1625 K Street, N.W.
Washington, D.C. 20006-1656

Phone: (202) 393-6100
Fax: (202) 331-8539

July 18, 2007

The Honorable Samuel W. Bodman
Secretary of Energy
Washington, D.C. 20585

Dear Mr. Secretary:

In response to the questions posed in your letter of October 5, 2005, the National Petroleum Council conducted a comprehensive study considering the future of oil and natural gas to 2030 in the context of the global energy system. The complexity of today's integrated energy markets and the urgency surrounding today's energy issues demanded a study that included:

- An integrated view of supply, demand, infrastructure, technology, and geopolitics

- A comprehensive review of public and aggregated proprietary energy outlooks

- In-depth analysis of technology trends and opportunities

- Policy options viewed through economic, security, and environmental lenses

- More than 350 participants from diverse backgrounds and organizations

- Dialogue with more than 1,000 persons and groups actively involved in energy.

The Council found that total global demand for energy is projected to grow by 50-60 percent by 2030, driven by increasing population and the pursuit of improving living standards. At the same time, there are accumulating risks to the supply of reliable, affordable energy to meet this growth, including political hurdles, infrastructure requirements, and availability of a trained work force. We will need all economic, environmentally responsible energy sources to assure adequate, reliable supply.

There is no single, easy solution to the global challenges ahead. Given the massive scale of the global energy system and the long lead-times necessary to make material changes, actions must be initiated now and sustained over the long term.

Over the next 25 years, the United States and the world face hard truths about the global energy future:

- Coal, oil, and natural gas will remain indispensable to meeting total projected energy demand growth.

- The world is not running out of energy resources, but there are accumulating risks to continuing expansion of oil and natural gas production from the conventional sources relied upon historically. These risks create significant challenges to meeting projected total energy demand.

- To mitigate these risks, expansion of all economic energy sources will be required, including coal, nuclear, biomass, other renewables, and unconventional oil and natural gas. Each of these sources faces significant challenges including safety, environmental, political, or economic hurdles, and imposes infrastructure requirements for development and delivery.

- "Energy Independence" should not be confused with strengthening energy security. The concept of energy independence is not realistic in the foreseeable future, whereas U.S. energy security can be enhanced by moderating demand, expanding and diversifying domestic energy supplies, and strengthening global energy trade and investment. There can be no U.S. energy security without global energy security.

- A majority of the U.S. energy sector workforce, including skilled scientists and engineers, is eligible to retire within the next decade. The workforce must be replenished and trained.

- Policies aimed at curbing carbon dioxide emissions will alter the energy mix, increase energy-related costs, and require reductions in demand growth.

The Council proposes five core strategies to assist markets in meeting the energy challenges to 2030 and beyond. All five strategies are essential—there is no single, easy solution to the multiple challenges we face. However, we are confident that the prompt adoption of these strategies, along with a sustained commitment to implementation, will promote U.S. competitiveness by balancing economic, security, and environmental goals.

The United States must:

- Moderate the growing demand for energy by increasing efficiency of transportation, residential, commercial, and industrial uses.

- Expand and diversify production from clean coal, nuclear, biomass, other renewables, and unconventional oil and gas; moderate the decline of conventional domestic oil and gas production; and increase access for development of new resources.

- Integrate energy policy into trade, economic, environmental, security, and foreign policies; strengthen global energy trade and investment; and broaden dialog with both producing and consuming nations to improve global energy security.

- Enhance science and engineering capabilities and create long-term opportunities for research and development in all phases of the energy supply and demand system.

- Develop the legal and regulatory framework to enable carbon capture and sequestration. In addition, as policymakers consider options to reduce carbon dioxide emissions, provide an effective global framework for carbon management, including establishment of a transparent, predictable, economy-wide cost for carbon dioxide emissions.

The attached report, *Facing the Hard Truths about Energy*, details findings and recommendations based on comprehensive analyses developed by the study teams.

The Council looks forward to sharing this study and its results with you, your colleagues, and broader government and public audiences.

Respectfully submitted,

Lee R. Raymond
Chair

Andrew Gould
Vice Chair, Technology

John J. Hamre
Vice Chair, Geopolitics
& Policy

David J. O'Reilly
Vice Chair, Supply

Daniel H. Yergin
Vice Chair, Demand

Attachment

HARDTRUTHS

Facing the Hard Truths about Energy

A comprehensive
view to 2030 of
global oil and
natural gas

A report of the National Petroleum Council
July 2007

Committee on Global Oil and Gas
Lee R. Raymond, Chair

NATIONAL PETROLEUM COUNCIL

Lee R. Raymond, *Chair*
Claiborne P. Deming, *Vice Chair*
Marshall W. Nichols, *Executive Director*

U.S. DEPARTMENT OF ENERGY

Samuel W. Bodman, *Secretary*

The National Petroleum Council is a federal
advisory committee to the Secretary of Energy.

The sole purpose of the National Petroleum Council
is to advise, inform, and make recommendations
to the Secretary of Energy on any matter
requested by the Secretary
relating to oil and natural gas
or to the oil and gas industries.

TABLE OF CONTENTS

Appendices

**A detailed glossary of terms used in this report is available at www.npc.org
and on the CD that accompanies the printed report.*

PREFACE

NATIONAL PETROLEUM COUNCIL

The National Petroleum Council (NPC) is an organization whose sole purpose is to provide advice to the federal government. At President Harry Truman's request, this federally chartered and privately funded advisory group was established by the Secretary of the Interior in 1946 to represent the oil and gas industries' views to the federal government: advising, informing, and recommending policy options. During World War II, under President Franklin Roosevelt, the federal government and the Petroleum Industry War Council had worked closely together to mobilize the oil supplies that fueled the Allied victory. President Truman's goal was to continue that successful cooperation in the uncertain postwar years. Today, the NPC is chartered by the Secretary of Energy under the Federal Advisory Committee Act of 1972.

About 175 in number, Council members are selected by the Energy Secretary to assure well-balanced representation from all segments of the oil and gas industries, all sections of the country, and from large and small companies. Members are also selected from outside the oil and gas industries, representing academic, financial, research, Native-American, and public-interest organizations and institutions. The Council provides a forum for informed dialogue on issues involving energy, security, the economy, and the environment in an ever-changing world.

STUDY REQUEST

By letter dated October 5, 2005, Secretary of Energy Samuel W. Bodman requested that the National Petroleum Council undertake a study on the ability of global oil and natural gas supply to keep pace with growing world demand. Specifically, the Secretary stated that key questions to be addressed in the study may include:

- What does the future hold for global oil and natural gas supply?

- Can incremental oil and natural gas supply be brought on-line, on-time, and at a reasonable price to meet future demand without jeopardizing economic growth?

- What oil and gas supply strategies and/or demand-side strategies does the Council recommend the U.S. pursue to ensure greater economic stability and prosperity?

(Appendix A contains a copy of the Secretary's request letter and a description of the NPC.)

STUDY ORGANIZATION

Responding to the Secretary's request, the Council established a Committee on Global Oil and Gas to study this topic and to supervise preparation of a draft report for the Council's consideration. The Council also established a Coordinating Subcommittee and four Task Groups—on Demand, Supply, Technology, and Geopolitics & Policy—to assist the Committee in conducting the study. These study groups were supported by three dozen Subgroups focused on specific subject areas. The box on the next page lists those who served as leaders of the study.

The members of the various study groups were drawn from NPC members' organizations as well as from many other U.S. and international industries, U.S. and international governments, non-governmental organizations, financial institutions,

Chair
Lee R. Raymond
Retired Chairman and
    Chief Executive Officer
Exxon Mobil Corporation

Chair – Coordinating Subcommittee
Alan J. Kelly
Former General Manager, Corporate Planning
    and Manager, Global Logistics Optimization
Exxon Mobil Corporation

Government Cochair
Jeffrey Clay Sell
Deputy Secretary of Energy
U.S. Department of Energy

Cochair – Coordinating Subcommittee
James A. Slutz
Deputy Assistant Secretary for Oil and Natural Gas
U.S. Department of Energy

Vice Chair – Demand
Daniel H. Yergin
Chairman
Cambridge Energy Research Associates

Chair – Demand Task Group
James Burkhard
Managing Director, Global Oil Group
Cambridge Energy Research Associates

Vice Chair – Supply
David J. O'Reilly
Chairman of the Board and
    Chief Executive Officer
Chevron Corporation

Chair – Supply Task Group
Donald L. Paul
Vice President and Chief Technology Officer
Chevron Corporation

Vice Chair – Technology
Andrew Gould
Chairman and Chief Executive Officer
Schlumberger Limited

Chair – Technology Task Group
Rodney F. Nelson
Vice President
Innovation and Collaboration
Schlumberger Limited

Vice Chair – Geopolitics & Policy
John J. Hamre
President and Chief Executive Officer
Center for Strategic & International Studies

Chair – Geopolitics & Policy Task Group
Frank A. Verrastro
Director and Senior Fellow
Center for Strategic & International Studies

consultancies, academia, and research groups. More than 350 people served on the study's Committee, Subcommittee, Task Groups, and Subgroups. (Appendix B contains rosters of these study groups.)

In addition to these study group participants, many more people were involved through outreach activities. These efforts were an integral part of the study with the goal of informing and soliciting input from a broad range of interested parties. More than two dozen sessions were held with staff of U.S. executive branch agencies, U.S. congressional committees, and state and local governments; non-governmental organizations; academia; professional societies; and industries. The outreach process also included key consuming and producing countries. Secretary Bod-

man contacted 19 energy ministries around the world to encourage supply and demand data from governments and national energy companies. Many countries provided constructive responses.

The data and feedback provided by the global energy community and other interested parties involved in the outreach sessions were documented and used to develop the insights for the future of the energy sector and to ensure that the study was addressing the critical issues associated with energy. This stakeholder input represented a wide range of views/opinions. This information was an integral part of the data sets analyzed and considered to develop the key findings and recommendations. (Appendix C provides a description of the study's outreach process and sessions.)

Figure P-1 illustrates the diversity of participation in the study process.

Study group and outreach participants contributed in a variety of ways, ranging from full-time work in multiple study areas, to involvement on a specific topic, to reviewing proposed materials, or to participating solely in an outreach session. Involvement in these activities should not be construed as endorsement or agreement with all the statements, findings, and recommendations in this report. Additionally, while U.S. government participants provided significant assistance in the identification and compilation of data and other information, they did not take positions on the study's policy recommendations. As a federally appointed and chartered advisory committee, the National Petroleum Council is solely responsible for the final advice provided to the Secretary of Energy. However, the Council believes that the broad and diverse study group and outreach participation has informed and enhanced its study and advice. The Council is very appreciative of the commitment and contributions from all who participated in the process.

STUDY SCOPE AND APPROACH

The study's primary focus was on oil and natural gas. However, all energy forms were assessed as they are elements of an interrelated and competitive global energy market. In fact, an understanding of all energy forms was necessary in order to provide meaningful advice on oil and natural gas. The study was conducted with a set of guiding principles that the study would:

- Not create another "grassroots" energy forecast of demand, supply, or prices, but rather focus on analysis of existing projections to identify underlying assumptions, understand why they differ, and thereby identify important factors governing the future of oil and gas

- Gather and analyze public data (from government, academia, and others) and aggregated proprietary data (from international oil companies and consultants)

- Solicit input from a broad range of interested parties including non-governmental organizations and foreign countries

- Emphasize long-term conditions to 2030 and beyond, not near-term energy market volatility

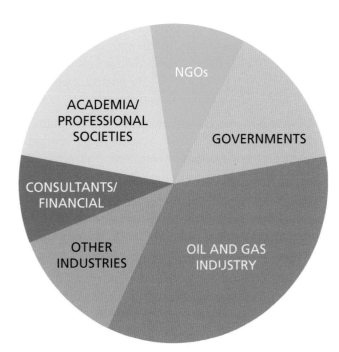

65% PARTICIPANTS FROM OUTSIDE OF OIL AND GAS INDUSTRY

350+ PARTICIPANTS, PLUS INPUT FROM 1,000+ OTHERS

FIGURE P-1. Broad Participation

- Make recommendations supported by data and science, and develop policy options and recommendations only after completing the study analyses, interpretation, and findings phase to guard against predetermined conclusions

- Frame detailed questions to ensure all study teams work within their scope and on time

- Comply fully with antitrust laws and regulations, and the Federal Advisory Committee Act. While the Council recognizes the important role price plays in both demand and supply actions, antitrust sensitivities precluded the study from addressing such impacts or accessing future price levels.

A large, broad, and diverse group of other studies and projections served as the underpinning of the NPC analyses. The NPC attempted to examine and use the full range of available projections:

- Data were provided by the International Energy Agency (IEA) and U.S. Energy Information Administration (EIA)—the two most widely used and respected sources of energy projections.

- A broad survey of proprietary energy projections was also conducted. As an integral part of this process, the NPC engaged the public accounting firm Argy, Wiltse & Robinson, P.C. to receive, aggregate, and protect proprietary data responses.

- A Wide-Net process collected additional publicly available projections from academia, governmental organizations, non-governmental groups, and other interests.

- A Data Warehouse was developed to store and assist in analysis of all collected projections. The warehouse data are included on the CD accompanying printed copies of this report.

- A Parallel Studies process examined numerous other recent reports regarding aspects of energy policy to inform the work of the NPC study's Coordinating Subcommittee. (Appendix D provides summaries of the studies.)

The Demand and Supply Task Groups focused primarily on the analysis and interpretation of the range of projections for world energy demand and supply to 2030 and the key assumptions/drivers underlying those projections. The Technology Task Group examined the range of technology assumptions in the projections surveyed and how these technologies might affect world energy supply/demand over the next 25 years. The Geopolitics & Policy Task Group had two focus areas. Its geopolitical analyses assessed how sovereign national, regional, and global policy decisions might affect global supply and demand outlooks. Its policy work involved the integration of options from the various study groups into a concise set of recommendations for the Secretary of Energy reflecting the tradeoffs among the economy, security, and the environment. In addition to the work of the Task Groups, the study addressed several overarching themes: energy efficiency, carbon management, and macroeconomic issues.

The output from these multiple efforts underpin the NPC's recommended supply- and demand-side strategies, and form the basis for its policy recommendations to the Secretary of Energy.

(See the Report Chapters and Topic Papers for more detailed descriptions of the scopes of work, framing questions, and approaches used by the various study groups.)

STUDY REPORT

In the interest of transparency and to help readers better understand this study, the NPC is making the study results and many of the documents developed by the study groups available to all interested parties as follows:

- *Executive Summary* provides insights on energy market dynamics as well as advice on an integrated set of actions needed immediately to ensure adequate and reliable supplies of energy, while assuring continued expansion of prosperity including economic growth, global security, and environmental responsibility.

- *Report Chapters* contain summary results of the analyses conducted by the Demand, Supply, Technology, and Geopolitics & Policy Task Groups; a discussion on Carbon Management; a full listing of the study's recommendations; and a description of the study's methodology. These chapters provide supporting data and analyses for the findings and recommendations presented in the *Executive Summary*.

- *Appendices* contain Council and study group rosters, a description of the study's outreach process, and other information.

- *Topic Papers,* which can be found on the CD inside the back cover of this report, include detailed, specific subject matter papers and reports prepared by the Task Groups and their Subgroups. These Topic Papers formed the basis for the analyses that led to development of the summary results presented in the report's Executive Summary and Chapters. The Council believes that these materials will be of interest to the readers of the report and will help them better understand the results. The members of the National Petroleum Council were not asked to endorse or approve all of the statements and conclusions contained in these documents but, rather, to approve the publication of these materials as part of the study process. (See the description of the CD in Appendix E for abstracts on topic papers and a list of other documents included.)

(Published copies of the report and the CD can be purchased from the NPC or viewed and downloaded from its website: www.npc.org)

EXECUTIVE SUMMARY

The American people are very concerned about energy—its availability, reliability, cost, and environmental impact. Energy also has become a subject of urgent policy discussions. But energy is a complex subject, touching every part of daily life and the overall economy, involving a wide variety of technologies, and deeply affecting many aspects of our foreign relations. The United States is the largest participant in the global energy system—the largest consumer, the second largest producer of coal and natural gas, and the largest importer and third largest producer of oil. Developing a framework for considering America's oil and natural gas position now and for the future requires a broad view and a long-term perspective; both are provided in this study.

During the last quarter-century, world energy demand has increased about 60 percent, supported by a global infrastructure that has expanded to a massive scale. Most forecasts for the next quarter-century project a similar percentage increase in energy demand from a much larger base. Oil and natural gas have played a significant role in supporting economic activity in the past, and will likely continue to do so in combination with other energy types. Over the coming decades, the world will need better energy efficiency and all economic, environmentally responsible energy sources available to support and sustain future growth.

Fortunately, the world is not running out of energy resources. But many complex challenges could keep these diverse energy resources from becoming the sufficient, reliable, and economic energy supplies upon which people depend. These challenges are compounded by emerging uncertainties: geopolitical influences on energy development, trade, and security; and increasing constraints on carbon dioxide (CO_2) emissions that could impose changes in future energy use. While risks have always typified the energy business, they are now accumulating and converging in new ways.

The National Petroleum Council (NPC) examined a broad range of global energy supply, demand, and technology projections through 2030. The Council identified risks and challenges to a reliable and secure energy future, and developed strategies and recommendations aimed at balancing future economic, security, and environmental goals.

The United States and the world face hard truths about the global energy future over the next 25 years:

- Coal, oil, and natural gas will remain indispensable to meeting total projected energy demand growth.

- The world is not running out of energy resources, but there are accumulating risks to continuing expansion of oil and natural gas production from the conventional sources relied upon historically. These risks create significant challenges to meeting projected energy demand.

- To mitigate these risks, expansion of all economic energy sources will be required, including coal, nuclear, renewables, and unconventional oil and natural gas. Each of these sources faces significant challenges—including safety, environmental, political, or economic hurdles—and imposes infrastructure requirements for development and delivery.

- "Energy Independence" should not be confused with strengthening energy security. The concept of energy independence is not realistic in the foreseeable future, whereas U.S. energy security can be enhanced by moderating demand, expanding and diversifying domestic energy supplies, and strengthening global energy trade and investment. There can be no U.S. energy security without global energy security.

- A majority of the U.S. energy sector workforce, including skilled scientists and engineers, is eligible to retire within the next decade. The workforce must be replenished and trained.

- Policies aimed at curbing CO_2 emissions will alter the energy mix, increase energy-related costs, and require reductions in demand growth.

Free and open markets should be relied upon wherever possible to produce efficient solutions. Where markets need to be bolstered, policies should be implemented with care and consideration of possible unintended consequences. The Council proposes five core strategies to assist markets in meeting the energy challenges to 2030 and beyond. All five strategies are essential—there is no single, easy solution to the multiple challenges we face. However, the Council is confident that the prompt adoption of these strategies, along with a sustained commitment to implementation, will promote U.S. competitiveness by balancing economic, security, and environmental goals. The United States must:

- Moderate the growing demand for energy by increasing efficiency of transportation, residential, commercial, and industrial uses.

- Expand and diversify production from clean coal, nuclear, biomass, other renewables, and unconventional oil and natural gas; moderate the decline of conventional domestic oil and natural gas production; and increase access for development of new resources.

- Integrate energy policy into trade, economic, environmental, security, and foreign policies; strengthen global energy trade and investment; and broaden dialogue with both producing and consuming nations to improve global energy security.

- Enhance science and engineering capabilities and create long-term opportunities for research and development in all phases of the energy supply and demand system.

- Develop the legal and regulatory framework to enable carbon capture and sequestration (CCS). In addition, as policymakers consider options to reduce CO_2 emissions, provide an effective global framework for carbon management, including establishment of a transparent, predictable, economy-wide cost for CO_2 emissions.

The Council identified these strategies by drawing upon more than 350 expert participants with wide-ranging backgrounds to provide analysis, information, and insight. Additionally, extensive outreach efforts involved more than 1,000 people actively engaged in energy. Task Groups for this study reviewed a broad range of public and aggregated proprietary studies in order to understand and evaluate the many assumptions and forces behind recent global energy projections.

Given the massive scale of the global energy system and the long lead times necessary to make significant changes, concerted actions must be taken now, and sustained over the long term, to promote U.S. competitiveness by balancing economic, security, and environmental goals. The Council's findings and recommendations are summarized below and explained in detail in the report chapters.

THE GROWING DEMAND FOR ENERGY

Over the coming decades, energy demand will grow to increasingly higher levels as economies and populations expand. This will pressure the supply system and require increased emphasis on energy-use efficiency.

Energy is essential to the economic activity that sustains and improves the quality of life. Projections for future energy needs generally assume expanding economies and populations, which drive continued energy demand growth. Over time, the efficiency of energy use has improved, thanks to the combined effects of technological advancement, education of consumers, and policy initiatives. These developments have allowed growth in economic activity to outpace growth in energy use. Differing assumptions for the world's population, economic activity, and energy efficiency result in varying projections for future energy demand, as shown in Figure ES-1.

Historically, energy consumption has been concentrated in the developed world, where economic activity has been centered. Today, the developed world, represented by the Organisation for Economic Co-operation and Development (OECD),[1] uses half of the world's total energy to produce half of the world's

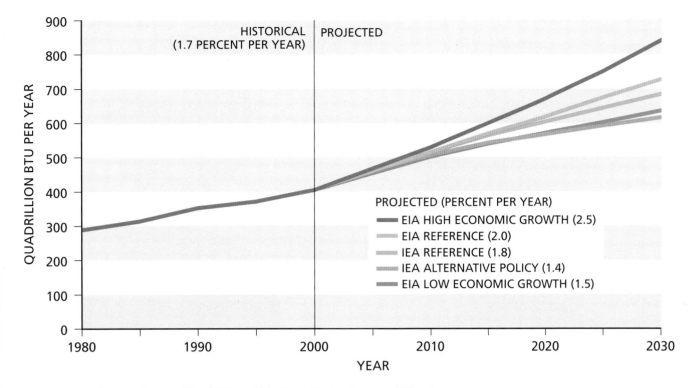

Note: A quadrillion Btu is one million billion British thermal units. One quadrillion Btu per year
      is the energy equivalent of about 500,000 barrels per day of oil.
Sources: EIA: U.S. Energy Information Administration, *International Energy Outlook 2006*.
      IEA: International Energy Agency, *World Energy Outlook 2006*.

FIGURE ES-1. *World Energy Demand — Average Annual Growth Rates*

Gross Domestic Product.[2] However, over 80 percent of the world's population is projected to live in developing countries by 2030, as shown in Figure ES-2.

Many developing countries are just reaching the point where individual wealth and energy consumption start to accelerate. For example, while the number of cars in China more than doubled between 2000 and 2006, there remains just one car for every 40 people[3] whereas the United States has one car for every two people.[4] Thus, dramatic further growth in vehicle sales and demand for fuel in China are very likely. As this accelerating consumption combines with large and growing populations, it becomes likely that most new energy demand growth will occur in the developing world, with one projection shown in Figure ES-3.

THE ENERGY SUPPLY LANDSCAPE

The world uses a wide variety of energy sources today. Oil and natural gas now provide nearly 60 percent of

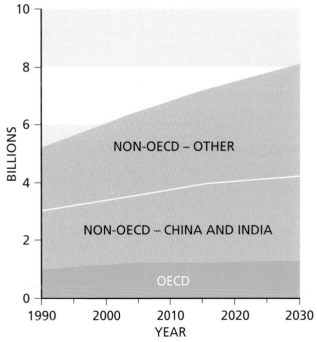

Source: *UN World Population Prospects.*

FIGURE ES-2. *World Population*

2004 – 445 QUADRILLION BTU PER YEAR

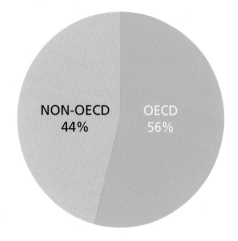

NON-OECD
44%

OECD
56%

2030 – 678 QUADRILLION BTU PER YEAR

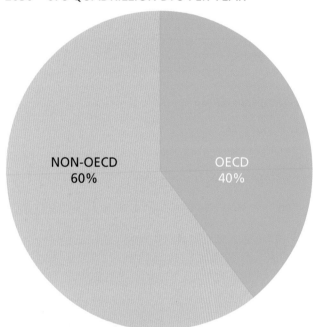

NON-OECD
60%

OECD
40%

Source: IEA, *World Energy Outlook 2006.*

FIGURE ES-3. *World Energy Demand Growth*
from 2004 to 2030

1980 – 288 QUADRILLION BTU PER YEAR

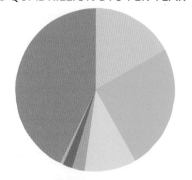

2004 – 445 QUADRILLION BTU PER YEAR

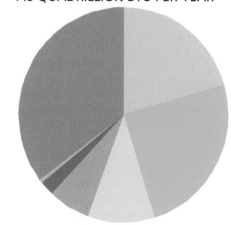

2030 – 678 QUADRILLION BTU PER YEAR

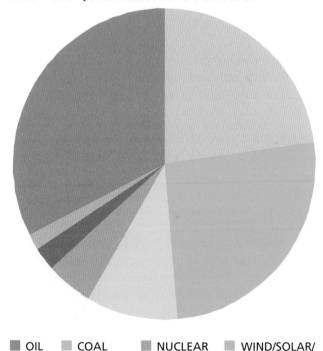

■ OIL   ■ COAL   ■ NUCLEAR   ■ WIND/SOLAR/
■ GAS   ■ BIOMASS   ■ HYDRO   GEOTHERMAL

Source: IEA, *World Energy Outlook 2006.*

FIGURE ES-4. *World Energy Supply –*
Historical and Projected

world primary energy,[5] as shown in Figure ES-4, and it is a hard truth that oil and natural gas will remain indispensable to meeting the projected growth in energy demand.

It is another hard truth that a rapidly growing world economy will require large increases in energy supplies over the next quarter-century. Expansion of all economic energy sources will be required to meet demand reliably, including coal, nuclear, renewables, and unconventional oil and natural gas. All energy sources have their own challenges that must be overcome to be produced, delivered, and used on an ever-increasing scale.

Current assessments for both oil and natural gas indicate large in-place volumes of resource. The natural gas resource appears more than adequate to meet the increased natural gas production typically anticipated by energy outlooks over the study period.

Future oil supply will come from a variety of sources, including existing production capacities, development of existing reserves, application of enhanced oil recovery, expansion of unconventional liquids, and development of new discoveries. Figure ES-5 is an illustrative example of these sources as depicted by the IEA in its *World Energy Outlook 2004*. There is uncertainty about the potential of the oil resource base to sustain growing oil production rates. Additional uncertainty surrounds the industry's potential to overcome multiple increasing risks, including access to promising areas for development, and the rate and timing

of investment, technology development, and infrastructure expansion. This study observed a range of oil projections from less than 80 to 120 million barrels per day in 2030. This wide range results from differing assumptions about these uncertainties.

Biomass, mainly wood and dung burned for heat, is today's largest non-fossil energy source. Liquid fuels from biomass, such as ethanol from corn and sugarcane, have grown rapidly in recent years, but given the scale of total oil consumption, liquids from biomass contribute only about 1 percent of the energy provided by oil. Potential cellulosic biomass resources, from wood, energy crops, and food crop waste, are large in the United States; the U.S. Departments of Agriculture and Energy estimate that the United States could generate sufficient biomass to produce up to 4 million barrels per day of oil-equivalent liquids.[6] As with the expansion of any energy source, challenges must be overcome before biofuels production can achieve significant volumes. For example, technology does not yet exist to convert cellulosic material economically at scale to liquid fuels. Ethanol expansion in the

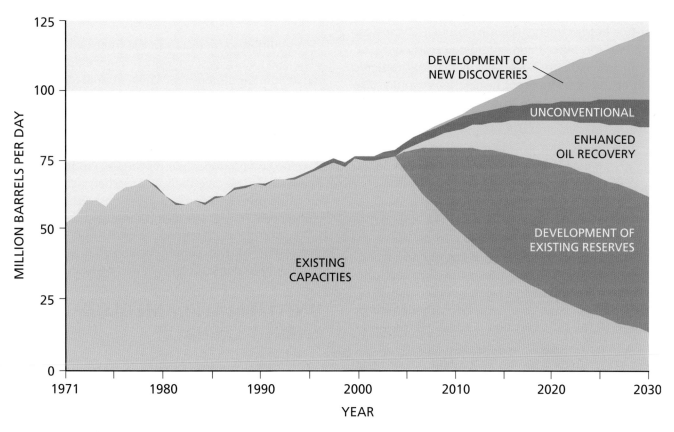

Source: IEA, *World Energy Outlook 2004*.

FIGURE ES-5. *Illustrative Total Liquids Supply*

United States faces compound challenges: increasing rail, waterway, and pipeline transport capacity; scaling up distribution systems; and balancing food uses and water requirements.

Wind and solar energy have also grown rapidly, now contributing about 1 percent to the world's energy mix. Wind and solar energy are expected to continue their rapid expansion, with associated challenges that include economics, intermittent availability, land-use considerations, and the need for grid interconnection and long distance transmission lines.

Hydroelectric power supplies about 2 percent of today's energy. It is not generally expected to grow significantly, except in developing Asia-Pacific areas, since the most suitable locations in developed countries are already in use.

Nuclear power contributes about 6 percent of world energy today, and its use is generally expected to increase outside the United States. Nuclear power expansion faces concerns about safety and security, the management and disposal of radioactive waste, and weapons proliferation. Further expansion of nuclear power could be promoted to limit CO_2 emissions or bolster energy security through diversification. On the other hand, additional restrictions on the nuclear industry, such as early plant retirements or limits on projected new installations, would raise demand for alternatives to generate electricity, such as natural gas, coal, wind, and solar.

Coal supplies the second largest share of world energy today, after oil. In forecasts where CO_2 emissions are not constrained, coal is generally expected to increase its share. Projected increases in coal use are driven mainly by growing electricity demand in developing countries. Remaining coal resources are far larger than for oil and natural gas; at current consumption rates, the United States has economically recoverable resources for at least another 100 years.[7] China also has large coal resources, although major deposits are far from consuming areas, and transportation infrastructure is limiting. In addition to the logistical challenges of rail, water, and power lines, coal combustion also produces more CO_2 per unit of energy than natural gas or oil from conventional sources. The combination of coal, natural gas, and oil is generally expected to provide over 80 percent of global energy needs in 2030, exacerbating the challenge of constraining CO_2 emissions.

THE CHANGING WORLD ENERGY MAP

Growth in energy production has been supported by global trade and open markets, combined with capital investment to produce and deliver energy. Energy consumption in the developing world is projected to increase dramatically, while oil and natural gas production in the United States and Europe decline. This combination will require a substantial increase in international oil and natural gas trade, profoundly redrawing the world energy map.

Forecasts for growth in oil and liquefied natural gas (LNG) shipments place greater emphasis on reliable transport, trade, and delivery systems while raising geopolitical, environmental, and security concerns. Today, more than half the world's inter-regional oil movements pass through a handful of potential "choke points," including the Suez Canal, the Bosporus, and the Straits of Hormuz and Malacca.[8]

Figure ES-6 shows one projection of significant changes in regional oil imports and exports between now and 2030. Natural gas supply and demand are projected to make similar shifts.

In addition to increases in the international trade of oil and natural gas, the world energy map is changing in another dimension. Conventional oil and natural gas resources are increasingly concentrated in a handful of non-OECD countries. The national oil companies and energy ministries in these countries play central roles in policy decisions about how to develop and produce their resources. Producers may increasingly leverage their assets when dealing with oil companies and consumer nations, either to gain commercial benefits or to further national or foreign policy objectives. The trend of market liberalization that expanded global energy trade and investment in the 1990s has come under renewed pressure.

UNITED STATES AND GLOBAL ENERGY SECURITY

U.S. and global energy security depend upon reliable, sufficient energy supplies freely traded among nations. This dependence will rise with the growth required in international oil and natural gas trade, and may be increasingly influenced by political goals and tensions. These trends are prompting renewed concerns about U.S. energy security.

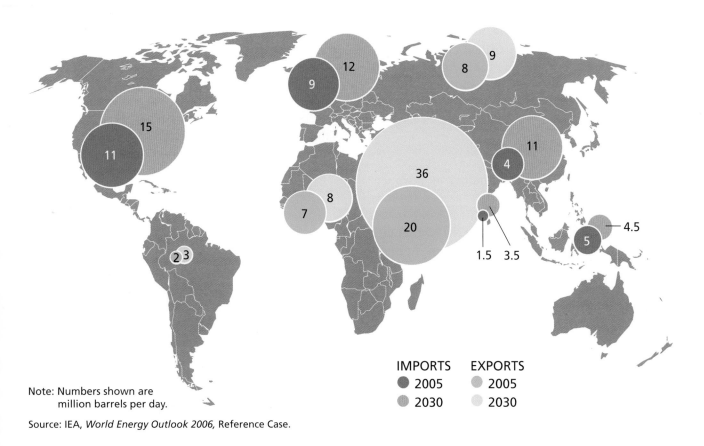

Note: Numbers shown are
       million barrels per day.

Source: IEA, *World Energy Outlook 2006,* Reference Case.

FIGURE ES-6. *Net Regional Oil Imports and Exports*

These energy security concerns have spurred calls for the United States to become totally self-sufficient in energy supply, often referred to as "energy independence." This concept is unrealistic in the foreseeable future and incompatible with broader foreign policy objectives and treaty obligations. Policies espousing "energy independence" may create considerable uncertainty among international trading partners and hinder investment in international energy supply development.[9]

It is a hard truth that energy independence is not necessary for energy security. Rather than pursuing energy independence, the United States should enhance its energy security by moderating demand, expanding and diversifying domestic energy supplies, and strengthening global energy trade and investment. Indeed, even if the United States could become physically self-sufficient in energy, it could not disengage from global energy activity, trade, and finance. There can be no U.S. energy security without global energy security.

INVESTMENT IN GLOBAL ENERGY DEVELOPMENT

Building new, multi-billion-dollar oil platforms in water thousands of feet deep, laying pipelines in difficult terrain and across country borders, expanding refineries, constructing vessels and terminals to ship and store liquefied natural gas, building railroads to transport coal and biomass, and stringing new high-voltage transmission lines from remote wind farms—all will require large investments over decades. Higher investment in real terms will be needed to grow production capacity. Future projects are likely to be more complex and remote, resulting in higher costs per unit of energy produced.[10] A stable and attractive investment climate will be necessary to attract adequate capital for evolution and expansion of the energy infrastructure.

The United States should actively engage energy suppliers, encouraging open trade and investment to expand international energy production and infrastructure. International trade and diplomatic negotiations should routinely incorporate energy issues to promote the rule-of-law, fiscal stability, equitable access, and the environmentally responsible development of all energy resources.

TECHNOLOGY ADVANCEMENTS

Human ingenuity and technological advances create the potential to develop new energy sources, to further develop existing resources, and to use energy in more efficient and environmentally friendly ways. The oil and natural gas industry has a long history of technological advancement, and today it operates using materials, chemistry, engineering, computing, and sensing techniques well beyond anything envisioned several decades ago. Technology has led to large savings in energy demand and additions to supply while reducing the industry's environmental "footprint." Technology advances are expected to continue, although broad-ranging technology impact can take over a decade from initial concept to large-scale implementation.[11]

There is no single technology capable of ensuring that the world's future energy needs will be met in an economical and environmentally responsible way. Many advances and breakthroughs will be required on numerous fronts. To do this, significant financial and human resources must be engaged over a sustained period. Meanwhile, the U.S. energy industry faces a dramatic human resource shortage that could undermine the future development of technological advances needed to meet the demand for increasingly diversified energy sources. A majority of the industry's technical workforce is nearing retirement eligibility, and the number of American graduates in engineering and geosciences has dropped substantially during the last quarter century, compromising future delivery of technology advances.

The Council's findings echo many in the National Academy of Sciences report "Rising Above the Gathering Storm: Energizing and Employing America for a Brighter Economic Future," which calls for a focus on mathematics and science education, long-term basic research, and ensuring that the United States is the premier place in the world for research and technological innovation.

■ Key Information: Energy Systems Scale and Timeline

The scale of the world energy system and the time required to make significant changes, both on the demand and on the supply sides, are frequently underestimated. A few examples:

- The world currently uses about 86 million barrels per day of oil—40,000 gallons every second.

- New, large oil discoveries can take 15-20 years from exploration until production actually begins, and production can continue for 50 years or more.

- A major new oil platform can cost billions and take a decade or more to complete. The Hibernia platform off the east coast of Canada cost $5 billion, took 19 years from discovery to production, and produces only 0.2 percent of world oil demand.[12] The Thunder Horse platform in the U.S. Gulf of Mexico cost $4 billion, is not yet operating eight years after discovery, and has a capacity of 0.3 percent of world oil demand.[13]

- A new average-sized U.S. refinery (120,000 barrels per day of crude oil distillation capacity) would cost $3 billion or more[14] and would increase U.S. refining capacity less than 1 percent.

- The United States has about 200,000 miles of oil[15] and about 280,000[16] miles of natural gas pipeline, built up over the last century.

- It can take over two decades for a newly commercialized technology to be broadly applied in the vehicle fleet actually on the road—examples include fuel injection and front-wheel drive.

- Buildings typically last for decades. Many of the attributes that affect energy consumption are costly and difficult to retrofit after initial installation, for example wall thickness, insulation, structural tightness, and windows.

- Commercializing new technology in the oil and gas market takes an average of 16 years to progress from concept to widespread commercial adoption.

ADDRESSING CARBON CONSTRAINTS

Constraints on CO_2 emissions are emerging, with profound implications for energy supply and demand. Worldwide CO_2 emissions from energy use are generally predicted to grow, as shown in Figure ES-7. Rising concerns about climate change may lead to further limits on these emissions. It is a hard truth that policies aimed at curbing carbon emissions will alter the energy mix, increase energy-related costs, and require reductions in demand growth.

Significantly reducing CO_2 emissions will require major changes in energy production, infrastructure, and use: reducing demand, substituting low-carbon or carbon-neutral fuels, and capturing and sequestering the emissions from burning coal, oil, and natural gas. Implementing effective changes on a sufficient scale will require time, money, and technology. It can take over two decades for newly commercialized vehicle technology to be incorporated into the vehicle fleet actually on the road. Improvements in building efficiency are made slowly—because buildings can stand for many decades, and retrofitting efficiency steps such as increased insulation and better windows can be difficult and costly. Power plants and industrial facilities often last fifty years or more, limiting the rate of capital turnover in these sectors. Achieving any significant increase in efficiency, shift in fuels used, and capture of CO_2 emissions for storage will require major changes over decades to vehicles, buildings, industrial plants, electric generation facilities, and infrastructure.

STRATEGIES FOR U.S. ENERGY POLICY

No single, easy solution can solve the world's energy challenges. The world will need all the economic, environmentally responsible energy sources that can be found to support and sustain prosperity in the coming decades. To assure this, actions on multiple fronts must be taken now, and sustained over the long term. The NPC study participants developed recommendations to achieve the following five strategic goals:

- Moderate demand by increasing energy efficiency

- Expand and diversify U.S. energy supply

- Strengthen global and U.S. energy security

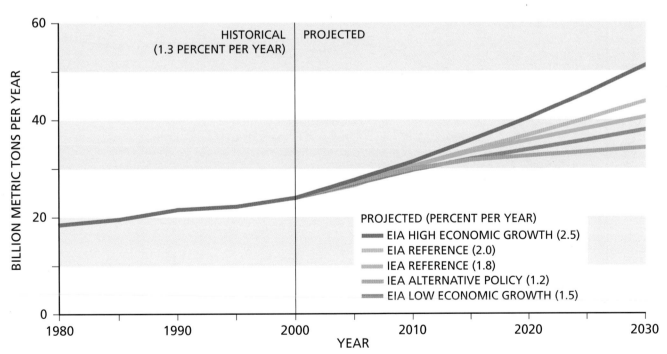

Sources: EIA: U.S. Energy Information Administration, *International Energy Outlook 2006.*
　　　　IEA: International Energy Agency, *World Energy Outlook 2006.*

FIGURE ES-7. *World Carbon Dioxide Emissions — Growth Projections*

- Reinforce capabilities to meet new challenges

- Address carbon constraints.

While the focus of this report has been concentrated on identifying key findings and relevant and effective recommendations, it is prudent to be mindful of the lessons of the past. The prospect of unintended consequences or the adverse impacts of poor policy choices should not be underestimated.[17] Policies aimed at penalizing industry segments may have political appeal but often undermine security goals and broader national objectives.

Moderate Demand by Increasing Energy Efficiency

Improve Vehicle Fuel Economy

Nearly half of the 21 million barrels of oil products that the United States consumes each day is gasoline used for cars and light trucks. The Reference Case in the U.S. Energy Information Administration's (EIA) *Annual Energy Outlook 2007* projects that gasoline consumption will increase by an average of 1.3 percent per year, totaling an increase of 3 million barrels per day between 2005 and 2030.

The Corporate Average Fuel Economy (CAFE) standards have been the primary policy used to promote improved car and light-truck fuel economy in the United States over the last three decades. The original standards created one economy requirement for cars, and another less stringent one for light trucks to avoid penalizing users of work trucks. At the time, light-truck sales were about one-quarter of car sales. Since then, sport utility vehicles and minivans classified as light trucks have increased their share of the market. Now, these light-truck sales exceed car sales, and the increase at the lower truck fuel economy standard has limited overall fuel economy improvement.

Cars and trucks sold today are more technically efficient than those sold two decades ago. However, the fuel economy improvements that could have been gained from this technology over the last two decades have been used to increase vehicle weight, horsepower, and to add amenities. Consequently, car and truck fuel economy levels have been about flat for two decades, as shown in Figure ES-8.

Based on a detailed review of technological potential, a doubling of fuel economy of new cars and light trucks by 2030 is possible through the use of existing

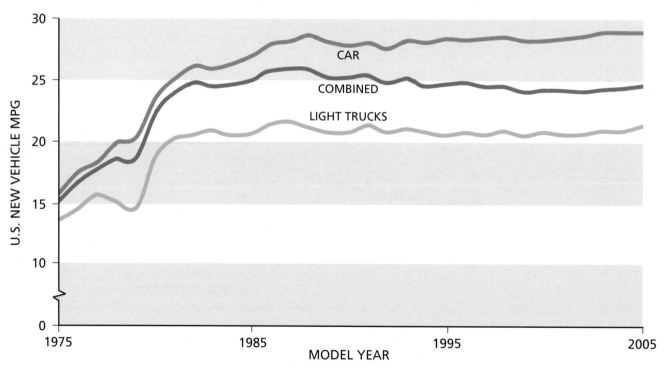

Source: U.S. EPA, *Light Duty Automotive Technology and Fuel Economy Trends: 1975 through 2006.*

FIGURE ES-8. *U.S. Car and Light-Truck Fuel Economy*

Facing the Hard Truths about Energy

and anticipated technologies, assuming vehicle performance and other attributes remain the same as today.[18] This economy improvement will entail higher vehicle cost. The 4 percent annual gain in CAFE standards starting in 2010 that President George W. Bush suggested in his 2007 State of the Union speech is not inconsistent with a potential doubling of fuel economy for new light duty vehicles by 2030. Depending upon how quickly new vehicle improvements are incorporated in the on-road light duty vehicle fleet, U.S. oil demand would be reduced by about 3-5 million barrels per day in 2030.[19] Additional fuel economy improvements would be possible by reducing vehicle weight, horsepower, and amenities, or by developing more expensive, step-out technologies.

Recommendation

The NPC makes the following recommendations to increase vehicle fuel economy:

- Improve car and light-truck fuel economy standards at the maximum rate possible by applying economic, available technology.

  – Update the standards on a regular basis.

  – Avoid further erosion of fuel economy standards resulting from increased sales of light trucks, or, alternatively, adjust light-truck standards to reflect changes in relative light-truck and car market shares.

Potential Effect: 3-5 million barrels of oil per day in the United States from the increased base in 2030.

Reduce Energy Consumption in the Residential and Commercial Sectors

Forty percent of U.S. energy is consumed in the residential and commercial sectors, including the energy lost while generating and distributing the electricity used. The EIA projects that U.S. residential and commercial energy use will increase almost one-third by 2030.

Significant efficiency improvements have been made in buildings over the last several decades. Improvement areas include the building structure itself; heating, cooling, and lighting systems; and appliances. However, these improvements have been partly offset by increased building sizes and by use of larger and multiple appliances. Cost-effective energy efficiency

building technologies have outpaced current U.S. federal, state, and local policies. If applied, currently available efficiency technology would reduce energy use an additional 15-20 percent.[20]

Buildings typically last for decades. Many of the features of buildings that affect their energy consumption, such as wall thickness, insulation, structural tightness, and windows, will go largely unchanged throughout the life of the building. Technologies and practices affecting these long-lived systems will be slow to penetrate the building stock and affect their overall efficiency, making it important to implement policies early to achieve significant long-term savings.

Major barriers to energy efficiency investments include initial costs, insufficient energy price signals, split incentive (where the consumer is different from the facility provider), and individual consumer's limited information. To reduce energy consumption significantly below the projected baseline will require policy-driven improvements in energy efficiency.

Building Energy Codes

Building energy codes have proved to be a significant policy tool to encourage increased energy efficiency in new buildings, and in buildings undergoing major renovations. Building codes are administered by the 50 states and by thousands of local authorities. To help state and local governments, national model energy codes are developed and updated every few years. Under federal law, states are not obligated to impose energy codes for buildings, although at least 41 states have adopted some form of building energy code.

Adopting a building code does not guarantee energy savings. Code enforcement and compliance are also essential. Some jurisdictions have reported that one-third or more of new buildings do not comply with critical energy code requirements for windows and air conditioning equipment, which are among the easiest energy saving features to verify.[21]

Building energy codes typically target only new buildings and major renovations. Additional policies are needed to encourage incremental, significant savings in existing buildings.

Appliance and Equipment Standards

Standards for appliances and other equipment are major policy measures that reduce energy use in existing buildings. These products may not consume much energy individually, but collectively they represent a significant portion of the nation's energy use.[22]

Energy efficiency standards currently do not apply to many increasingly common products, including those based on expanded digital technologies. Product coverage must be continuously evaluated and expanded when appropriate to assure inclusion of all significant energy consuming devices. In addition, industry and other stakeholders have negotiated standards for other products, such as residential furnaces and boilers. Implementing and enforcing expanded and strengthened standards would reduce energy consumption below the levels that will result from current Department of Energy requirements.[23]

Residential and commercial efficiency gains are partially consumed by increased use of the services and products that become more efficient. For example, U.S. house sizes have increased steadily over the years, offsetting much of the energy efficiency improvements that would have resulted had house sizes not swelled. Similarly, household refrigerators have increased in number and size, consuming much of the reduced energy use per refrigerator gained by efficiency standards. Energy efficiency programs should consider steps to avoid increasing the demand for energy services.

Recommendation

The NPC makes the following recommendations to improve efficiency in the residential and commercial sectors:

- Encourage states to implement and enforce more aggressive energy efficiency building codes, updated on a regular basis.

- Establish appliance standards for new products.

- Update federal appliance standards on a regular basis.

Potential Effect: 7-9 quadrillion Btu per year by 2030 in the United States, including 2-3 quadrillion Btu per year of natural gas (5-8 billion cubic feet per day), 4-5 quadrillion Btu per year of coal, and ~1 quadrillion Btu per year (0.5 million barrels per day) of oil.

Increase Industrial Sector Efficiency

The industrial sector consumes about one-third of U.S. energy, and contributes to a large share of the projected growth in both oil and natural gas use globally and in the United States. Worldwide, industrial demand for natural gas is expected to double by 2030. Worldwide, industrial sector demand for oil is expected to increase by 5 million barrels per day, or 15 percent of total oil demand growth through 2030.

The industrial sector is a price-responsive energy consumer. U.S. energy-intensive industries and manufacturers rely on internationally competitive energy supplies to remain globally competitive. In recent years, U.S. natural gas prices have risen faster than those in the rest of the world. As a result, U.S. energy-intensive manufacturers using natural gas as a fuel or feedstock have responded by increasing the efficiency of their operations and/or by shifting more of their operations to lower energy cost regions outside the United States.

Across the industrial sector, there are opportunities to increase energy efficiency by about 15 percent.[24] Areas for energy savings include waste-heat recovery, separation processes, and combined heat and power.[25] While 40 percent of that opportunity could be implemented now, further research, development, demonstration, and deployment are required before the remaining savings can be achieved. Providing programs that encourage deployment of energy efficiency technologies and practices will hasten their implementation. Making the federal research and development tax credit permanent is one way to encourage private investment in these areas. However, a lack of technically trained workers can impede the implementation of efficiency projects while the uncertainty from price volatility can make justifying those projects difficult.

Recommendation

The NPC makes the following recommendations to improve efficiency in the industrial sector:

- The Department of Energy should conduct and promote research, development, demonstration, and deployment of industrial energy efficiency technologies and best practices.

Facing the Hard Truths about Energy

- The research and development tax credit should be permanently extended to spur private research and development investments.

  Potential Effect: 4-7 quadrillion Btu per year by 2030 in the United States, about equal parts coal, gas, and oil.

Generation of electricity uses a significant amount of energy. In the United States, about 30 percent of primary energy is used by the electric power generating sector. Only modest generation efficiency improvements appear economically feasible in existing plants (2 to 6 percent), as efficiency improvements are incorporated during routine maintenance. The major potential for efficiency improvement comes when existing generation plants are replaced with facilities using updated technology and designs. Retirement of existing facilities and selection of replacement technology and design is driven by economics affected by fuel cost, plant reliability, and electricity dispatching considerations.

Expand and Diversify U.S. Energy Supply

Oil, natural gas, and coal—the fossil fuels used for transportation, heating, power, and industrial uses—are by far the largest energy sources in industrial economies. While alternative sources, particularly fuel from biomass and other renewables, are likely to contribute increasingly to total energy supply, these three fossil fuels are projected to dominate through at least 2030.

The prospects for oil and natural gas production raise complex questions. It is a hard truth that the global supply of oil and natural gas from the conventional sources relied upon historically is unlikely to meet projected 50-60 percent growth in demand over the next 25 years. There are accumulating risks to replacing current production and increasing supplies of conventional oil and natural gas. They involve a growing set of global uncertainties ranging from production capabilities through environmental constraints, infrastructure needs, and geopolitical complications.

While risks have always typified the energy business, they are now accumulating and converging in new ways. Geopolitical changes coincide with in-creasingly large and complex technical challenges. Environmental concerns that limit access to some U.S. resources may compete with security concerns that would promote expanded access. Carbon issues challenge coal use while energy security considerations may encourage it. Carbon constraints would require huge capital investments to maintain energy production. These uncertainties, and the risks they generate, describe the background for understanding energy supply prospects during the next few decades.

Endowment and recoverable resources are fundamental concepts in any discussion of fossil fuel supplies. *Endowment* refers to the earth's physical store of potential energy sources: barrels of oil, cubic feet of natural gas, and tons of coal. The endowment of fossil fuels is fixed: it can be depleted but not replenished. *Recoverable resources* are a subset of the endowment—the portion that can be produced and converted to fuel and power.

The total global fossil endowment estimates appear huge, but only a fraction of these estimated volumes can be technically produced. The total endowment of oil is estimated at 13-15 trillion barrels, natural gas at 50 quadrillion cubic feet, and coal at 14 trillion tons.

Renewable resources such as biomass, wind, and solar represent huge additional energy endowments that are continuously replenished, unlike fossil fuels.

Understanding the Range of Production Forecasts

This study examined a comprehensive range of oil production forecasts including integrated supply/demand studies from EIA and IEA; publicly available projections from a diverse range of other sources; and a unique set of aggregated proprietary forecasts from international oil companies (IOCs) and energy consulting groups. The diversity of this range of projections is shown in Figure ES-9, which highlights the EIA reference, the Association for the Study of Peak Oil (ASPO) – France, and the average of the IOC forecasts for 2030. The distribution of production forecasts, spanning a range from less than 80 million to more than 120 million barrels per day, highlights the effect of assigning different levels of risk and uncertainty to both resource and above-ground factors. This distribution of outcomes, along with evaluation of assessments of the total resource base, indicates that the key consideration for energy supplies is not endowment

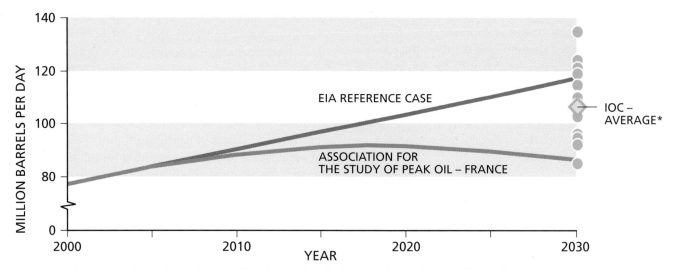

* Average of aggregated proprietary forecasts from international oil companies (IOC) responding to the NPC survey. See Chapter Two (Energy Supply), Analysis of Energy Outlooks, Global Total Liquids Production, for identification of other aggregations and outlooks shown here.

Source: EIA, *International Energy Outlook 2006*, and the NPC Survey of Outlooks.

FIGURE ES-9. *Understanding the Range of Global Oil Forecasts*

but "producibility." Over the next 25 years, risks above ground—geopolitical, technical, and infrastructure—are more likely to affect oil and natural gas production rates than are limitations of the below-ground endowment. This range of outcomes emphasizes the need for proactive strategies to manage the accumulating risks to liquids delivery in 2030.

Explanations for the variance in projections for both conventional oil and natural gas production are widely discussed as part of the "peak oil" debate. As a result, this study sees the need for a new assessment of the global oil and natural gas endowment and resources to provide more current data for the continuing debate.

■ Key Information: The Peak Oil Debate

Concerns about the reliability of production forecasts and estimates of recoverable oil resources raise questions about future oil supply and deliverability. These concerns are strongly expressed in peak oil forecasts in which (1) oil production does not grow significantly beyond current levels and (2) an inevitable decline in oil production is increasingly near at hand. Views about oil supply tend to diverge after 2015, with peak oil forecasts providing the lower bound. These forecasts generally consider oil supply independently of demand and point to supply shortfalls. Such views contrast with forecasts and economic models that expect market forces to provide incentives for developing global hydrocarbon and other resources to meet energy needs through at least 2030.

Forecasts that see an imminent peak in oil production use several indicators to support their case, including: historical peaks in production for individual countries; extrapolations of the production cycle from individual wells to fields, basins, and the world; and the historical dominance of large reservoirs in supplying the world's oil. These historical indicators for production of conventional oil are countered by expectations for new discoveries, enhanced recovery techniques, advancing technology for producing oil from unconventional sources, and reassessments and revisions of known resources. The economic and investment climate, as well as access to resources, will also affect the production base.

For further discussion of peak oil forecasts and related issues, please see Chapter 2, "Energy Supply," in this report.

Reduce Declines in U.S. Conventional Oil and Natural Gas Production

The United States was once the largest oil producer in the world, but is now the third largest daily producer, after Saudi Arabia and Russia. U.S. oil production has declined steadily over the past 35 years, as shown by Figure ES-10. U.S. natural gas production has been more stable, as shown by Figure ES-11, but demand for both oil and natural gas has increased steadily, creating a gap that is filled by imports. Many forecasts project that the gap between supply and demand for domestic oil and natural gas will widen over the next 25 years and beyond. Historically, technology advances have increased the recovery from existing wells and reservoirs. Technology such as enhanced oil recovery (EOR) has the potential to improve recovery factors and reduce declining production.[26]

In 2005, over 17 percent of oil and 9 percent of natural gas produced onshore in the United States came from marginal oil wells. The nation has more than 400,000 marginal oil wells[27] each producing on average 2.2 barrels per day. Without these wells, U.S. imports would increase by nearly 7 percent to make up for the shortage. Increasing operational and regulatory costs, and diminishing access to markets via pipelines, are all key factors that can contribute to the premature abandonment of marginal wells. When wells and fields are prematurely abandoned, the associated oil and gas resources may never be recovered due to economics, lease termination, and related issues. Access to existing fields provides the opportunity to deploy new technologies to enhance the ultimate recovery of oil and natural gas from these fields.

Recommendation

The NPC makes the following recommendations to promote enhanced oil recovery (EOR) from existing reservoirs:

- Support regulatory streamlining and research and development programs for marginal wells.

- Expedite permitting of EOR projects, pipelines, and associated infrastructure.

Potential Effect: An additional 90 to 200 billion barrels of recoverable oil in the United States alone, which could help moderate the current decline in production.

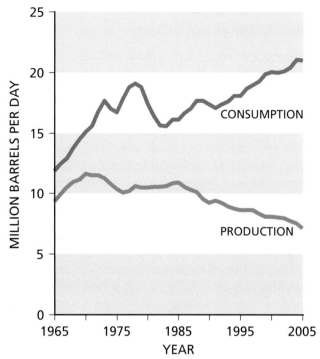

Source: *BP Statistical Review of World Energy 2006.*

FIGURE ES-10. *U.S. Oil Production and Consumption*

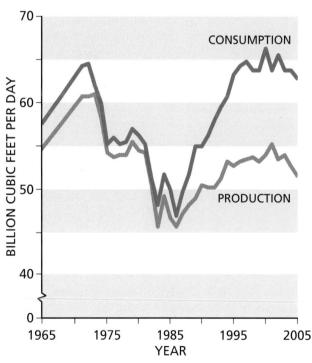

Source: *BP Statistical Review of World Energy 2006.*

FIGURE ES-11. *U.S. Natural Gas Production and Consumption*

Increase Access for New Energy Development

For various reasons, access to some domestic energy resources has become restricted. In the United States, an estimated 40 billion barrels of technically recoverable oil resources are either completely off-limits or are subject to significant lease restrictions. These resources are evenly split between onshore and offshore locations, as shown in Figure ES-12. Similar restrictions apply to more than 250 trillion cubic feet of natural gas. Another estimated 11 billion barrels of oil resources and 51 trillion cubic feet of natural gas resources are restricted in Canada. Advancements in technology and operating practices may now be able to alleviate the environmental concerns that originally contributed to some of these access restrictions.

Recommendation

The NPC makes the following recommendations to expand access to the most favorable U.S. oil and natural gas basins:

- Conduct national and regional basin-oriented resource and market assessments to identify opportunities for increasing oil and natural gas supply.

- Use technology and operational advancements to allow environmentally responsible development of high potential onshore and offshore areas currently restricted by moratoria or access limitations.

Potential Effect: Material increases to current reserves within 5 to 10 years from currently inaccessible areas could approach 40 billion barrels of oil and 250 trillion cubic feet of natural gas with current technology.

There is vast potential for oil and natural gas from "unconventional" resources that could be significant contributors to U.S. oil and natural gas production over the next 25 years. Unconventional natural gas exists in formations of "tight" or physically constrained deposits, in coalbeds, and in shale formations. This represents a significant and growing segment of U.S. natural gas production, estimated to be 20-25 percent of current U.S. natural gas production. Typically, unconventional natural gas wells are productive longer than conventional wells, and they can contribute to sustaining supply over a longer period. Similarly, there are large deposits of crude oil in unconventional formations where production is currently increasing with recent technology innovations.

Vast hydrocarbon deposits exist in the oil shales in the Rocky Mountain region of the United States. Until recently, technology has been unavailable to produce these oil shale deposits at a competitive cost and with acceptable environmental impact. Research, development, and demonstration programs are increasing to advance the technologies required to expand economically and environmentally sustainable resource production. However, successful production at scale may still be several decades away.

Recommendation

The NPC makes the following recommendations to increase unconventional oil and natural gas production:

- Accelerate U.S. oil shale and oil sands research and development and leasing.

- Accelerate U.S. unconventional natural gas leasing and development.

Potential Effect: Double U.S. unconventional natural gas production to more than 10 billion cubic feet per day, increasing total U.S. natural gas production by about 10 percent.

Implementing these strategies can slow the inevitable decline in U.S. oil and natural gas production, but is unlikely to reverse it. The gap between U.S. production and demand will continue to widen, particularly for oil. Long lead-times and higher capital requirements to develop economical energy from new or remote locales, and from unconventional oil and natural gas resources, all contribute to the challenge of moderating the U.S. production decline.

Diversify Long-Term Energy Production

Accelerate the Development of Energy from Biomass

As total U.S. energy demand grows, there will be an increasing need to supplement energy supplies

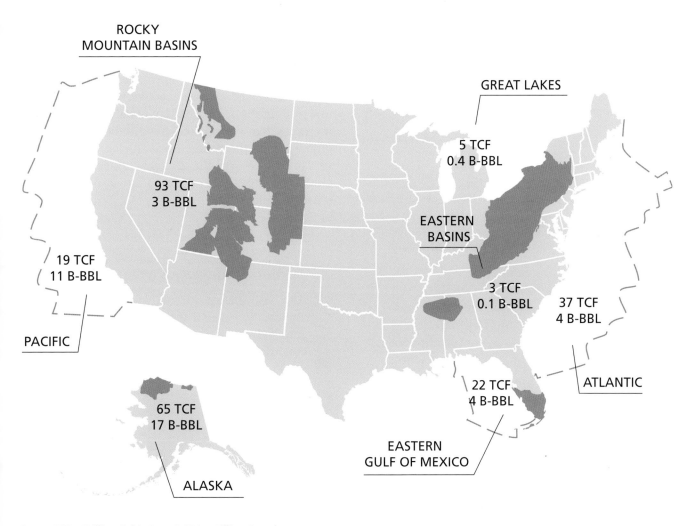

ROCKY
MOUNTAIN BASINS

GREAT LAKES

5 TCF
0.4 B-BBL

93 TCF
3 B-BBL

EASTERN
BASINS

19 TCF
11 B-BBL

3 TCF
0.1 B-BBL

37 TCF
4 B-BBL

PACIFIC

ATLANTIC

22 TCF
4 B-BBL

65 TCF
17 B-BBL

EASTERN
GULF OF MEXICO

ALASKA

Note: TCF = Trillion Cubic Feet; B-BBL = Billion Barrels.
Source: U.S. Department of the Interior.

FIGURE ES-12. *U.S. Oil and Natural Gas Resources Affected by Access Restrictions*

with diversified domestic energy sources that are economically and environmentally viable and can be developed at commercial scale. Coal and nuclear power already play a significant role, and biomass is emerging as an option, primarily for conversion to transportation fuels. Wind and solar energy are forecast to grow faster than overall energy demand, although their total projected contribution will remain small over this study period. Taken together, all these energy sources can contribute to reducing risks posed to energy supply security.

Biomass includes wood, cultivated crops, and naturally growing vegetation that potentially can be converted to energy sources. First-generation biomass conversion to fuels has been based on

crops like corn, sugarcane, soybeans, and palm oil. Developing second-generation biomass conversion technologies, such as cellulosic ethanol, which would use trees, energy crops, and plant waste as a feedstock, could allow non-food vegetation to become a significant resource for fuel production.

As with any newly developed energy sources, certain technical, logistical, and market requirements must be met for biofuels to achieve significant scale. Challenges include: expanding rail, waterway, and pipeline transportation; scaling up ethanol production plants and distribution systems; developing successful cellulosic ethanol conversion technology; and maximizing the potential of arable land.

Enable the Long-Term Environmental Viability of Coal for Power, Fuel, and Feedstock

Given the vast coal resource base in the United States—by some estimates, the world's largest—and the major contribution that coal makes to electricity generation today, coal needs to remain a viable long-term component of U.S. energy supply. Many studies forecast growth in coal use for power, plus additional growth for direct conversion of coal to liquids to diversify the fuel supply. However, coal combustion is also the largest source of CO_2 emissions from energy production. Adding coal-to-liquids production at scale, as with conversion of most heavy unconventional hydrocarbons, would generate large additional CO_2 volumes. Therefore, addressing carbon constraints at scale will likely be an essential requirement for retaining coal as a viable part of the energy supply system. Recommendations for maintaining coal's long-term viability are discussed specifically in the section entitled "Address Carbon Constraints" later in this Executive Summary.

Expand Domestic Nuclear Capability

Energy projections generally show a continuing role for nuclear energy, notwithstanding concerns about safety, security, radioactive waste, and weapons proliferation. In a carbon constrained environment, nuclear energy may need to become a much larger part of the energy mix. Nuclear energy must remain viable over the 25 years considered in this study—both to meet projected demand and to provide expanded capacity, if necessary, to reduce CO_2 emissions.

Strengthen Global and U.S. Energy Security

Besides expanding U.S. oil and natural gas production and developing additional domestic energy types at commercial scale, it will be necessary to enlarge and diversify oil and natural gas supplies from global markets. The long lead-times needed to build domestic energy alternatives at commercial scale will require the United States to remain engaged in international energy markets beyond the time frame considered in this study. Moreover, oil and natural gas supplies from major resource-

■ Key Information: Energy Security and Strategic Petroleum Stocks

This study examined the long-term energy future and focused on fundamental supply and demand, since a robust supply/demand balance is necessary for global energy security. In the short term, there is another aspect to energy security—the availability of strategic stocks to respond to a short-term disruption in supplies.

Following the oil supply shocks of 1973-74, the OECD countries agreed to maintain strategic petroleum stocks and created the International Energy Agency to coordinate measures in times of oil supply emergencies. Today, OECD countries are committed to individually hold oil stocks equal to 90 days of their imports.

This strategic stockholding proved its worth in the aftermath of Hurricanes Katrina and Rita in the U.S. Gulf of Mexico in the fall of 2005. At one point, the hurricanes shut down all Gulf Coast crude oil production and nearly 30 percent of U.S. refining capacity. The IEA coordinated a release of oil from stockpiles worldwide, and the global market quickly rebalanced, with the United States receiving petroleum product supplies from around the world—including Europe and Japan.

In total, the OECD countries currently hold about 1.4 billion barrels of strategic oil stocks. The U.S. Strategic Petroleum Reserve (SPR) alone holds nearly 700 million barrels of crude oil today. To put the U.S. SPR in perspective, its volume currently represents sixteen months of United States oil imports from Venezuela.

The total OECD strategic stockpile volume represents almost 19 months of the entire volume of Iranian crude oil exports[30] (none of which are currently imported into the United States).

holding countries often bear lower production and development costs than do U.S. domestic sources. Maintaining U.S. access to these sources will contribute to an affordable U.S. energy supply and promote U.S. competitiveness in the global marketplace.

The world is entering a period in which international energy development and trade are likely to be influenced more by geopolitical considerations and less by the free play of open markets and traditional commercial interactions among international energy companies. Global competition for oil and natural gas will likely intensify as demand grows, as new parties enter the market, as some suppliers seek to exploit their resources for political ends, and as consumers explore new ways to guarantee their sources of supply.

These shifts pose profound implications for U.S. interests, strategies, and policy making as well as for the ways that energy companies conduct business. Many of the expected changes could heighten risks to U.S. energy security in a world where U.S. influence is likely to decline as economic power shifts to other nations. In years to come, security threats to the world's main sources of oil and natural gas may worsen.

In geoeconomic terms, the biggest impact will come from increasing demand for oil and natural gas from developing countries. This demand may outpace timely development of new supply sources, thereby pressuring prices to rise. In geopolitical terms, the consequences of shifting the balance between developed and developing countries will be magnified by the accelerating demand coming most strongly from China, India, and other emerging economies.

These developments are taking place against a background of rising hostility to globalization in large parts of the world, including in many industrialized countries that benefit from it. This hostility could possibly fracture the global trading system. The political will to complete multilateral trade negotiations may be ebbing as major producers and consumers seek bilateral or regional preferential agreements that can fragment world trade, increase costs, and diminish market efficiency.

- Integrate energy policy into trade, economic, environmental, security, and foreign policies by having the Department of Energy share an equal role with the Departments of Defense, State, Treasury, and Commerce on policy issues relating to energy and energy security.

- Continue to develop the international energy marketplace by expanding the energy dialogue with major consuming and producing nations, including China, India, Canada, Mexico, Russia, and Saudi Arabia.

- Promote an effective global energy marketplace by sustaining and intensifying efforts to encourage global adoption of transparent, market-based approaches to energy through multilateral and international institutions—including the World Trade Organization, G8, Asia-Pacific Economic Cooperation (APEC), IEA, International Energy Forum, and the Joint Oil Data Initiative (JODI).

- Assist and encourage global adoption of energy efficiency technologies through technology transfer programs and lend-lease arrangements.

Potential Effect: Restricted resource access and curtailed production could put potential 2030 global liquid (25-35+ million barrels per day) and gas (150-200+ billion cubic feet per day) incremental growth at risk.

Reinforce Capabilities to Meet New Challenges

To meet the world's growing energy needs, critical capabilities for delivering energy supplies will need to be improved. These critical capabilities include:

- Assessing future infrastructure requirements

- Developing human resources

- Encouraging technology advancement

- Enhancing the quality of energy data and information, including expanding knowledge of resource endowments.

Develop a Comprehensive Forecast of U.S. Infrastructure Requirements

Transportation infrastructure plays a vital role in delivering energy and other commodities from resource locations to shipping centers, to manufacturing plants for processing, and ultimately to demand centers for consumption. The transportation system as a whole is an immense network of pipelines, railways, waterways, ports, terminals, and roadways that has evolved over the past two centuries. The system today is a highly complex, robust delivery network that operates in a safe, reliable manner and serves as the foundation for the country's economic activity.

Shipments of goods have increased substantially using all modes of transport. The spare capacity and redundancies in the various infrastructure systems that existed 25 to 30 years ago have diminished. Continuing growth will require additions to infrastructure.

New infrastructure investments will also be required as nontraditional energy sources grow. Infrastructure requirements for many alternative energy sources, such as biofuels and unconventional oil and natural gas, will be significant and yet are often underestimated. The potential scale of CCS activities would also require significant new infrastructure.

Energy supply and demand projections to 2030 generally assume infrastructure will be built if it is economic to do so. These forecasts generally assume no constraints on the ability to finance, permit, and build the infrastructure required to supply increasing kinds and amounts of energy. In practice, however, social, environmental, and land-use constraints do affect infrastructure planning and development. Complex permitting processes lengthen the time and cost of infrastructure construction and maintenance or may entirely preclude the infrastructure needed for certain energy options. Additional information is needed to understand the full requirements for energy infrastructure additions and the potential limitations to timely investment.

Rebuild U.S. Science and Engineering Capabilities

As the post-World-War-II baby-boom generation begins to retire, the energy industry faces a severe human resource challenge. Nearly half of personnel in the U.S. energy industries will be eligible for retirement within the next 10 years, and fewer people have entered the workforce over the past generation. A "demographic cliff" is looming in all areas of energy industry employment.[31] A hard truth is that the U.S. energy workforce must be replenished and trained, although too few young people are preparing for the opportunities.

An American Petroleum Institute survey in 2004 indicated that by 2009 there will be a 38-percent shortage of engineers and geoscientists and a 28-percent shortage of instrumentation and electrical workers in the U.S. oil and gas industry. Statistics for other science, engineering, and technology professions specifically within the energy industry are not available, but the problem extends to those areas as well. One of the more important predictors for the future supply of potential employees in oil and natural gas is the number of students earning university degrees in petroleum engineering and geosciences. Enrollment in these petrotechnical programs has dropped about 75 percent over the last quarter-century.

The United States has traditionally been a leader in the global energy industry, but that position is threatened by the anticipated loss of experience through retirements, without adequate replacements. The U.S. government and the energy industry should work actively to renew this vital workforce through education, recruitment, development, and retention—much as companies strive to develop and renew energy supplies.

Federal and state governments can play an important role by funding university research and development in science and technology. Consistent support for university research programs relating to the energy industry will signal prospective students that these subjects are vital to the country. For example, several universities have recently increased petrotechnical enrollment by active recruiting aimed at high school seniors, their parents, and their counselors. These results indicate that vigorous recruiting can yield positive results, but efforts need to be more widespread.

There is insufficient time to train enough young professionals to fill the positions opening over the next decade. Accelerating competencies through knowledge sharing, coaching, and mentoring will become critical. Many retirees might prefer to phase-in retirement, but face regulatory barriers that restrict their part-time work. These individuals' expertise should be harnessed to prepare the next generation in both professional and vocational training programs.

Across continents, there is a geographical disparity in the supply of new graduates for some energy related fields (Figure ES-13). Over the next ten years, the number of foreign nationals allowed to work in the United States will be restricted by the number of work permits issued each year. Increasing the quotas on work and study permits can help alleviate this geographical imbalance, and support U.S. energy productivity.

Recommendation

The NPC makes the following recommendation to increase the supply of trained energy professionals in the United States:

- Increase student and immigration quotas for trained professionals in energy and technical fields.

Create Research and Development Opportunities

The oil and natural gas industry uses advanced, state-of-the-art technology. Exploration specialists interpret geologic structures miles beneath the earth's surface. Drilling engineers access the resources found at extreme depths, at high temperature and pressure, and often in remote and physically challenging places. Production engineers bring the oil and natural gas to the surface through miles of pipeline, also under sometimes extreme conditions, and deliver them to refineries. Once there, increasingly heavy and sulfurous crude oils are refined into useful products. All these accomplishments are achieved today with a smaller environmental "footprint" than even a decade ago, and are conducted more economically than ever before.

Most energy technology is developed by industry in response to a resource opportunity, such as opening

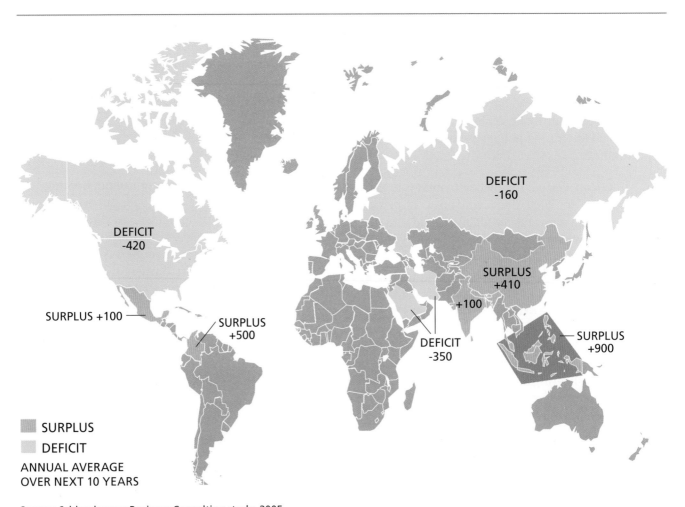

Source: Schlumberger Business Consulting study, 2005.

FIGURE ES-13. *The Regional Imbalance of Petrotechnical Graduates*

Facing the Hard Truths about Energy

exploration in the deepwater Gulf of Mexico. Fewer investments are being directed to researching possibilities for energy production in the continental United States, where accessible conventional opportunities are maturing. Government has a role in creating new opportunities and developing the regulatory framework and infrastructure needed to extract new resources. Enhanced oil recovery is an activity for which funding by the DOE for research could pay significant dividends through increased domestic production. Coalbed methane and oil shale present additional opportunities.

The decline in DOE-funded oil and natural gas-related research and development in the past two years has affected both universities and the National Laboratories. Government funding in engineering and science, when distributed to universities and National Laboratories, sustains these important institutions. It is vital that this funding is accompanied by contracts that call for spending accountability and research delivery.

The national interest is also well served when the government supports large-scale demonstration projects, such as the FutureGen program to integrate large-scale electricity generation with carbon capture and sequestration. In addition, government and industry would benefit from collaborating in several critical areas, including advanced materials, bioprocess, and meteorological and oceanic (metocean) research.

Recommendation

The NPC makes the following recommendations to expand research and development opportunities to support long-term study goals:

- Review the current DOE research and development portfolio to refocus spending on innovative, applied research in areas such as EOR, unconventional oil and natural gas, biofuels, nuclear energy, coal-to-fuels, and CCS.

- Maintain a fundamental research budget in the DOE Office of Science to support novel technologies.

- Focus and enhance research in the U.S. universities and National Laboratories.

- Encourage DOE, Department of Defense, and industry cooperation in innovative areas of development, such as advanced materials and metocean information and analyses.

Improve the Quality of Energy Data and Information

As the study teams examined multiple forecasts, they observed that some of the important basic data and information were incomplete, inconsistent, dated, or oversimplified. Investment and policy decisions are increasingly informed by such uncertain data. For example, some disparities in predictions for future oil and natural gas supplies result from divergent estimates of the underlying resources and their deliverability. Additionally, little or no quantitative data are available to clearly understand the need for additional infrastructure capacity.

Recommendation

The NPC makes the following recommendations to enhance the quality of energy data and information:

- Expand data collected by EIA and IEA to provide additional sources of production and consumption data for inclusion in annually prepared public domain energy outlooks.

- Expand funding for data collection and analysis of energy transportation systems to enable informed infrastructure decisions.

There are many energy outlooks, but most base their projections for future fossil-fuel production on a few publicly available resource estimates, most notably the U.S. Geological Survey (USGS) assessments. Since these assessments are comprehensively updated only every decade or so, the fundamental data for energy policy decisions may not reflect the most current perspectives. In addition, the many organizations involved in energy forecasting and analysis often apply different methodologies and assumptions to the assessments, which can create misunderstandings about future production capabilities.

This study's results confirm the primary importance of maintaining comprehensive, up-to-date, fundamental assessments of the global oil, natural gas, and coal endowment and recoverable resources. Although each such assessment produces inherent uncertainties based on the state of geological knowledge and observational information, a new, comprehensive assessment would more accurately frame the condition of the fossil resource base for policy decision making and strategy. Additionally, given the growing contribution expected from biomass-based energy sources by 2030, a global assessment of this renewable resource would provide a more complete outlook for the available energy endowment.

In order to increase the reliability and timeliness of fundamental endowment and resource data, the United States should collaborate with other global stakeholders to improve the collection, management, interpretation, and communication of data and estimates for energy endowments and recoverable resources.

Recommendation

The NPC makes the following recommendations to update publicly available global endowment and resource estimates:

- The USGS should conduct a comprehensive geological assessment of U.S. and global oil and natural gas endowment and recoverable resources.

  - Incorporate wider participation of industry and international experts and current data.

- The USGS should conduct a new, comprehensive survey of U.S. and global recoverable coal resources and reserves using common analysis and reporting methodologies.

- The U.S. Departments of Energy and Agriculture should conduct a global biomass resource assessment.

Potential Effect: Timely and better informed policy decisions based on shared understanding of critical resource data.

Address Carbon Constraints

There is growing concern that the global climate is warming, and that CO_2 emissions from human activity play a role. The NPC did not examine the science of climate change. But recognizing that an increasing number of initiatives to reduce these emissions are emerging, the NPC considered the potential effect of

Source: IEA, *World Energy Outlook 2006,* Reference Case.

FIGURE ES-14. *World Carbon Dioxide Emissions*

CO_2 emissions constraints on energy and opportunities for technology application. Limits on CO_2 emissions could restrict fossil fuel use, which currently provides more than 80 percent of the world's energy. Therefore, it is increasingly important to plan for potential constraints on CO_2 emissions as part of any overall energy strategy.

By its nature, climate change is global. CO_2 emissions from burning fossil fuels contribute to the overall flux of carbon between the atmosphere, the land, and the oceans. By mixing in the atmosphere, CO_2 emitted anywhere in the world is distributed around the globe.

The United States was the world's largest CO_2 emitter from energy use as of 2005,[32] both in total emissions and on a per-capita basis, but most projected growth of CO_2 emissions is in the developing world, as illustrated in Figure ES-14. Significantly reducing CO_2 emissions would require global, broad-based actions over decades, with major and sustained investment.

Enable Carbon Capture and Sequestration

Coal combustion is the largest source of CO_2 emissions from energy use, and coal is projected to remain a major fuel for electricity generation in most forecasts. The resource base for coal is much larger than that for oil and natural gas, and the United States has the world's largest coal resource by some estimates.[33] One opportunity for reducing CO_2 emissions is carbon capture and sequestration, which traps CO_2 and stores it underground. Extensive, commercial scale deployment of this technology could allow continued coal use in a carbon constrained future. Additionally, some unconventional oil production requires substantial energy, increasing CO_2 emissions per unit of delivered energy, and future development could be influenced by the availability of CCS. An initial suite of technologies for large-scale CCS implementation already exists within the oil and natural gas industry, although such technologies have yet to be demonstrated in combination and at commercial scale. More importantly, a legal and regulatory framework for long-term CO_2 storage is still lacking.

Scale is also a major consideration for CCS. In the United States, if all the CO_2 from today's coal-fired electricity generation were collected and compressed, it would total 50 million barrels per day.[34] This amounts to 2½ times the volume of oil handled daily in the United States. To accommodate such volumes, potential storage sites need to be mapped and assessed.

Recommendation

The NPC makes the following recommendations to enable long-term environmental viability of coal for both power and fuel:

- Establish a legal and regulatory framework which is conducive to CCS.

  - Provide regulatory clarity for land use and liability policies.

  - Provide access to federal lands for storage.

- Enable full scale CCS and clean coal technology demonstration.

  - Organize efforts between the power and oil/natural gas industries.

- Undertake a national CO_2 sequestration capacity assessment.

  - Build on the existing efforts being undertaken by the DOE Regional Partnerships.

  - Encourage global application.

- Continue federal research and development support for advanced coal-to-fuel technologies.

Potential Effect: Maintaining coal's projected 25 percent contribution to the future U.S. energy mix, including potential coal-to-liquids production, even in carbon-constrained circumstances.

A comprehensive approach to carbon management would include measures to: boost energy efficiency and reduce demand; increase use of power that is not carbon based (nuclear, wind, solar, tidal, ocean-thermal, and geo-thermal); shift to lower carbon fuels, including renewables; and deploy CCS. Putting a cost on carbon emissions across all economic sectors, whether through a carbon tax or a carbon cap-and-trade mechanism, would allow the marketplace to find the lowest cost combination of steps to achieve carbon reduction. Any cost should be imposed in a predictable manner over the long term, since regulatory uncertainty weakens the investment climate and has the potential to disrupt economic activity. Any cost imposed should also consider the actions of other countries and the resulting effect on U.S. competitiveness.

Recommendation

As policymakers consider actions to reduce CO_2 emissions, the NPC recommends including:

- An effective global framework for carbon management incorporating all major emitters of CO_2 and focusing particularly on opportunities for U.S.–China cooperation.

- A U.S. mechanism for setting an effective cost for emitting CO_2 that is:

  - Economy-wide, market-based, visible, transparent, applicable to all fuels.

  - Predictable over the long term for a stable investment climate.

- A credit for CO_2 used in enhanced oil and natural gas recovery.

Direct regulation: CO_2 emissions could be constrained by imposing limits on emissions from individual sources, such as power plants and industrial facilities. Economists generally regard this sort of regulation as inefficient, because it does not allow for the likelihood that some sources may be able to achieve emissions reductions more economically than others. Encouraging greater emissions reductions by the sources that can do so most economically would yield a larger total reduction for a given total cost, but this can be difficult to accomplish with fixed regulatory targets.

Cap-and-trade regulation: Cap-and-trade systems seek to overcome the inefficiency of direct regulation by providing a market-based mechanism to encourage those who can reduce CO_2 emissions most economically to do so. Regulators must determine which sources will be covered by the system and the total amount of emissions that will be allowed within a specified period of time. Permits to emit a given amount, such as one metric ton of CO_2, are then allocated or auctioned. The permits can be traded, encouraging sources that can eliminate emissions for less than the market price of a permit to do so, while sources for whom emissions control is more costly can buy permits from others.

Creating a cap-and-trade system involves important policy choices:

- Which sectors to include.

- What level of emissions should be permitted and whether any "safety valve" is provided to limit the volatility or price of permits.

- Whether permits should be allocated at no cost or auctioned.

- Whether there should be a single permitting system covering all affected sectors or multiple systems for different sectors.

Fundamentally, a cap-and-trade system establishes a level of emissions, and the marketplace then establishes the cost.

Carbon taxes or fees: A tax or fee could be levied on CO_2 emissions, establishing the cost of emissions while letting the market then establish the emissions level. In principle, any level of emissions reduction that could be achieved with a cap-and-trade scheme could also be achieved with taxes or fees. For CO_2 emissions from combustion, the simplest method would levy the fee on the primary fuel, with a credit system for any use that doesn't emit CO_2 such as production of petrochemicals.

A tax or fee system has the advantages of establishing a predictable cost, thus encouraging long-term planning and investment, and not requiring the regulatory complexity of determining the equitable emissions allowance levels by sector and facility. A tax or fee system has the disadvantage that the level of resulting emissions is not established in advance. A tax or fee system also poses the challenge of how to equitably return the revenues to the economy.

Potential Effect of Recommended Strategies

The Council proposes five core strategies to assist markets in meeting the energy challenges to 2030 and beyond. An illustration of the potential effect of implementing all the recommended strategies is shown in Figure ES-15. Starting with the EIA Reference Case for U.S. liquid fuel demand, the potential effect of the recommended demand reduction strategies is shown in light green. The potential effects of recommended strategies to moderate the decline of conventional supplies, and strategies to further expand and diversify supplies are shown in dark green. The combined effect of the recommended strategies would reduce the gap between domestic demand and supply by about one-third from 2006 to 2030 in this illustration—improving the outlook for energy availability, reliability, cost, and environmental impact.

Given the massive scale of the global energy system and the long lead-times necessary to make significant changes, concerted actions to implement these recommendations must be taken now, and sustained over the long term, to promote U.S. competitiveness

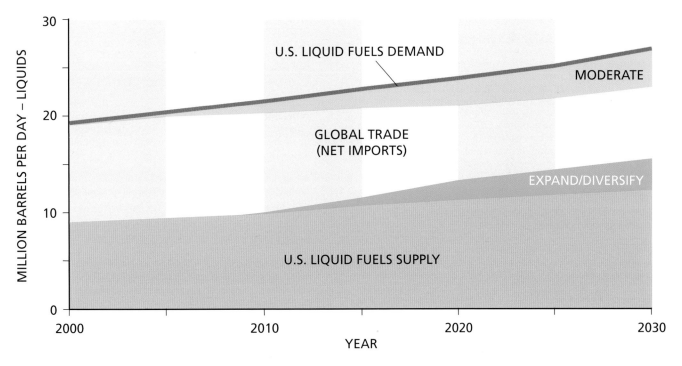

Source: EIA, *International Energy Outlook 2006*, Reference Case / NPC Global Oil and Gas study estimates.

FIGURE ES-15. *Illustrative Effect of Recommended Strategies for the United States*

by balancing economic, security, and environmental goals. The following report chapters detail more fully the challenges posed by the complexity of the world's integrated energy system and the opportunities to secure a more reliable energy future.

Endnotes

1   The OECD (Organisation for Economic Co-operation and Development) includes Australia, Austria, Belgium, Canada, Czech Republic, Denmark, Finland, France, Germany, Greece, Hungary, Iceland, Italy, Japan, Korea, Luxembourg, Mexico, Netherlands, New Zealand, Norway, Poland, Portugal, Slovak Republic, Spain, Sweden, Switzerland, Turkey, United Kingdom, and United States of America.

2   For 2003, per the IEA's *World Energy Outlook 2005* and the EIA's *International Energy Outlook 2006*.

3   As of year-end 2005, 31.6 million cars and 1.3 billion people, as reported by the China National Statistics Bureau.

4   Per the U.S Bureau of Transportation Statistics, the United States had 137 million cars in 2004; population was 281 million. But the U.S. also has a large number of trucks/SUVs used as passenger vehicles, which are unfortunately not reported separately. A close approximation would be the category of "other vehicles—two axle, four wheel," which would add 92 million vehicles and bring the total for U.S. "passenger vehicles" to 228 million, for a ratio of 8 passenger vehicles for 10 people.

5   "Primary Energy" refers to first use of an energy source. For example, coal can be burned to produce electricity. There are losses of energy in the process of generating and transmitting the electricity to the end user, such that the energy value of electricity finally used is less than the energy value of the coal initially burned. In this example, coal is the primary energy, not the final electricity used.

6   The "Billion Ton Study" – *Biomass as a Feedstock for a Bioenergy and Bioproducts Industry: The Technical Feasibility of a Billion-Ton Annual Supply*, USDA and USDOE, April 2005, available at http://www.osti.gov/bridge.

7   About 240 years based on the most recent study by USGS in 1974. Just prior to publication of this NPC study, the National Academy of Sciences issued a report suggesting that economically recoverable coal reserves in the U.S. might be lower than the 1974 USGS study—approximately 100 years of current consumption.

8   See in this report, "New Patterns of Trade" section in Chapter 4, Geopolitics.

9   See *World Oil Outlook 2007*, OPEC Secretariat, especially pages 2, 7, and 8.

10 IEA *World Energy Outlook 2006*, Chapter 12, page 315.

11 Refer to the *Technology Development Topic Report* accompanying this report, Section F.

12 The Hibernia platform discovery in 1979, first production in 1997, producing 180,000 barrels per day. *http://www.hibernia.ca*

13 The Thunder Horse Platform discovery in 1999, design capacity 250,000 barrels per day. *http://www.bp.com*

14 Per reported estimates for a proposed new refinery by the Arizona Refining Company, *http://www.arizonacleanfuels.com*

15 American Association of Oil Pipelines.

16 National Petroleum Council, *Balancing Natural Gas Policy*, 2003.

17 For example, see *The Crude Oil Windfall Profit Tax of the 1980s—Implications for Current Energy Policy*, Congressional Research Service, 2006, available at http://nationaljournal.com/policy-council/energy/legnar/031406CRS_Crude.pdf.

18 See in this report, "Transportation Efficiency" section of Chapter 3, Technology. The extent to which technologies translate into reductions in fuel consumption depends on several factors, including costs, consumer preferences, availability, deployment, and timing.

19 The potential fuel savings of 3 to 5 million barrels per day in 2030 is relative to a scenario where current fuel economy standards remain unchanged through 2030.

20 Baseline projections taken from Energy Information Administration, *Annual Energy Outlook 2007 with Projections to 2030*, Table 2, February 2007, http://www.eia.doe.gov/oiaf/aeo/excel/aeotab_2.xls; savings estimates taken from several studies including *Building on Success, Policies to Reduce Energy Waste in Buildings*, Joe Loper, Lowell Ungar, David Weitz and Harry Misuriello – Alliance to Save Energy, July 2005. "Achievable" used here means that the measures are currently available and the savings can be realized with a reasonable level of effort and with acceptable reductions, if any, in perceived amenity value.

For additional discussion, see the *National Action Plan for Energy Efficiency*, which is available at: http://www.epa.gov/cleanrgy/actionplan/eeactionplan.htm.

21 From *Building on Success, Policies to Reduce Energy Waste in Buildings*, Joe Loper, Lowell Ungar, David Weitz and Harry Misuriello – Alliance to Save Energy, July 2005, pp. 18-19. For a compilation of compliance studies, see U.S. Department of Energy, *Baseline Studies*, on web site (http://www.energycodes.gov/implement/baseline_studies.stm). Arkansas reports 36 of 100 homes in the study sample did not meet the HVAC requirements of the state energy code.

22 From *Building on Success, Policies to Reduce Energy Waste in Buildings*, Joe Loper, Lowell Ungar, David Weitz and Harry Misuriello – Alliance to Save Energy, July 2005, p. 24.

23 For additional savings potential see Steven Nadel, Andrew deLaski, Maggie Eldridge, & Jim Kleisch, *Leading the Way: Continued Opportunities for New State Appliance and Equipment Efficiency Standards*, March 2006, http://www.standardsasap.org/a062.pdf.

24 From the *Chemical Bandwidth Study*, DOE, 2004; *Energy Bandwidth for Petroleum Refining Processes*, DOE, 2006; *Pulp and Paper Industry Energy Bandwidth Study*, AIChE, 2006.

See also *Curbing Global Energy Demand Growth: The Energy Productivity Opportunity*, McKinsey Global Institute, May 2007.

25 "Combined heat and power" refers to using the excess heat from generating electricity to meet processing or building heat needs. This combination is frequently called "cogeneration" and results in a substantial increase in efficiency versus generating electricity and heat separately.

26 See in this report, "Conventional Oil" section in Chapter 3, Technology, for a full discussion of potential technologies that may increase conventional oil and gas recovery.

27 A "marginal well" is one that produces less than 10 barrels of oil per day.

28 The "Billion Ton Study" – *Biomass as a Feedstock for a Bioenergy and Bioproducts Industry: The Technical Feasibility of a Billion-Ton Annual Supply*, USDA and USDOE, April 2005, available at http://www.osti.gov/bridge.

29 See www.energycommission.org/files/contentFiles/report_noninteractive_44566feaabc5d.pdf, page IV.

30 Iranian oil exports were 2.5 million barrels per day in 2006 per the EIA.

31 U.S. Department of Labor: "Identifying and Addressing Workforce Challenges in America's Energy Industry," President's High Growth Job Training Initiative, U.S. DOL Employment Training Administration (March 2007).

32 According to a preliminary estimate by the Netherlands Environmental Assessment Agency, China overtook the United States in total CO_2 emissions for the year 2006. More information at http://www.mnp.nl/en/dossiers/Climatechange/moreinfo/Chinanowno1inCO2emissionsUSAinsecondposition.html.

33 Based on the 1974 USGS assessment. A very recent study by the National Academy of Science suggests that the U.S. economically recoverable coal resource may only be ~40% of the USGS estimate.

34 Based on 150,000 barrels per day of supercritical CO_2 from a one-gigawatt coal-fired power plant and 2,090 terawatt-hours of coal-fired electricity generation in the United States in 2004 per the EIA.

Chapter
ENERGY DEMAND

Abstract

Demand for energy is growing steadily, and is likely to reach increasingly higher levels as populations and economies expand. During the last quarter-century, world energy demand increased by over half, and a similar increase is projected between now and 2030. However, future growth builds from today's much larger base, meaning that tomorrow's energy requirements are unprecedented in scale. This will pressure the global supply system and require increased emphasis on energy-use efficiency in transportation, residential, commercial, and industrial sectors.

This chapter examines how credible, integrated modeling efforts portray the future world energy situation, and identifies the implications of those projections. Subgroups examined a wide range of demand data from public and aggregated proprietary sources, making no attempt to produce a new, consensus projection. Expert teams assessed technologies that hold potential for critical efficiency gains; coal demand and supply trends; and how cultural, social, and economic conditions and other non-technical forces shape energy demand.

The outline of the Energy Demand chapter is as follows:

- Demand Study Observations
- Demand Summary
- Demand Data Evaluation
- Electric Generation Efficiency
- Coal Impact
- Industrial Efficiency
- Cultural/Social/Economic Trends
- Residential/Commercial Efficiency
- Demand Study Potential Policy Options
- Policy Recommendations.

The Demand Task Group organized its activities into six subgroups (Demand Data Evaluation, Electric Generation Efficiency, Coal Impact, Industrial Efficiency, Cultural/Social/Economic Trends, and Residential/Commercial Efficiency). The output of these efforts led to a series of observations and development of potential policy options. Detailed discussions of the work of each subgroup have been included in the report as topic papers. These topic papers are included on the CD distributed with the report (a list of all the topic papers can be found in Appendix E).

- The purpose of the Demand Data Evaluation subgroup was to summarize and compare the output from publicly available, integrated energy projections for the world, to understand the underlying basis of those projections, and to compare the results with other projections that were either non-integrated or available only as aggregated proprietary studies.

- The intent of the Electric Generation Efficiency subgroup was to understand the efficiency potential in the electric generation sector and estimate the portion of that potential that is included in the available projections.

- The Coal Impact subgroup examined both the coal supply and demand trends. The primary goals were to compare the projected demand for coal in the outlooks examined with the potential future supply of coal on a worldwide and regional basis and to evaluate coal transportation factors.

- The focus of the Industrial Efficiency subgroup was to define the potential for energy-efficiency improvement in the industrial energy sector and to compare that potential to an estimate of the efficiency that is embedded in the outlooks examined for the study. This effort also investigated historical patterns of industrial feedstock use and how they changed over time.

- The Cultural/Social/Economic Trends subgroup undertook a broad area of investigation aimed at examining how non-technical factors affect energy demand, including how these factors have changed over time and how they might be expected to change in the future.

- The Residential/Commercial Efficiency subgroup looked at the potential for energy-efficiency improvement in the residential and commercial end-use sectors. Much of this effort focused on the potential to reduce energy losses in existing structures, the potential impact of appliance standards on energy use, and the potential impact of new building standards.

- Each of these subgroup efforts resulted in formation of observations associated with the respective areas. The Demand Task Group reviewed all of the observations and organized them into a list of those that appear to be the most significant.

- The next step in the process was to develop potential policy options, which were used as input into the study recommendations process after the Demand Task Group reduced the overall list to those it identified as most significant.

DEMAND STUDY OBSERVATIONS

The output of each of the demand subgroups provides a broad view of historical and projected worldwide and regional energy use. Many observations were derived from the subgroups' efforts. The list of observations were reduced to eighteen that the Demand Task Group deemed to be the most significant and broad

based.[1] The rest of the observations can be found in the individual demand subgroup reports located in the topic papers.

1. **Income and population are prime drivers of energy demand.**

   The assumed rate of economic growth is a key variable in projections of global energy demand. Population growth and the size of a region's population are also important variables. Projected annual average global economic growth from 2000 to 2030 ranges from 3 percent to 4.4 percent in the publicly available integrated energy outlooks. From 1980 to 2000, global economic growth averaged 3.1 percent.

2. **There are varying views on the rate of global energy demand growth.**

   Projected annual average global energy demand growth from 2000 to 2030 ranges from 1.5 percent to 2.5 percent. Global energy demand growth averaged 1.7 percent from 1980 to 2000. High and low projections of economic growth result in high and low projections, respectively, of future energy growth. The difference in energy demand in 2030 between the high and low growth rates is 224 quadrillion Btu—equivalent to roughly half of global demand in 2005.

3. **There is a range of views on the rate of U.S. economic and energy demand growth.**

   Projections of annual average U.S. economic growth from 2000 to 2030 in the public energy outlooks range from 2.3 percent to 3.3 percent. The 1980 to 2000 average was 3.2 percent. Projected annual average U.S. energy demand growth ranges from 0.5 percent to 1.3 percent. The 1980 to 2000 average was 1.2 percent. The difference between the high and low energy demand growth rates from 2000 to 2030 is 37 quadrillion Btu—equivalent to 37 percent of 2005 total U.S. energy demand.

4. **In most cases, carbon dioxide emissions are closely related to projected energy use.**

   Projected global carbon dioxide emissions generally grow at roughly the same rate as projected

---

1 Unless otherwise noted, data referred to in this chapter and used in its figures and tables are from the Energy Information Administration's (EIA) *International Energy Outlook 2006* and the International Energy Agency's (IEA) *World Energy Outlook 2006*. These data were gathered by the NPC Survey of Global Energy Supply/Demand Outlooks.

energy demand, while growth in the United States is slightly slower than energy demand growth.

5. **Fossil fuels remain the largest source of energy.**

    In 2030, fossils fuels (oil, natural gas, and coal) are projected to account for between 83 and 87 percent of total world energy demand compared with 85 percent in 2000. The share for the United States ranges from 81 to 87 percent in 2030. The U.S. share in 2000 was 86 percent.

6. **The projections indicate that a large and, in many cases, growing share of energy use will be met by coal.**

    In all of the projections but one, annual average demand growth for coal is faster than in the past for both the United States and the world. Resources do not appear to be limiting the projected growth in coal use. However, use of coal will require infrastructure development, especially for transportation and unconventional uses such as coal to liquids.

7. **In most of the outlooks, world natural gas demand is projected to increase at a slower rate than in the past (1980 to 2000).**

    Natural gas demand growth is still faster than total energy demand from 2000 to 2030. The result is natural gas gaining in market share.

8. **Growth in U.S. natural gas demand is projected to be significantly slower than in the past (1980 to 2000), which results in a decline in its share of total U.S. energy.**

    Despite slower demand growth, absolute U.S. consumption of natural gas is projected to continue to grow.

9. **Projected world demand growth for oil is faster than in the past (1980-2000), but less than the projected overall increase in energy demand resulting in a declining market share for oil.**

    Annual average growth in world oil demand between 2000 and 2030 is projected to increase at an annual average rate ranging from 1.0 to 1.9 percent. From 1980 to 2000, annual growth in world oil demand averaged 0.9 percent. In most cases, U.S. oil demand growth equals or exceeds the 0.6 percent annual average growth rate from 1980 to 2000.

10. **Nuclear energy use is projected to contribute a declining share to world energy and U.S. energy consumption, but it grows in absolute terms.**

    Both world and U.S. projections show nuclear energy use growing slower than total energy demand, and losing its share of the energy mix.

11. **Transportation oil use is the largest component of oil demand growth in the world and the United States.**

    Transportation increases its share of world and U.S. oil use.

12. **The share of natural gas use in the major end-use sectors—residential/commercial, industrial, and electric generation—changes over time.**

    The publicly available projections show a declining share of world natural gas use in the residential and commercial sectors, essentially a constant share for industrial purposes, and an increasing share for electric generation. In the United States, the natural gas share remains essentially constant in the residential/commercial sector, while it declines in the industrial sector and grows for electric generation.

13. **Energy demand in Asia/Oceania is projected to grow at a faster rate than the global and U.S. averages.**

    Projected energy growth in the publicly available integrated projections indicates that Asia/Oceania's share of total world energy demand will increase by about 10 percent between 2000 and 2030. Over the same period, despite rising absolute consumption, the United States' share of total world energy use is projected to decline by about 2 percent.

14. **Energy use is projected to grow slower than economic activity in both the world and the United States, resulting in a projected decline in energy intensity.**

    World energy use is projected to grow slower than economic growth. This is a continuation of past trends. The United States is expected to exhibit a similar profile. Energy intensity (energy use per unit of gross domestic product, GDP) declines at a faster rate in Asia/Oceania than in North America.

15. Global and U.S. energy consumption, per capita, is projected to increase.

With the exception of one case, in all the publicly available integrated projections, energy use per capita increases in the world, Asia, and the United States. From 1980 to 2000, energy use per capita was essentially constant in the United States, while it increased in Asia.

16. U.S. per capita energy consumption is projected to remain higher than the world average.

In most publicly available projections, U.S. energy use per capita in 2030 is projected to be 4 times greater than the world average and 6 times greater than in Asia. In 2000, the U.S. to world ratio was 5 and U.S. to Asia ratio was 11.

17. U.S. energy efficiency improvement, as measured by energy intensity, is projected to be equal to—or less than—the historical rate from 1980 to 2000.

Data limitations constrain insights into the amount of efficiency increase outside the United States that is built into the projections. However, the decrease in energy intensity suggests that there is an increase in energy efficiency underpinning many of the projections. U.S. new light duty vehicle miles per gallon (mpg) appears to be projected to increase at 0.6 percent per year. U.S. industrial efficiency is estimated to increase by 5 percent over the projection period. There is potential for further energy efficiency improvement in both of these sectors as well as in the residential/commercial sectors.

18. Applying additional policy initiatives could change the energy, economic, and environmental outlook.

In a projection that assumed the enactment of several additional policies—the IEA Alternative Policy Case—total world energy demand growth from 2000 to 2030 was about 0.4 percent per year lower then in the IEA Reference Case. In the same Alternative Policy Case, growth in U.S. energy demand was 0.3 percent per year lower than in the Reference Case. Global carbon dioxide emissions are 6 billion metric tons lower (34 billion metric tons) in 2030 in the IEA Alternative Policy Case than in the IEA Reference Case (40 billion metric tons).

DEMAND SUMMARY

The NPC Demand Task Group reviewed, analyzed, and compared projections of world energy demand. These projection data were gathered by the NPC Survey of Global Energy Supply/Demand Outlooks and collected in the NPC data warehouse, a repository for data and information used in this study, which is discussed in the Methodology chapter. Publicly available demand data from the U.S. Department of Energy's Energy Information Administration and the International Energy Agency were the main focus of the analysis. Aggregated proprietary data and data from other, generally less complete, public outlooks were used primarily to establish whether the EIA and IEA outlooks provided a reasonable range of projections for analysis.

The three major input assumptions behind both the EIA and the IEA projections are economic growth, population, and energy policies. In general, the economic growth projections (2000 to 2030) for the world exceed past (1980 to 2000) growth. World population growth projections in all cases are essentially the same. Population growth rates are projected to be generally lower than historical growth rates.

The EIA projections generally include only those energy policies that are currently in effect and allow most policies to expire as currently enacted at their sunset dates. The IEA Reference Case, however, assumes the likely extension of public policies. The IEA Alternative Policy Case provides a significantly different energy policy approach, assuming not only existing energy policies and their logical extension, but also other policies that are under consideration around the world. Projected worldwide energy demand is shown in Figure 1-1, while projected U.S. energy demand is shown in Figure 1-2.

World demand for petroleum liquids is projected to grow from about 76 million barrels per day in 2000 to between 98 and 138 million barrels per day in 2030 (Figure 1-3). U.S. petroleum liquids demand is projected to grow from about 19 million barrels per day in 2000 to between 21 and 30 million barrels per day in 2030 (Figure 1-4).

World natural gas demand is projected to range from 356 to 581 billion cubic feet per day in 2030, compared with 243 billion cubic feet per day in 2000 (Figure 1-5). U.S. natural gas demand, which was 64 billion cubic feet per day in 2000, is projected to

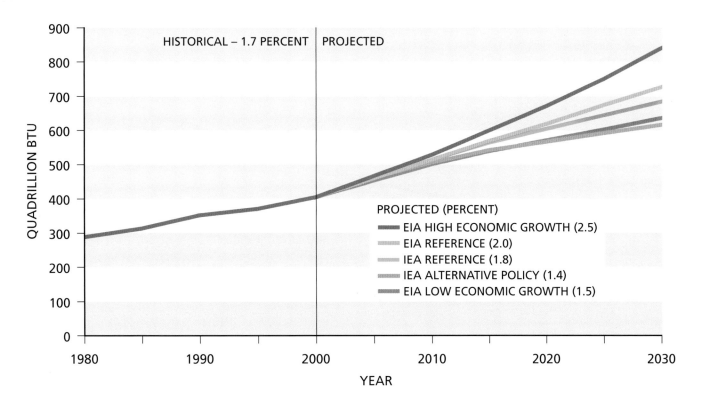

FIGURE 1-1. *World Energy Demand — Average Annual Growth Rates*

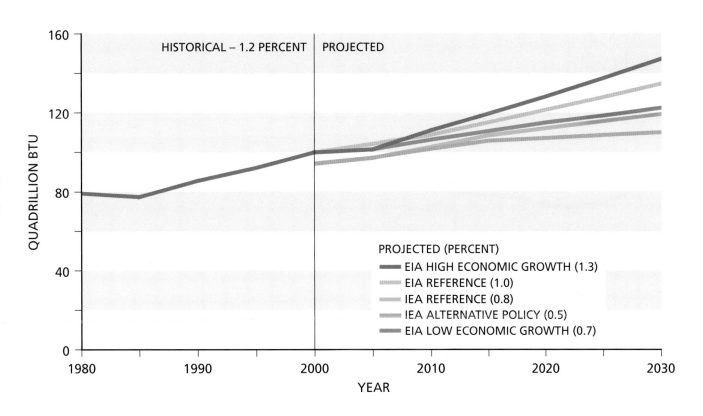

FIGURE 1-2. *U.S. Energy Demand — Average Annual Growth Rates*

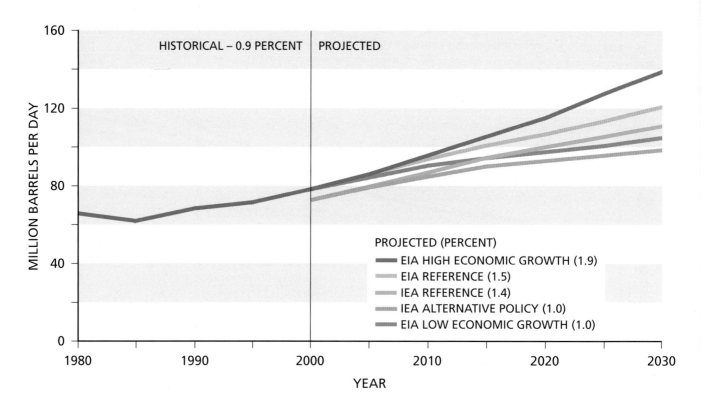

FIGURE 1-3. *World Petroleum Demand — Average Annual Growth Rates*

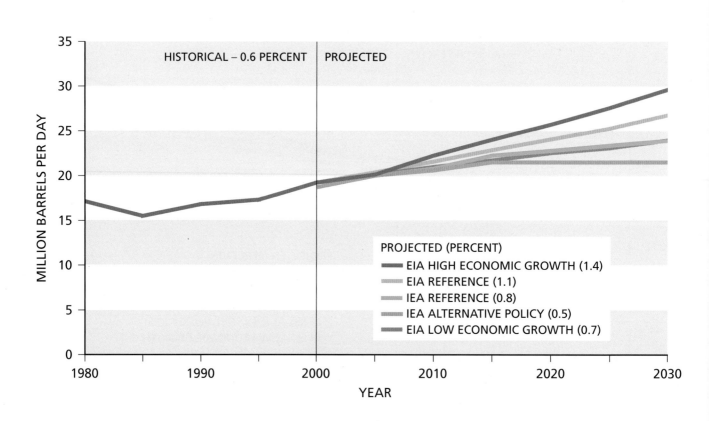

FIGURE 1-4. *U.S. Petroleum Demand — Average Annual Growth Rates*

Facing the Hard Truths about Energy

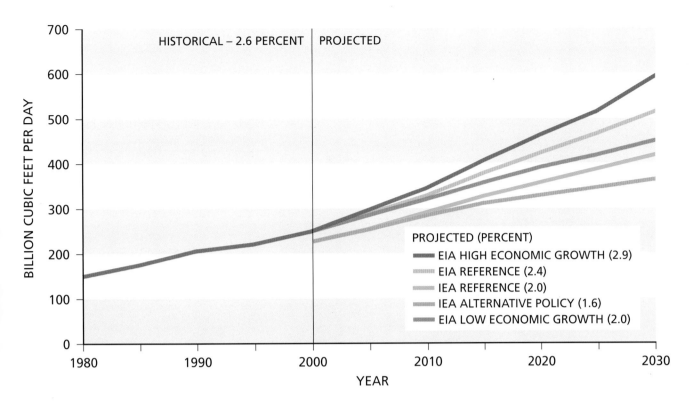

FIGURE 1-5. *World Natural Gas Demand — Average Annual Growth Rates*

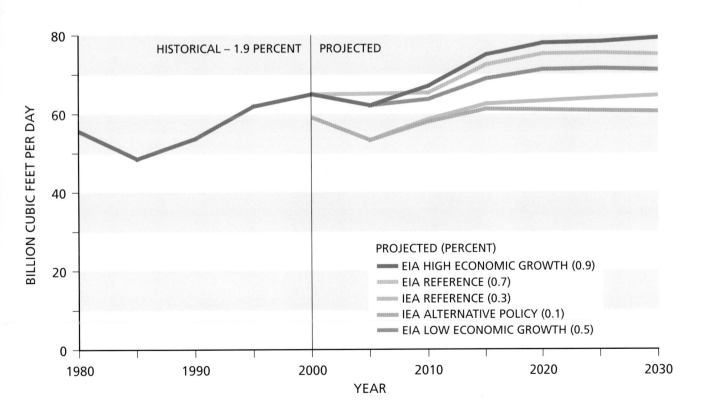

FIGURE 1-6. *U.S. Natural Gas Demand — Average Annual Growth Rates*

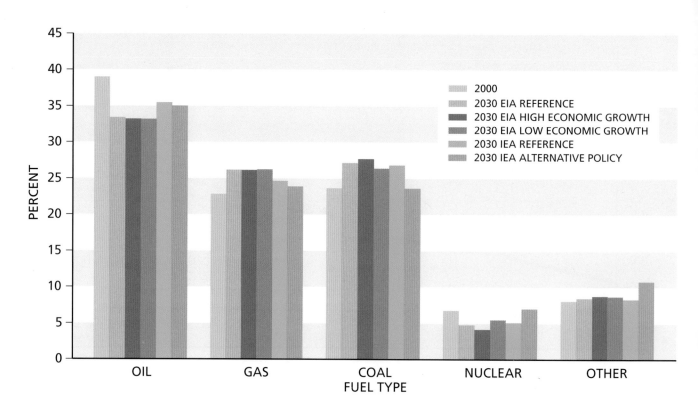

FIGURE 1-7. *World Energy Supply Shares*

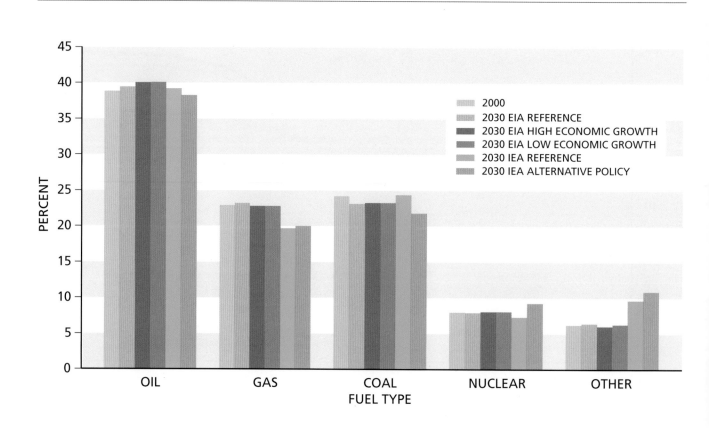

FIGURE 1-8. *U.S. Energy Supply Shares*

range from 59 to 78 billion cubic feet per day in 2030 (Figure 1-6).

On a world basis, oil use is generally expected to lose share, while share gain is expected in the United States. On the other hand, worldwide natural gas use share is projected to increase (Figure 1-7). In the United States, the projections indicate little change to a slight decline in natural gas use share (Figure 1-8).

Worldwide carbon dioxide emissions grow from 24 billion metric tons in 2000 and are projected to range from 34 to 51 billion metric tons in 2030 (Figure 1-9). In all cases, carbon dioxide emissions increase at about the same rate as energy demand. In 2030, projected carbon dioxide emissions in the United States range from 6.3 to 9 billion metric tons compared with 5.8 billion metric tons in 2000.

Regional shares of energy use are projected to change over time. The share of total worldwide energy consumed in North America, OECD Europe, and Non-OECD Europe & Eurasia is projected to fall in all of the cases, while the share in Asia/Oceania grows (Table 1-1). In general, the change in the oil share of total worldwide oil consumed by region parallels

	2000 IEA	2030 IEA Ref. Case
North America	27%	21%
Central and South America	5%	5%
OECD Europe	18%	13%
Non-OECD Europe & Eurasia	10%	8%
Middle East	4%	6%
Asia/Oceania	31%	41%
Africa	5%	6%

TABLE 1-1. *Regional Energy Shares*

the change in the share of total energy consumption, with industrialized regions losing share and the Asia/Oceania oil share increasing significantly.

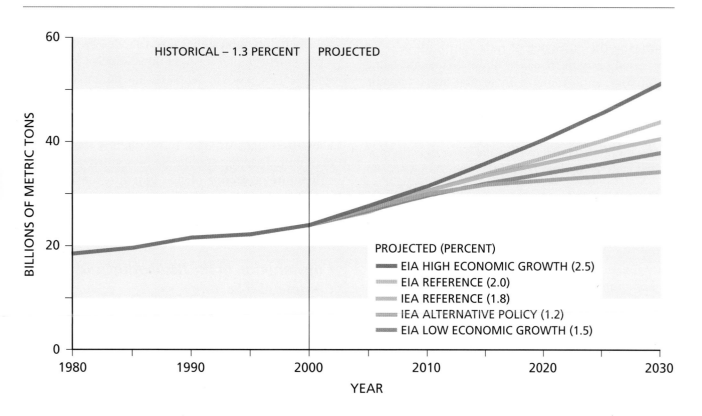

FIGURE 1-9. *World Carbon Dioxide Emissions — Average Annual Growth Rates*

Improvement in the efficiency of energy use is an important factor determining future energy use. The models used to project future energy use are complex, which makes it difficult to provide precise estimates of the efficiency improvement built into the projections. However, energy use intensity (energy use per unit of GDP) provides a useful proxy and is projected to decline in all regions.

Major Areas to Moderate Demand by Increasing Energy Efficiency

Vehicle Fuel Economy

The major use of liquid fuels in the United States is for transportation. The projections that were studied indicate that transportation will likely remain the primary use of liquid fuels in the United States. Among various transportation uses, light duty vehicle use (automobiles and light trucks) is the largest component. Significant potential exists for efficiency improvements, but most projections do not expect this potential to be fully realized. In most of the other transportation uses, the EIA Reference Case projection uses most or all of the potential for efficiency improvement now or expected to be available.

Technically, there appears to be a potential for improving the efficiency of new light duty vehicles (fuel used per unit travel) by about 50 percent using technology improvements in several areas: engine efficiency; body improvements; driveline changes; accessory modifications; and hybrid technology use. Some of the changes are likely to have costs associated with them as well as possible broader economic effects (see Technology chapter).

The NPC global oil and gas study has not been conducted in a way that provides for internally generated projections. However, it is possible to understand the potential size of an impact on U.S. light duty fuel consumption from incorporating an efficiency improvement of 50 percent in the U.S. new vehicle sales mix by 2030. By removing assumptions that relate to changes in the vehicle sales mix, increases in vehicle performance, increases in vehicle energy use created by added comfort and convenience options, and increases in miles driven per licensed driver, most of the factors that complicate direct understanding of a single factor like vehicle efficiency increase are set aside.

The 50 percent improvement in new vehicle efficiency that has been discussed thus far is not consistent with the general public understanding of light duty vehicle efficiency. The general measure used to indicate the fuel-use characteristic of a vehicle is miles traveled per gallon of fuel used (mpg). A 50 percent reduction in fuel used per mile of travel (efficiency) is, mathematically, equivalent to a doubling of—or a 100 percent increase in—mpg.

There are many ways to build a fuel use estimate of the impact of incorporating a new light duty vehicle efficiency improvement. Consequently, any estimate is, at best, an indication of magnitude and not a projected actual outcome. If it is assumed that the total 100 percent improvement in new vehicle fuel economy is implemented by the year 2030, the potential impact appears to lower light duty vehicle fuel consumption by 3 to 5 million barrels per day relative to a future with no improvement in new vehicle fuel economy. Factors such as rate of new vehicle technology penetration and new vehicle replacement in the on-road fleet have impacts on reduction in fuel use. New vehicle fuel economy improvement might vary from the rapid improvement rate in new vehicle fuel economy that occurred when the Corporate Average Fuel Economy program was instituted in the 1970s to a gradual incorporation of new vehicle efficiency over the period to 2030. Replacement of on-road light duty vehicles by new light duty vehicles has taken about 15 years. If the replacement period for light duty vehicles in the on-road fleet increases or decreases, the potential fuel use reduction decreases or increases.

Obviously there are many other factors that are likely to change with time. Consequently, the estimate of potential savings should not be applied to any specific future projection of U.S. light duty fuel demand, but should be used to indicate potential magnitude. The ultimate outcome will depend on the specifics of program design and implementation.

Consumption in the Residential and Commercial Sectors

There appears to be sizeable potential to reduce energy consumption in U.S. residential and commercial sectors. The EIA *Annual Energy Outlook 2007* (AEO 2007) reported the residential/commercial efficiency factors that are included in the projection. The factors shown in Table 1-2 are greatly influenced by the replacement of old, relatively inefficient

Category	Appliance	Efficiency Improvement
Appliance	Refrigerators	22%
	Freezers	8%
Space heating	Electric heat pumps	10%
	Natural gas heat pumps	14%
	Geothermal heat pumps	5%
	Natural gas furnaces	6%
	Distillate furnaces	2%
Space cooling	Electric heat pumps	20%
	Natural gas heat pumps	10%
	Geothermal heat pumps	6%
	Central air conditioners	22%
	Room air conditioners	7%
Water heaters	Electric	3%
	Natural gas	6%
	Distillate fuel oil	0%
	Liquefied petroleum gases	6%
Building shell efficiency Note: Index includes size of structure in the calculation	Space heating – Pre 1998 homes	7%
	Space cooling – Pre 1998 homes	2%
	Space heating – New construction	2%
	Space cooling – New construction	2%

Source: Energy Information Administration, *Annual Energy Outlook 2007,* table 21, http://www.eia.doe.gov/oiaf/aeo/supplement/sup_rci.xls.

TABLE 1-2. *Residential Stock Efficiency Improvements, 2007-2030*

equipment. Efficiency improvement in new equipment is expected to be less than the aggregated improvements in the table.

Studies for efficiency improvements are largely specific to regions, and often to energy types. A review of these studies suggests that anticipated energy use in the residential and commercial sectors could be reduced by roughly 15 to 20 percent through deployment of cost-effective energy-efficiency measures that use existing, commercially available technologies. Assuming that all these measures are put in place over the next decades and that all other factors such as level of services are held constant, U.S. residential/commercial energy consumption could be reduced by 7 to 9 quadrillion Btu. Technologies to accom-

plish savings of these magnitudes are indicated to be available in the marketplace. However, some of these measures have initial cost and retrofit issues associated with their use.

While significant efficiency improvements have been made over the last several decades in building shells, systems, and appliances, these have been offset in part by additional energy service demand requirements that have been imposed as a result of increased structure sizes and larger and multiple appliance use. As much as possible, programs to increase the efficiency in the U.S. residential/commercial sector need to avoid inclusion of measures that inadvertently encourage using energy services that decrease the effectiveness of energy-efficiency measures.

U.S. Industrial Sector Efficiency

The industrial sector is a price-responsive consumer of energy. U.S. energy-intensive industries and manufacturers rely on internationally competitive energy supplies to remain globally competitive. In recent years, U.S. natural gas prices have risen relative to those in the rest of the world. As a result, U.S. energy-intensive industries and manufacturers using natural gas as a fuel or feedstock have responded by increasing the efficiency of their operations and/or by shifting a greater proportion of their operations outside the United States.

Energy efficiency opportunities exist for reducing energy use by about 15 percent broadly across the industrial sector. Areas of opportunity include waste heat recovery, separations, and combined heat and power. While 40 percent of that opportunity could be implemented now, research, development, demonstration, and deployment are required before the rest can be implemented. If all of this efficiency could be put in place over the next 20 years, U.S. energy demand could be reduced by 4 to 7 quadrillion Btu compared with what it would be without the improvements.

Table 1-3 indicates some of the barriers to adopting industrial energy efficiency measures.

Research, development, and demonstration are needed to prove the technologies. However, focus on deployment of improved technologies and practices is particularly important because of the risk-averse character of manufacturing companies, the high capital cost of new equipment, the long life cycle of existing industrial equipment, access to unbiased information on technology performance, and lack of technically trained human resources. Addressing these issues will speed the diffusion of improved technologies and practices.

Making the federal research and development tax credit permanent, instead of legislatively renewing it every few years, is a way to encourage private investment in industrial energy-efficiency research, development, demonstration, and deployment.

U.S. Electric Power Generation Efficiency

U.S. electricity generation efficiencies indicated in both the EIA and IEA outlooks show improvements over time. The expected improvements come mainly

Energy Cost Environment	• Price volatility • Lack of transparency to end-users of the real cost of energy
Business Environment	• Technical and economic risk (uncertain return on investment) associated with efficiency projects • Initial capital costs influence decisions more than long-term energy costs • Lack of incentives for development and use of new technology • Lack of R&D investments in efficiency • Long service life of existing equipment
Regulatory Environment	• Election cycles and impact on R&D priorities • Uncertainty related to future regulation, particularly environmental, and power • Permitting hurdles for upgrading existing equipment
Education Environment	• Inadequate industry awareness of new technology • Lack of technical expertise

Sources: Energetics, Technology Roadmap: Energy Loss Reduction and Recovery in Industrial Energy Systems, 2004; Global Environmental Facility (GEF), Operation Program Number 5: Removal of Barriers to Energy Efficiency and Energy Conservation, 2003; Marilyn Brown, Market Failures and Barriers as a Basis for Clean Energy Policies, 2001; A.B. Jaffe, R.G. Newell, R.N. Stavins, "Energy-Efficient Technologies and Climate Change Policies: Issues and Evidence," Resources for the Future, Climate Issue Brief No. 19, 1999.

TABLE 1-3. *Barriers to Adopting Energy Efficiency Measures*

Facing the Hard Truths about Energy

from the replacement of retired plants with new plants that have better efficiencies. However, installation of environmental control systems will add internal energy requirements reducing the efficiency of a power generation plant.

There are a few changes that can be made to make an existing power generation plant more efficient. Studies suggest the potential to improve the efficiency of existing U.S. power plants by 2 to 6 percent. Existing electric generation plant efficiency improvements generally fall into the following categories.

- Improved operation and maintenance practices

- Replacement/upgrade of:
  - steam turbines
  - forced draft, primary air, and induced draft fans
  - condensers
  - air heaters
  - operating controls
  - soot blowers
  - burners.

If these efficiency improvements could be captured in the next decades, energy savings would equal about 1 quadrillion Btu.

Capturing Efficiency Potential

Current energy-efficiency polices will place downward pressure on future U.S. energy consumption. However, further energy reduction would be possible if additional energy-conservation-related policy is put in place.

In commercially oriented end-uses such as industrial, electric generation, and commercially oriented transportation, the market price mechanism creates an incentive for using economically available energy efficiency technology. Programs to assist in research, development, demonstration, and deployment of energy-efficient technology would bolster the market mechanism in these areas.

Energy conservation and efficiency use in areas where individual consumers are faced with complex choices that are not well understood, and where decisions are made by third parties who are not con-

suming and paying for the energy, are likely to benefit from prudent application of technically practical and economically rational policies. Areas such as light duty vehicle fuel use and residential and commercial energy use could potentially benefit from well developed and implemented energy conservation/efficiency policies.

DEMAND DATA EVALUATION

The Demand Data Evaluation Subgroup of the Demand Task Group reviewed, analyzed, and compared projection data collected in the NPC data warehouse, which is discussed in the Methodology chapter. Publicly available demand data from EIA and IEA were the main focus of the analysis. The aggregated proprietary data available in the NPC data warehouse were used primarily to establish whether the EIA and IEA projections provided a reasonable range of projection results. Other public projections, generally less complete than the EIA and IEA projections, were also used as a reasonableness check.

The three major input assumptions behind both the EIA and the IEA projections are economic growth, population, and effect of associated energy policies. In general, the economic growth projections (2000 to 2030) for the world exceed past (1980 to 2000) growth except for that used in the EIA Low Economic Growth Case (Figure 1-10). By region and country, the pattern is somewhat different. Economically developed regions (North America and OECD Europe), and both developing and economically emerging Asia are projected to grow more slowly than in the past. Countries in Africa, Central and South America, the Middle East, and Non-OECD Europe and Eurasia are projected to grow more rapidly than historically. The faster global economic growth is driven by the rapidly growing emerging Asian economies becoming a larger share of the global economy.

World population growth in all cases is essentially the same, drawn from United Nations or U.S. Census projections of population growth. Population growth rates are projected to be generally lower then historical growth rates.

The EIA, generally, only included those energy policies that are currently in effect and allows most policies to expire at their currently enacted sunset date. The IEA Reference Case, however, assumes the likely extension of public policies. The IEA Alternative

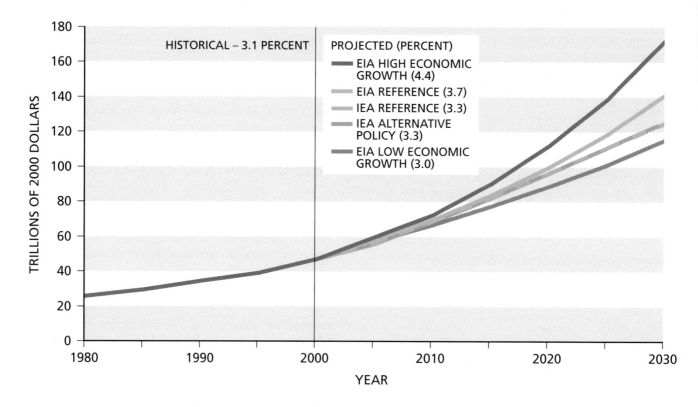

FIGURE 1-10. *World Economy — Average Annual Growth Rates*

Policy Case provides a significantly different energy policy approach, assuming not only existing energy policies and their logical extension, but also other policies now under consideration around the world. IEA used the same economic projections in its Reference Case and Alternative Policy Case.

Worldwide energy demand is projected to grow 1.4 to 2.5 percent per year, versus the historical growth rate of 1.7 percent per year (Figure 1-11). The projected U.S. energy demand growth of 0.5 to 1.3 percent per year was generally less than the historical rate of growth of 1.2 percent per year (Figure 1-12).

World demand for petroleum liquids is projected to grow at 1.0 to 1.9 percent per year versus the historical growth rate of 0.9 percent per year. In 2030, petroleum demand is projected to range from 98 to 138 million barrels per day, up from 76 million barrels per day in 2000 (Figure 1-13). Despite this growth, petroleum as a share of total energy declines in all cases. U.S. petroleum demand is projected to grow 0.5 to 1.4 percent per year versus 0.6 percent per year historically. In 2030, U.S. petroleum liquids demand is projected to range from 21 to 30 million barrels per day, compared to 19 million barrels per

day in 2000 (Figure 1-14). The IEA Alternative Policy Case is the only public case in which growth in U.S. petroleum liquids demand is slower than in the past. This indicates that the policies assumed in this case could have a significant impact on the growth in petroleum liquids demand relative to the policies in place today.

According to the EIA projection for the United States, two-thirds of the volume and most of the projected growth in demand for petroleum liquids is in transportation services (Figure 1-15). That projected growth in transportation is led by increased demand by light duty vehicles (60 percent) (Figure 1-16). The key drivers of light duty vehicle growth are increased vehicle penetration and annual miles traveled per vehicle, which more than offset improvement in vehicle efficiency (miles per gallon).

The transportation sector provides the greatest potential for reducing oil consumption. The Technology Task Group, through its Transportation Efficiency subgroup, developed an estimate of transportation efficiency potential for five classes of transportation: light duty vehicles, heavy duty vehicles, air, marine, and rail (see Technology chapter).

Facing the Hard Truths about Energy

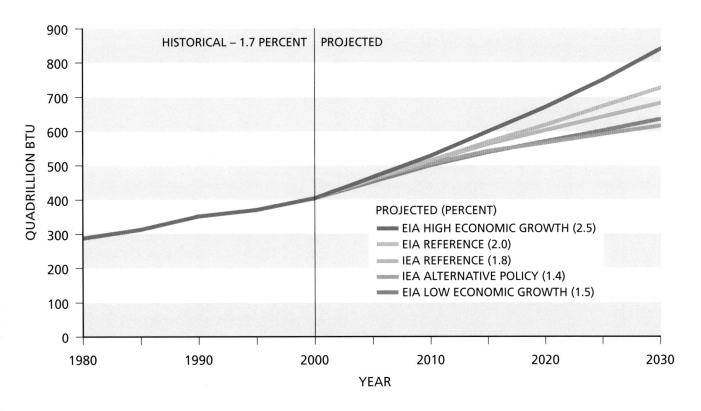

FIGURE 1-11. *World Energy Demand — Average Annual Growth Rates*

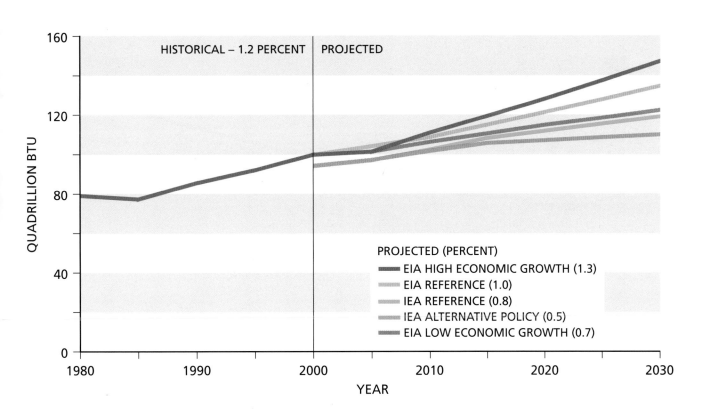

FIGURE 1-12. *U.S. Energy Demand — Average Annual Growth Rates*

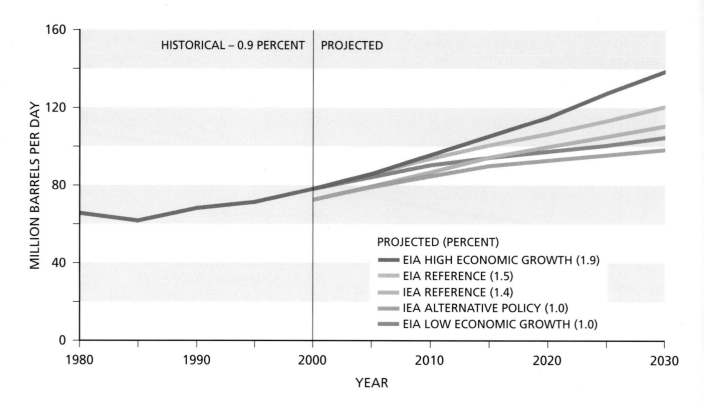

FIGURE 1-13. *World Petroleum Demand — Average Annual Growth Rates*

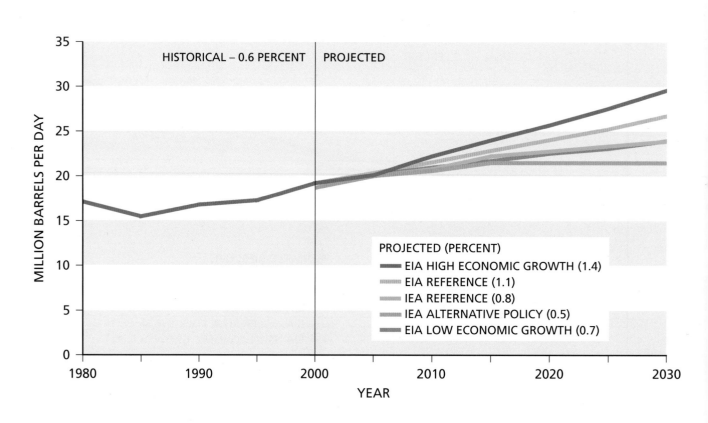

FIGURE 1-14. *U.S. Petroleum Demand — Average Annual Growth Rates*

Facing the Hard Truths about Energy

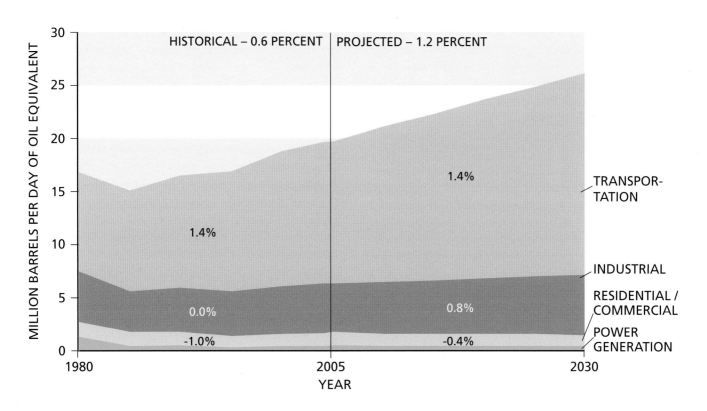

FIGURE 1-15. *U.S. Demand for Petroleum Liquids by Sector (EIA Reference Case) — Average Annual Growth Rates*

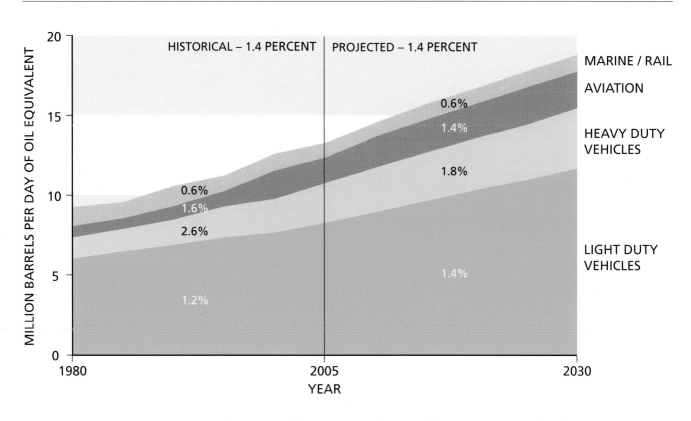

FIGURE 1-16. *U.S. Demand for Transportation Fuels by Transportation Mode (EIA Reference Case) — Average Annual Growth Rates*

The EIA Reference Case for the United States projects that in 2030 technology improvements will result in ~10 percent improvement in new light duty vehicle fuel consumption (Btu per mile) from 2005 levels. It is estimated that this includes technological improvements of ~30 percent at constant vehicle performance, and vehicle attribute changes that reduce this improvement by about half. Based on this study's analysis, technologies (drive-train and body improvements, and hybridization) exist, or are expected to be developed, that have the potential to reduce fuel consumption by 50 percent relative to 2005. This assumes constant vehicle performance, characteristics, and sales mix between light trucks and autos and entails higher vehicle cost.

Improvements beyond 50 percent will require breakthroughs in batteries or fuel cells, resulting in significantly higher vehicle costs and potentially significant infrastructure investments. The fuel efficiency improvement estimates beyond the initial 50 percent warrant careful scrutiny as other energy forms such as electricity and hydrogen are incorporated in the fuel mix. The conversion and transformation of primary fuels to secondary energy types may significantly decrease the overall energy efficiency of these advanced technologies.

Technologies exist to reduce new heavy-duty-truck fuel consumption by 15-20 percent in the United States by 2030, which is about equal to the EIA Reference Case assumption. These technologies (e.g., engine efficiency, rolling resistance, and aerodynamic improvements) will involve higher cost and require appropriate incentives. Operational improvements such as reduced idling and improved logistics can provide a benefit of 5 to 10 percent across the fleet during this period.

Advanced technology solutions, such as hybridization and fuel cells, offer fuel consumption reductions of an additional 25 percent, and applications would likely be initiated in local delivery, short-haul, medium-duty delivery trucks, and buses. As in the light duty vehicles, the conversion and transformation of primary fuels to secondary energy types may significantly decrease the overall energy efficiency of these advanced technologies.

Fuel consumption improvements for aircraft on the order of 25 percent are the basis for the EIA Reference Case. This is an aggressive projection and all of the known technologies appear to be included in

the EIA estimates. New technologies will need to be discovered to achieve additional improvements in efficiency.

The EIA Reference Case is based on a 5 percent improvement in marine shipping fuel consumption by 2030. This improvement level is achievable with operational solutions and existing technologies. Improvements greater than 5 percent will require new hull designs and new propeller designs. Given the long life of ships (greater than 20 years), migration of these solutions into the fleet will not have a large impact until later in the study period. Operational changes, affecting the entire fleet, may be more significant sooner than technological improvements.

The EIA Reference Case assumes that fuel consumption will improve by 2.5 percent between 2005 and 2030 for rail use in the United States. Incremental improvements in engine design, aerodynamics, and use of hybrids have the potential to reduce new locomotive fuel consumption by up to 30 percent over 2005 technology. Rollout of new technology into the fleet is slow due to low turnover and will be difficult to achieve during the years considered in this study. More stringent emissions standards will tend to increase fuel consumption.

World natural gas demand is projected to grow 1.6 to 2.9 percent per year versus 2.6 percent per year historically (Figure 1-17). Despite the slowing of gas demand growth rates, gas is still projected to gain market share versus other energy sources in all cases. Natural gas demand grows in all regions. Gas demand ranges from 356 to 581 billion cubic feet per day in 2030, compared with world natural gas demand of 243 billion cubic feet per day in 2000. In all cases, the projected growth rate in U.S. natural gas demand is lower than the historical rate. U.S. natural gas demand ranges from 59 to 78 billion cubic feet per day in 2030, compared with 64 billion cubic feet per day in 2000 (Figure 1-18).

In contrast with projected U.S. oil demand, which is concentrated in the transportation sector (Figure 1-15), natural gas use in the United States is more evenly spread across three sectors: residential/commercial, industrial, and electric utility (Figure 1-19).

Worldwide, coal demand growth is projected to be faster in the future than in the past in all outlooks except for the Alternative Policy Case where the growth is slightly less than in the past. More than two-thirds

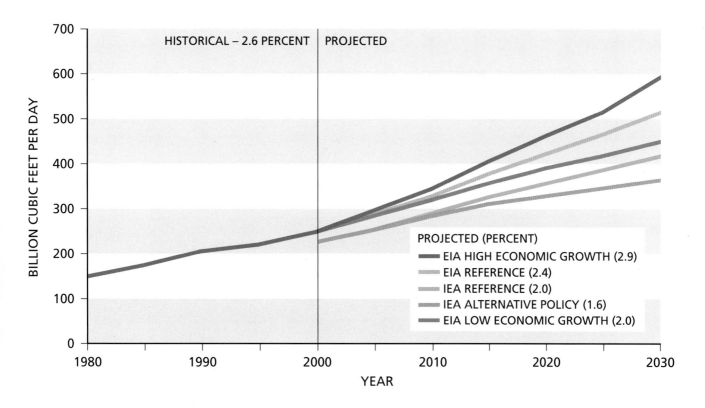

FIGURE 1-17. *World Natural Gas Demand — Average Annual Growth Rates*

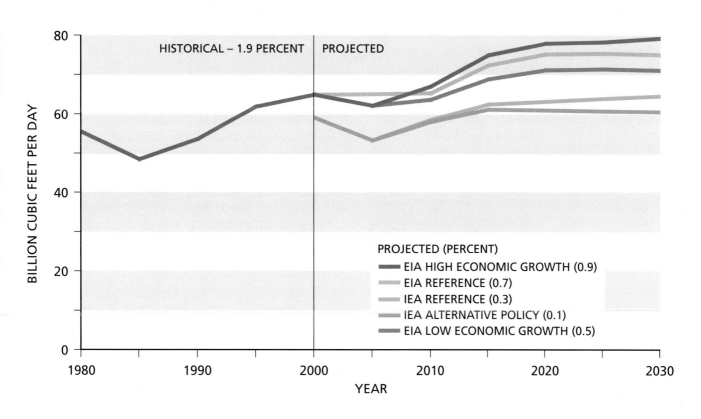

FIGURE 1-18. *U.S. Natural Gas Demand — Average Annual Growth Rates*

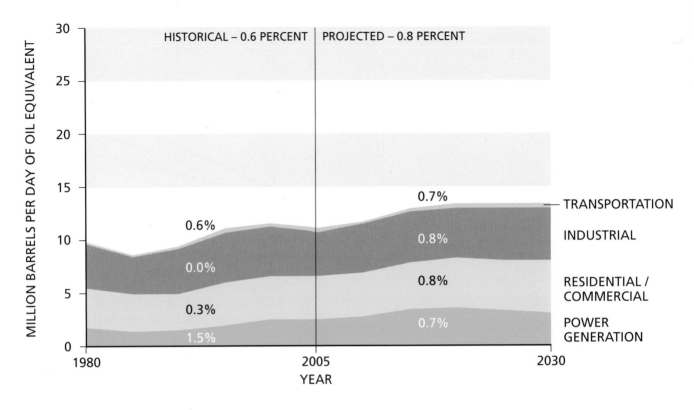

FIGURE 1-19. *U.S. Natural Gas Demand by Sector (EIA Reference Case) — Average Annual Growth Rates*

of the projected growth in coal demand from 2000 to 2030 is in China and India, where the economies are growing rapidly and coal is very competitive with other fuels. The indication is that share of total world energy consumption met by coal is projected to increase in all cases except where policies are enacted that place a limit on the use of coal.

Worldwide nuclear consumption growth in all outlooks is projected to be slower in the future than it has been in the past. The nuclear share of total worldwide energy demand declines in all projections except for the Alternative Policy Case, in which it increases very slightly. While the specific numbers are different in the U.S. projections, the trends are the same. The nuclear share of energy consumption is projected to decline slowly in the United States through 2030. The projections suggest that a major shift in nuclear policy will be required to increase the nuclear share of energy use.

The share of total worldwide energy consumption accounted for by other energy sources (hydro, biofuels, wind, solar, etc.) is projected to be higher in 2030 than in 2000.

As shown in Figure 1-20, worldwide carbon dioxide emissions grow in all of the projections. Carbon dioxide emissions are projected to range from 34 billion metric tons in 2030 in the IEA Alternative Policy Case to 51 billion metric tons in the EIA High Economic Growth Case, compared with 24 billion metric tons in 2000. In all cases, carbon dioxide emissions increase at about the same rate as energy demand. Carbon dioxide emissions in the United States are also expected to grow in all projections, although not as fast as for the world. In 2030, carbon dioxide emissions in the United States range from 6.3 billion metrics tons in the IEA Alternative Policy Case to 9 billion metric tons in EIA High Economic Growth Case (5.8 billion metrics tons in 2000).

The regional shares of energy use are projected to change over time. The share of total worldwide energy consumed in North America, OECD Europe, and Non-OECD Europe and Eurasia is projected to fall in all of the cases, while the share in Asia/Oceania grows. China is a major contributor to the substantial growth in Asia/Oceania share. In general, the change in the oil share of total worldwide oil consumed by region parallels the

Facing the Hard Truths about Energy

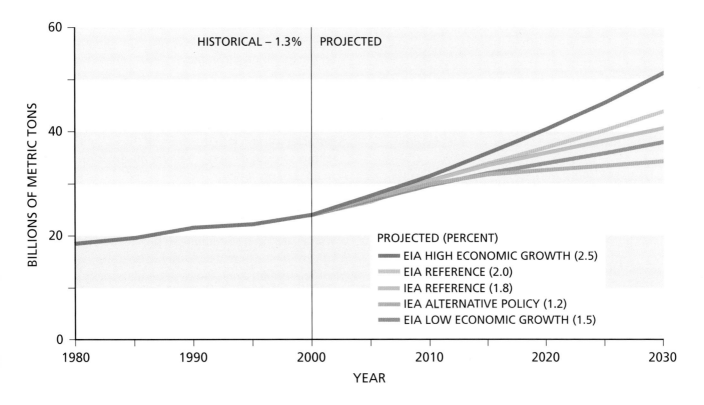

FIGURE 1-20. *World Carbon Dioxide Emissions — Average Annual Growth Rates*

change in the share of total energy consumption, with industrialized regions losing share and the Asia/Oceania oil share increasing significantly, as shown in Table 1-4.

Energy consumption per unit of GDP (energy intensity) is projected to decline in all regions. The Middle East, while not exhibiting the highest energy intensity in 2000, is projected to have the highest energy intensity in 2030 in all cases. North America, the region exhibiting the highest energy use per person in 2000, is still projected to have the highest energy use per person in 2030, but it declines in the IEA cases. Energy consumption per person in all other regions is projected to be higher than or equal to 2000 levels in 2030, as shown in Table 1-5.

Part of the study effort involved collecting energy demand projections from organizations other than EIA or IEA. Some of these projections were proprietary and, therefore, were collected by a third party with the data aggregated before being made available to study participants. Details of the aggregated data collection process are discussed in Chapter 7, "Methodology."

	2000 IEA	2030 IEA Ref. Case
North America	27%	21%
Central and South America	5%	5%
OECD Europe	18%	13%
Non-OECD Europe & Eurasia	10%	8%
Middle East	4%	6%
Asia/Oceania	31%	41%
Africa	5%	6%

TABLE 1-4. *Regional Energy Shares*

The results of the aggregated proprietary data collection effort confirmed that using the EIA and IEA projections was reasonable. As can be seen on

	2000 IEA	2030 IEA Ref. Case
North America	9.51	6.18
Central and South America	6.53	4.88
OECD Europe	6.49	4.35
Non-OECD Europe & Eurasia	21.27	9.40
Middle East	15.23	12.04
Asia/Oceania	8.04	4.64
Africa	12.00	7.07

TABLE 1-5. *Regional Energy Intensity (1,000 Btu/2000$ GDP)*

Figure 1-21, the aggregated proprietary projections for all three levels of the total submissions output (average of the two highest submissions, average of the two lowest submissions, and the average of all submissions) fall generally in the range of the EIA and IEA projections for total energy. The same is true for all the major energy types.

For the U.S. situation, there were an insufficient number of submissions to provide a high and low average. Figure 1-22 shows that the average for the proprietary data is in the range of the EIA and IEA projections for total energy. Similar observations hold for major energy types.

Other studies were provided to the study effort as public projections. Generally, the information in these studies was in less detail than provided in the EIA and IEA studies. There were other organizations that had sufficient data available to provide partially complete data input templates. The other studies support the finding that the EIA and IEA projections provide a reasonable range of results for assessing energy issues. With the exception of the IEA Alternative Policy Case, policy assumptions underpinning the projections are extensions of polices in place today. It is interesting to note that projections with lower energy demand growth rates are based on lower economic growth rates. As an example of the congruence of study results, the energy and carbon dioxide growth rates are shown in Table 1-6. There were other projections

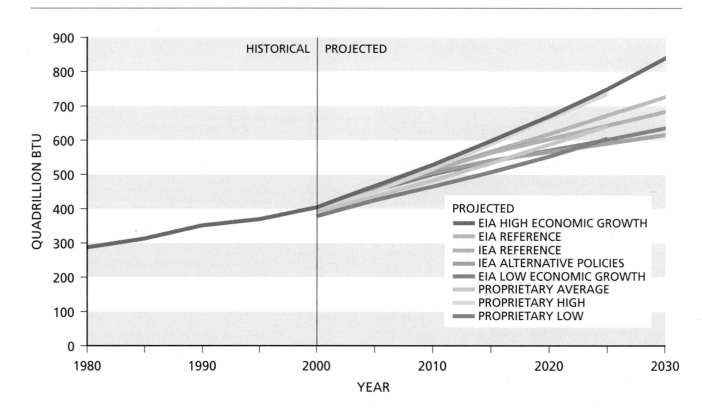

FIGURE 1-21. *World Energy Demand — Public and Proprietary Projections*

Facing the Hard Truths about Energy

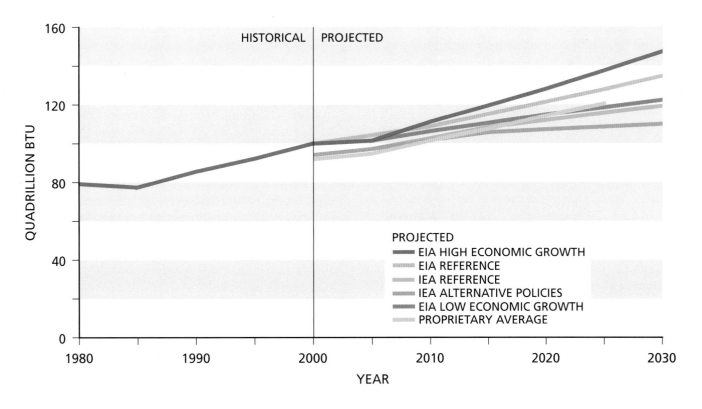

FIGURE 1-22. *U.S. Energy Demand — Public and Proprietary Projections*

	World Economy	World Population	World Energy	World CO_2
Energy Information Administration – reference	3.7%	1.0%	1.9%	2.0%
Energy Information Administration – low economic	2.9%	1.0%	1.4%	1.4%
Energy Information Administration – high economic	4.5%	1.0%	2.5%	2.6%
International Energy Agency – reference	3.7%	1.0%	1.6%	1.7%
International Energy Agency – alternative policy	3.4%	1.0%	1.2%	1.0%
European Commission	3.1%	0.9%	1.7%	1.6%
Institute of Energy Economics, Japan	3.1%	1.0%	1.7%	1.8%
Greenpeace & European Renewable Energy Council	3.1%	0.9%	1.4%	1.5%
U.S. Climate Change Science Program – MERGE	2.6%	0.8%	1.0%	1.2%
U.S. Climate Change Science Program – MINICAM	2.3%	0.9%	1.7%	1.5%
U.S. Climate Change Science Program – IGSM	3.1%	1.0%	1.9%	2.1%

TABLE 1-6. *Outside Study Comparison of Average Annual Growth Rates from 2004 to 2030*

that were submitted or captured in other efforts that did not have sufficient definition of underlying bases or data detail to be included in the comparison.

The Petroleum Federation of India (PFI) provided a series of outlooks for India. These projections offer perspective on the expected Indian energy situation. The data are limited, but there is sufficient information to look at the 2020 energy mix. The PFI total energy projection has a 2004 to 2020 energy demand growth rate of 3.3 percent per year for the Business as Usual Case. This growth rate is slightly higher than the 3.0 and 2.8 percent per growth rates developed in the EIA and IEA Reference Cases, respectively. One difference between the projections is in petroleum demand, where the PFI projection has an indicated 2004 to 2020 growth rate of 4.7 percent per year while the other two projections have indicated growth rates of 2.6 to 3.2 percent per year. Offsetting this difference, to some extent, is the lower growth in coal use expected by PFI relative to the other projections.

McKinsey Global Institute conducted a study in November 2006 that approached the issue of the potential for energy savings (*Productivity of Growing Global-Energy Demand: A Microeconomic Perspective*). The study provides an assessment of potential savings without regard for the time needed to achieve the estimated savings, or for the practicality of achieving them. The McKinsey study used 2020 as its horizon year. As indicated in Table 1-7, the McKinsey study suggests that between 2003 and 2020 essentially all U.S. energy growth, and about 75 percent of world energy growth, could be recovered by efficiency/conservation measures assuming they could be instituted within the time period. The McKinsey study adds support to the NPC study recommendations that efficiency/conservation measures are an important piece for providing a balanced U.S. energy program.

When preparing its International Energy Outlook, the EIA uses the Annual Energy Outlook as a major source of U.S. data. The EIA released an updated version of its Annual Energy Outlook during the first quarter of 2007. Table 1-8 contains a 2004 to 2030 growth rate comparison between the 2006 and 2007 Annual Energy Outlooks. There are only

	McKinsey		EIA	
	U.S.	World	U.S.	World
Energy consumption				
2003 – quadrillion Btu	92	422	101	433
2020 – quadrillion Btu	113	615	121	613
Growth – percent per year	1.2%	2.2%	1.0%	2.1%
2020-2003 – quadrillion Btu	21	193	19	181
Potential 2020 reduction				
Low estimate – quadrillion Btu	19	117	19	117
High estimate – quadrillion Btu	27	173	27	173
Percent of 2003 to 2020 growth				
Low – percent	90%	61%	99%	65%
High – percent	129%	90%	140%	96%

Sources: McKinsey Global Institute, *Productivity of Growing Global-Energy Demand: A Microeconomic Perspective,* November 2006; Energy Information Administration, *Annual Energy Outlook 2007.*

TABLE 1-7. *Comparison of Data from McKinsey Global Institute and Energy Information Administration*

Facing the Hard Truths about Energy

	AEO 2006	AEO 2007
Primary Energy		
Petroleum Products	1.1%	1.0%
Natural Gas	0.7%	0.6%
Coal	1.7%	1.6%
Nuclear	0.4%	0.5%
Other	1.7%	1.6%
Total	1.1%	1.1%
Sectors		
Residential	0.8%	0.7%
Commercial	1.6%	1.6%
Industrial	0.9%	0.7%
Transportation	1.4%	1.3%
Electric Generation	1.3%	1.2%
Subtotal	1.2%	1.1%
Electricity	1.6%	1.4%
Total	1.1%	1.1%
Gross Domestic Product	3.0%	2.9%

TABLE 1-8. Comparison of EIA Annual Energy Outlook 2006 and 2007 Reference Cases' Average Annual Growth Rates from 2004 to 2030

minor differences between the two projections, which suggests that the overall analysis that uses the 2006 International Energy Outlook (IEO 2006) is basically unchanged as a result of the recently released EIA U.S. outlook. Data availability issues have lead to some of the analyses that support various components of the demand effort being based on the AEO 2007, which should not present any difficulties.

The EIA released the 2007 version of the International Energy Outlook (IEO 2007) on May 21, 2007. IEO 2007 suggests no changes in the overall demand related conclusions of the National Petroleum Council's Global Oil and Gas Study. However, there are some interesting differences between IEO 2006 and IEO 2007 that should be noted. A comparison between the two Reference Case outlooks is shown in Table 1-9.

World economic growth is higher in IEO 2007. From a regional perspective, the major differences are in Asia/Oceania where projected economic growth is faster, and in North America, where it is slower. All other regions show a greater growth in economy than in IEO 2006 with the Non-OECD Europe and Eurasia region projected difference slightly greater than in other regions.

While the economic growth projections used as a basis for IEO 2007 are generally greater than in IEO 2006, energy growth projections are equal or less than they were in IEO 2006. This suggests that the energy efficiency/conservation assumptions underpinning IEO 2007 are greater than in IEO 2006. Energy intensities (energy use per unit of economic activity) calculated from the two outlooks show that in all regions except North America energy intensity is lower in IEO 2007, supporting the idea that there is more energy efficiency/conservation incorporated in IEO 2007 than in IEO 2006.

The projected regional energy consumption pattern in IEO 2007 is little different than in IEO 2006. The biggest difference is in Asia/Oceania, where projected 2030 energy use share increased from 37.6 percent to 39.2 percent.

Considering the type of energy consumption, the most significant difference appears to be a lower projection of world natural gas use. Both nuclear and coal use are projected to be higher. There was an accounting convention change between the two outlooks for the way in which renewable liquids were handled. In IEO 2007, liquids from renewables are shown as petroleum products instead of as "other." This change accounts for most of the reduction in other energy use, but suggests that petroleum liquids from more traditional sources are somewhat lower in IEO 2007 than in IEO 2006.

An output from both projections is an estimate of carbon dioxide emissions. In 2030, the IEO 2006 estimate for Reference Case carbon dioxide emissions was 43.7 billion metric tons. The IEO 2007 carbon dioxide emissions estimate for 2030 is 42.9 billion metric tons.

	2003–2030		2030	2030	2007-2006	2030	2030
	Growth Rate (%/Year)		Share (%)		Difference (Quadrillion Btu)	Intensity (1,000 Btu/ 2000$ GDP)	
	IEO 2006	IEO 2007	IEO 2006	IEO 2007		IEO 2006	IEO 2007
Primary Energy							
Petroleum Products	1.4%	1.4%	33.1%	34.1%	-0.2		
Natural Gas	2.4%	2.0%	26.3%	24.3%	-19.5		
Coal	2.5%	2.6%	27.1%	28.4%	3.6		
Nuclear	1.0%	1.5%	4.8%	5.7%	5.0		
Other	2.4%	1.8%	8.6%	7.6%	-8.9		
Total	2.0%	1.9%	100.0%	100.0%	-20.0		
Regions (Energy)							
North America	1.3%	1.2%	23.0%	23.0%	-4.6	5.99	6.01
OECD Europe	0.7%	0.5%	13.1%	12.7%	-5.3	4.87	4.48
Central and South America	2.8%	2.4%	6.3%	5.9%	-4.3	5.49	4.67
Middle East	2.5%	2.5%	5.2%	5.4%	0.5	9.23	9.03
Non-OECD Europe and Eurasia	1.8%	1.4%	10.9%	10.2%	-7.5	8.60	7.24
Africa	2.6%	2.3%	3.7%	3.5%	-1.9	3.85	3.36
Asia/Oceania	3.1%	3.1%	37.6%	39.2%	3.2	4.20	3.56
Total	2.0%	1.9%	100.0%	100.0%	-19.9	5.14	4.55
Gross Domestic Product (billion 2000 dollars)					**Difference (B $2000)**		
North America	3.1%	2.9%	19.8%	17.4%	-849		
OECD Europe	2.2%	2.3%	13.8%	12.9%	519		
Central and South America	3.8%	4.0%	5.9%	5.7%	541		
Middle East	4.2%	4.3%	2.9%	2.7%	145		
Non-OECD Europe and Eurasia	4.4%	4.7%	6.5%	6.4%	691		
Africa	4.4%	4.6%	5.0%	4.8%	438		
Asia/Oceania	4.8%	5.5%	46.1%	50.0%	12,498		
Total	3.8%	4.2%	100.0%	100.0%	13,983		

TABLE 1-9. *Comparison of EIA International Energy Outlook — 2006 and 2007 Reference Cases*

ELECTRIC GENERATION EFFICIENCY

Power plant efficiencies presented in the EIA and IEA outlooks both show improvements over time. These expected improvements mainly come from the replacement of retired old plants with new plants that have better efficiencies. There are a few changes that can be made to make an existing unit more efficient. However, these changes typically will only result in a few percentage point improvements to efficiency.

Given the large aggregate capacity of existing coal-fired power plants and their long useful lives, efforts to improve the average efficiency of the existing stock by 1 or 2 percent could have a significant near term impact on fuel consumption rates and greenhouse gas emissions. Efficiency improvement potential for existing U.S. power plants is related to the age of the plant, the age of specific pieces of equipment in a plant, a plant's design, and the economics of the specific plant situation. When all is considered, most plants will fall in the 3-6 percent range of possible improvement. The practical or economic values will be lower. The newer plants might be in the 2-4 percent range and a certain population might be 2 percent or less because they were already upgraded. The overall range of potential efficiency improvement for existing U.S. coal fired power plants should be in the 2 to 4 percent range.[2]

Much of the discussion surrounding power plant efficiency will focus on the heat rate (Btu per kilowatt-hour). This is an ideal measure of efficiency since it defines the ratio of the input as fuel (Btu) to output as power (kilowatt-hour). The efficiency of a new power plant is largely a function of economic choice. The technology is well understood in order to produce a highly efficient plant. In order to produce higher efficiencies, higher pressures and temperatures are required. This increases the cost of the plant as special alloy materials will be needed. Technology improvements could assist by lowering the cost of these special materials through discovery and better manufacturing process.

Coal power plant efficiency merits much focus since coal represents over 50 percent of current generation in the United States. Many countries in the world from Germany to Japan have demonstrated coal plants with heat rates of less than 9,000 Btu per

kilowatt-hour. The United States has also demonstrated such technology since the 1950s. However, the U.S. coal fleet current operating heat rate is nowhere near those levels, at 10,400 Btu per kilowatt-hour.

Existing coal-fired power plants worldwide do not achieve the highest efficiency possible based on their design. The efficiency loss can be categorized as controllable or non-controllable. Controllable losses are generally due to poor operation and maintenance practices. Non-controllable losses are due to environmental conditions (e.g., cooling-water temperature), dispatching requirements (e.g., customer demand), and normal deterioration.

Deterioration naturally occurs and, if left unchecked, can become substantial. Therefore, some amount of normal deterioration will always be present and non-controllable. Most of the normal deterioration can be recovered with regularly scheduled maintenance intervals, the frequency of which determines the average based on the resulting saw-tooth curve shown in Figure 1-23. There is a gradual increase in the unrecoverable portion as the unit ages, which would require a replacement rather than a refurbishment to eliminate. Poor maintenance practices regarding the timing of the intervals and the amount of refurbishment may result in excessive deterioration and is controllable.

Figure 1-24 shows historical and projected heat rates from U.S. natural gas and coal-fired power plants. Historical calculations are based upon EIA data that include both central station generation and end-use generation of electricity. The post-war boom of the late 1940s and 1950s saw a large increase in new power plants. However, these were, by today's standards, highly inefficient plants, with the overall fleet heat rate starting in 1949 at nearly 15,000 Btu per kilowatt-hour. By the end of the 1950s, more-efficient plant constructions drove the fleet heat rate to about 10,300 Btu per kilowatt-hour, where it remained relatively unchanged until the end of the century.

The overbuilding of natural gas combined-cycle units in the late 1990s decreased the natural gas fleet heat rate below 9,000 Btu per kilowatt-hour, where it currently resides. However, with the recent higher natural gas prices, coal generation still represents over 50 percent of current U.S. power generation. Therefore, overall U.S. fleet heat rate was not affected by the large gas combined-cycle build since coal-fired heat rates remain around 10,400 Btu per kilowatt-hour.

---

2   Equipment Refurbishing and Upgrading Options (taken from Asia Pacific Economic Cooperation document, June 2005).

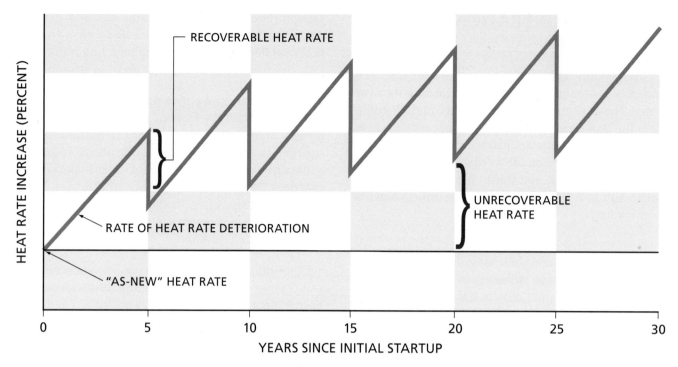

Source: General Electric GER-3696D, *Upgradable Opportunities for Steam Turbines*, 1996.

FIGURE 1-23. *Change in Heat Rate over Time*

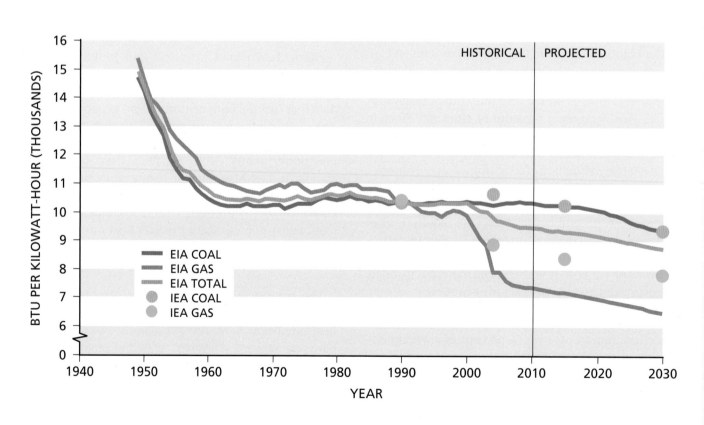

FIGURE 1-24. *U.S. Operating Heat Rates*

The EIA is projecting the natural gas fleet heat rate to continue to improve. Around the year 2023, electricity generation from natural gas units decreases faster than consumption, resulting in a slight increase to 8,300 Btu per kilowatt-hour. Currently, best technology combined-cycle units can achieve ~5,700 Btu per kilowatt-hour [General Electric H-System]. The gas heat rate includes combustion turbine plants that could have heat rates as high as 13,000 and as low as 8,550 Btu per kilowatt-hour in the future according to the EIA. These types of units will continue to be needed as they have the ability to turn on and off over a short time period leading to increased system stability.

The EIA projects moderate improvements in the coal fleet heat rate, achieving 9,700 Btu per kilowatt-hour by 2030. In terms of percentage improvement, it is about the same trend as gas units. This indicates many more new coal plants as compared to new gas plants in the projection. To see any appreciable improvement in fleet heat rate, a large number of new, efficient units would need to replace a large number of old, inefficient units and/or existing units would have to be retrofitted. With 40-year life spans and high capital costs

(vs. natural gas plants) to construct, and risk of a CO_2-constrained environment, this is not achieved very quickly. The difference in fuel price (coal vs. natural gas) is another major driver for increased efficiencies in gas plants compared to coal plants. Major increases in combined-cycle efficiencies will make those units more competitive with coal in dispatch. With coal's current fuel price advantage, there is less incentive to make wholesale improvements in efficiency versus focusing on availability. Table 1-10 shows the EIA assumptions for new build heat rates for 2005, nth-of-a-kind plant in the future and the best observed heat rates to date. Observed data for combustion turbines are not provided because efficiency is not their primary role in the supply stack. These units are used primarily as peakers, where efficiency is not of utmost concern.

Because historical data do not align properly between EIA and IEA due to differences in data definitions, heat-rate improvements were examined for the world and China, as opposed to absolute heat-rate values. Figures 1-25, 1-26, 1-27 show the percentage improvements in heat rate for EIA and IEA from each agency's base year. As expected, heat-rate improvements in

Technology	Heat Rate in 2005	Heat Rate nth-of-a-kind (% improvement from 2005)	Best Current (2004)*
Scrubbed Coal	8,844	8,600 (2.8%)	8,842†
Integrated Gasification Combined Cycle (IGCC)	8,309	7,200 (13.3%)	N/A
IGCC w/carbon sequestration	9,713	7,920 (18.5%)	N/A
Conventional Combined Cycle	7,196	6,800 (5.5%)	6,335‡
Advanced Combined Cycle	6,752	6,333 (6.2%)	N/A
Advanced Combined Cycle w/carbon sequestration	8,613	7,493 (13.0%)	N/A
Conventional Combustion Turbine	10,842	10,450 (3.6%)	N/A
Advanced Combustion Turbine	9,227	8,550 (7.3%)	N/A

* "Operating Performance Rankings Showcase Big Plants Running Full Time," Electric Light & Power, Nancy Spring, managing editor, November 2005.
† Coal = TVA, Bull Run Plant.
‡ Conventional Combined Cycle = Sempra, Elk Hills Power.

TABLE 1-10. *EIA Heat-Rate Assumptions (Btu per Kilowatt-Hour)*

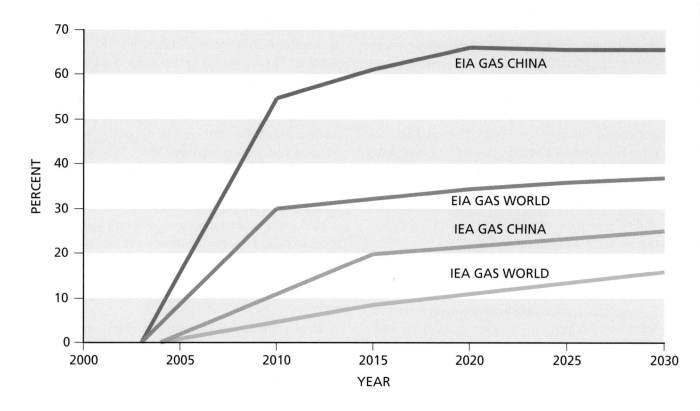

FIGURE 1-25. *Natural Gas Heat Rate Improvements*

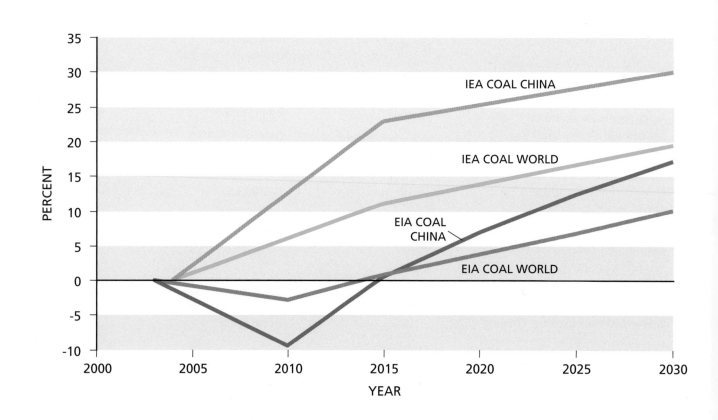

FIGURE 1-26. *Coal Heat Rate Improvements*

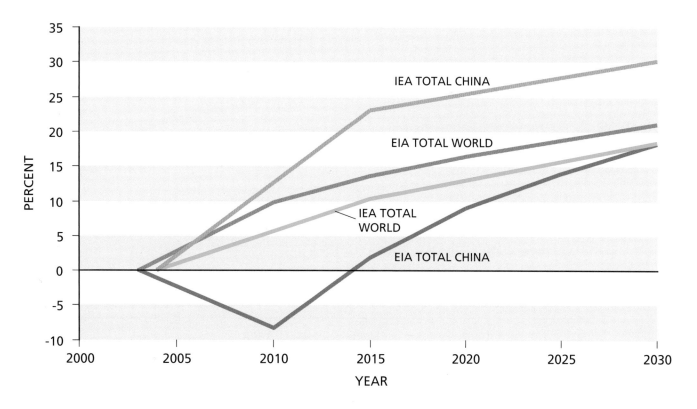

FIGURE 1-27. *Total Heat Rate Improvements*

China are projected to outpace worldwide improvements. Rapidly growing power demand is expected to drive a large increase in the number of new builds. With a larger percentage of fleet capacity coming from newer, efficient units, it is expected that overall improvements would increase rapidly in China. Worldwide heat-rate improvements are projected to increase moderately for both gas and coal plants according to both EIA and IEA. Again, this is the result of gradual replacement of older, inefficient units that have outlived their economic lives with new, efficient ones. The slower pace of this replacement leads to the slower increase in efficiency when compared with China alone.

An important distinction to note between the EIA and IEA projections is the heat-rate improvements for coal and natural gas. The EIA projects natural gas improvements for the world and China to greatly outpace improvements to coal-fired generation. Inversely, the IEA projects coal to improve more rapidly than for natural gas-fired plants. There are two schools of thought that can justify either scenario. One could argue that gas heat rates are expected to rapidly improve due to a large buildup of highly efficient combined-cycle units. This is the same phenomenon that was seen in the United States during the 1990s. With

a rapid increase of combined-cycle units, the gas heat rate quickly improves. The large improvements in coal-fired heat rates could be justified by determining that gas-fired heat rates are asymptotically approaching their maximum achievable efficiency (though not achievable, 100 percent efficiency is 3,412 Btu per kilowatt-hour). Steam cycle coal units theoretically have more room for improvement since they are less efficient from the start.

Recently, a blue book of energy in China (The Energy Development Report of China, Edited by M. Cui, etc., Social Sciences Academic Press of China, 2006) reports that the average heat rates of thermal power plants in China improved 15.2 percent from 1980 to 2002. Figure 1-28 shows the average heat rates of thermal power plants in China, compared with those in the United States and Japan. Natural gas consists of only a small percentage of China's energy mix on a Btu basis. For example, natural gas comprised only 2.62 percent in 2002, in comparison to 65.28 percent for coal. In 2002, 54.7 percent of coal consumption in China went to power plants, and the report does not give the percentage of natural gas consumed by the power plants, but states that most of its natural gas went to residential use. The IEA World Energy

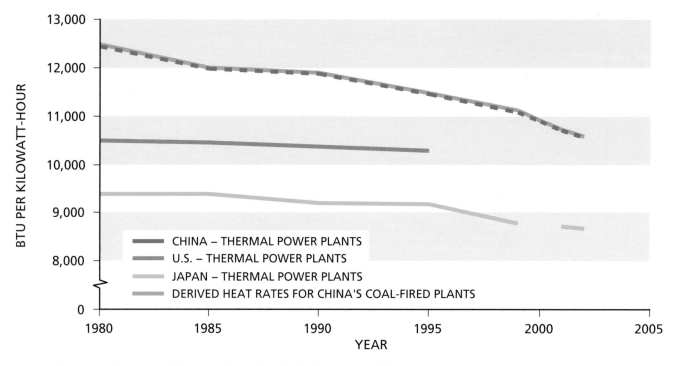

Source: The Energy Development Report of China, Edited by M. Cui, etc., Social Sciences Academic Press of China, 2006.

FIGURE 1-28. *Historical Heat Rates*

Outlook 2006 reports the electricity generation from thermal power plants. For China, coal consists of more than 90 percent of thermal power generation since 1990, and continues to increase its share.

Japan has the lowest coal percentage in its thermal-generated electricity of the three countries. To conservatively estimate the average heat rate for Chinese coal-fired power plants, it is assumed that 1 percent of electricity generated from thermal power plants came from natural gas before 2004, and assume that the average heat rate of gas-fired plants is 30 percent better than that of coal-fired plants and that the average heat rate of oil-fired power plants is the same as that of coal-fired power plants. The derived heat rates for coal-fired plants in China are about 0.2 percent higher than the average heat rates of its thermal power plants. Of the three countries, China had improved its thermal power plants efficiency the most from 1980 to 2002. The great improvement in efficiency in the thermal power plants in China can be attributed to a large number of new builds. Figure 1-29 also shows increases in China's electricity output in the same period, of which the coal-fired plants contributed the most. For example, thermal power plants generated 82.64 percent of electricity in China in 2004. The large percentage of higher-efficiency coal-fired new builds drives China's average heat rates down quickly.

COAL IMPACT

The primary consumer of coal in the United States is the electric power industry, consuming 92 percent of the 1.1 billion tons used in 2005. About half the U.S. electricity generated in 2005 was from coal. EIA projects that coal consumed to generate power in the electricity sector will account for 85 percent of total U.S. coal consumption by 2030 (Figure 1-30). In the AEO 2006 Reference Case projection, the emergence of a coal-to-liquids (CTL) industry accounts for virtually all of the growth in coal use in the non-electricity sectors.

Coal is consumed in large quantities throughout the United States. As shown in Figure 1-31, coal production is focused in relatively few states, meaning that huge amounts of coal must be transported long distances. Therefore, U.S. coal consumers and producers have access to the world's most comprehensive and efficient coal transportation system.

All major surface-transportation modes carry large amounts of coal. According to the EIA, about two-

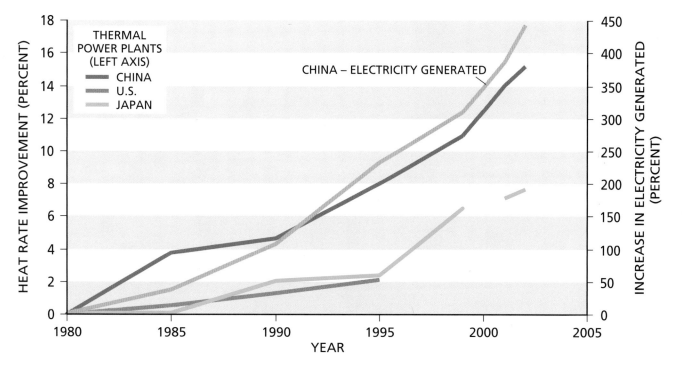

THERMAL
POWER PLANTS
(LEFT AXIS)
— CHINA
— U.S.
— JAPAN

CHINA – ELECTRICITY GENERATED

Source: The Energy Development Report of China, edited by M. Cui, etc., Social Sciences Academic Press of China, 2006.

FIGURE 1-29. *Changes in Efficiency and Electricity Generated in China*

thirds of U.S. coal shipments were delivered to their final domestic destinations by rail in 2004, followed by truck (12 percent), the aggregate of conveyor belts, slurry pipelines, and tramways (12 percent), and water (9 percent, of which 8 percent were inland waterways and the remainder tidewater or the Great Lakes).[3]

Over the past 15 years, the rail share of coal transport has trended upward, largely reflecting the growth of western coal moved long distances by rail. The truck share has fluctuated, but has also trended upward since 1990, while the waterborne share has fallen.

The extent to which coal is able to help meet U.S. future energy challenges will depend heavily on the performance of coal transporters. If the past is a reliable guide, the various modes will be able to accommodate increased coal transportation demand, albeit perhaps with occasional "hiccups" and "bottlenecks" along the way.

Railroads, barges, and trucks are all critical coal transportation providers. Each mode faces challenges,

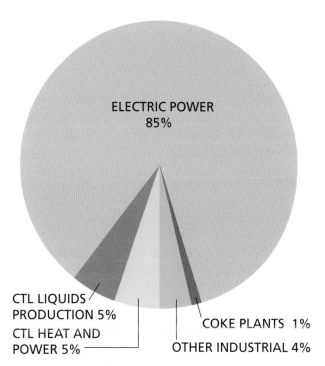

Source: EIA, *Annual Energy Outlook 2006.*

FIGURE 1-30. *U.S. Coal Consumption by Sector — 2030*

---

3 Energy Information Administration, "Coal Distribution Current and Back Issues," web site www.eia.doe.gov.

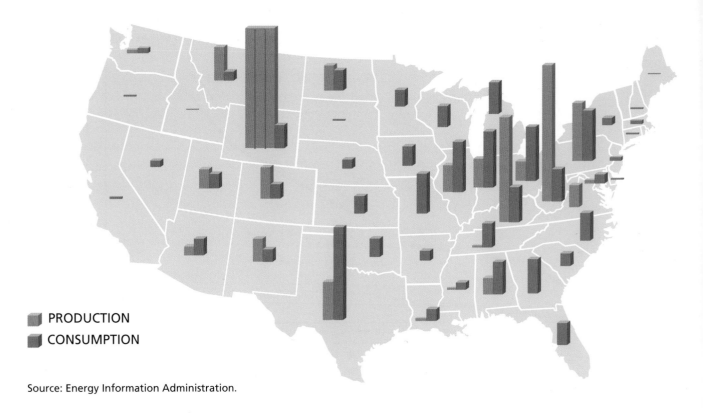

PRODUCTION
CONSUMPTION

Source: Energy Information Administration.

FIGURE 1-31. *U.S. Coal Consumption and Production by 2005*

some of which are unique to it and some of which are common to each of the modes. For each mode, having capacity that is adequate to meet growing demand is perhaps the most pressing need.

Available truck capacity will be determined by factors such as the amount of public spending on highways, how well the industry resolves the driver retention issue, and fuel costs.

Like trucks, waterways depend on publicly owned and maintained infrastructure. Waterway infrastructure is, in general, in need of significant maintenance and improvement. The availability of public funds to provide these improvements will feature prominently in how well waterways can handle future coal-transportation needs.

Railroads, on the other hand, rely overwhelmingly on privately owned, maintained, and operated infrastructure. As private-sector companies, railroads must be confident that traffic and revenue will remain high enough in the long term to justify the investments before they expand capacity. Railroads will continue to spend huge amounts of private capital to help ensure that adequate capacity exists, but

they can do so only if regulations or laws do not hinder their earnings.

Worldwide, coal trade patterns have shown a steady evolution since the early days of the international coal industry. As long ago as the early 1980s, Australia was still a minor coal exporter. Indonesia, now the world's largest thermal coal exporter, did not emerge as a force in the international market until the 1990s. A similar pattern exists on the demand side. In the 1970s, there was regional trade in Europe with supply coming from Germany and Poland. The 1980s were dominated by Japan's demand for coal, while the 1990s saw Korea and Taiwan as significant markets. The early years of this decade have seen rapid increases in demand from smaller countries in Asia, as well as the emergence of China as both a significant coal exporter and a major import market.

Trade patterns are hard to project because some countries have dedicated export facilities as well as mines that are intended for purely domestic purposes. The current major exporters of coal are Indonesia, Australia, China, South Africa, Russia, and Colombia. All of these countries, except Indonesia and China, have current reserves-to-production ratios in excess of 100.

INDUSTRIAL EFFICIENCY

The industrial sector is a large and price-responsive consumer of energy, consuming roughly one-third of the energy used in the United States. U.S. energy-intensive industry and manufacturers in associated value chains rely on competitive energy supplies to remain globally competitive.

As natural gas prices have risen in the United States relative to those in the rest of the world, manufacturers with energy-intensive processes have responded in two ways: (1) by increasing the efficiency of their operations (shown as energy intensity on Figure 1-32), and/or (2) by shifting a greater proportion of energy-intensive industry outside the United States (shown by declining industrial energy use).

Despite this decrease in energy intensity, energy-intensive manufacturers in the United States struggle to remain competitive in the global marketplace. U.S. manufacturers are investing for strategic growth in regions of the world where energy costs are lower. For example, over the last 10 years, the United States has gone from one of the world's largest exporters of chemicals to an importer. Although less dramatic, trends are similar in the paper and metals industries. Figure 1-33 tracks the aggregate trade balance for the steel, paper, and chemicals industries compared to the price of natural gas. Significantly, the correlation between the two data series is -89 percent, indicating that high natural gas prices have hurt U.S. competitiveness in these industries.

The extent to which U.S. industry can continue to compete for the domestic market is unclear. For instance, imports have provided 40 percent of the increase in U.S. gasoline use over the last 10 years. The impact of factors such as international supply and demand balances for oil and natural gas, geopolitical issues, the advent of disruptive technologies, and the evolution of the world's economies is unknown. The uncertainty in U.S. industrial energy consumption carries through to global balances. Since product consumption is unlikely to decline, product needs that are unmet by local production likely will be met by imports.

Projecting historical industrial energy patterns forward may illustrate this uncertainty. In the first scenario (called Stays), industrial use grows as it did between 1983 and 1996. In the second scenario (Flight), industrial consumption declines as it

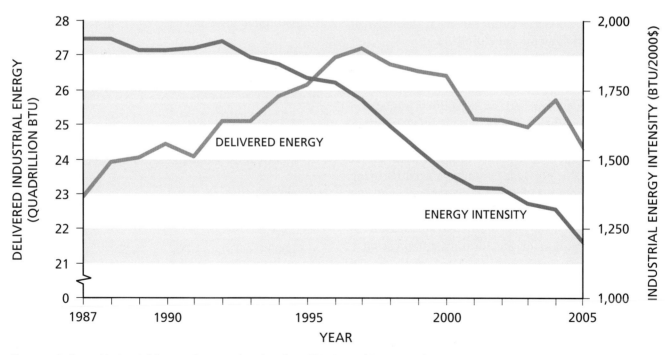

Sources: Delivered Industrial Energy Consumption data from EIA, *Annual Energy Review 2005*.
GDP data from Bureau of Economic Analysis website.

FIGURE 1-32. *U.S. Industrial Energy Consumption and Energy Intensity*

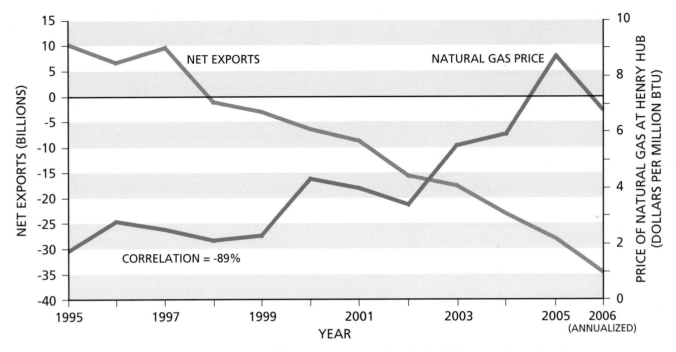

Source: U.S. Dept. of Commerce data for SITC Code 5 (Chemicals and Related Products), 64 (Paper and Paperboard), and 67 (Iron and Steel) from tse.export.gov web site. Price data from Platt's.

FIGURE 1-33. *Trade Balance for Energy-Intensive Industry*

did between 1996 and 2005. These projections are intended to bound the EIA's AEO 2007 Base Case projection. Energy use growth rates for each are shown in Table 1-11 and depicted in Figure 1-34.

Bandwidth studies conducted for the U.S. DOE on the most energy-intensive manufacturing sectors (chemical, petroleum, and forest products industries) suggest energy-efficiency opportunities of up to 5 quadrillion Btu per year, or just under 15 percent of 2005 industrial energy use. Of these opportunities, about 2 quadrillion Btu per year can be achieved by using existing technology (Table 1-12). Processes requiring additional research and development include separation, distillation, catalysts, alternate feedstocks, fouling, heat integration, drying, forming, and pressing.

Adopting existing technology for combined heat and power systems (CHP) and implementing "best practices" for steam systems would each yield savings of about 1 quadrillion Btu per year without requiring significant research. Despite its thermal efficiency advantages, CHP implementation in the U.S. industrial sector totals 72 gigawatts, which is about 50 percent of the total potential for CHP in the industrial sector (CHP Installation Database and Onsite Energy, 2000).

AEO 2007 projects a wide range of energy-intensity improvements in the manufacturing sector from 2005 to 2030, reflecting expected changes in that sector given

Growth Rates	Total Energy	Oil	Natural Gas
1949-1973	3.0%	3.9%	4.8%
1996-2005	-1.1%	0.5%	-2.2%
1983-1996	1.7%	1.4%	2.7%
Base 2005-2030	0.7%	0.4%	0.7%
Flight 2005-2030	-1.1%	0.5%	-2.2%
Stays 2005-2030	1.7%	1.4%	2.7%

Note: Growth rates average 2004/2005 values as a starting point to minimize the impact of Hurricanes Katrina and Rita on growth rate calculations.

Source: EIA, Table 2.1.d Industrial Sector Energy Consumption, 1949-2005, and *Annual Energy Outlook 2007*.

TABLE 1-11. *U.S. Industrial Energy Use Scenarios*

Facing the Hard Truths about Energy

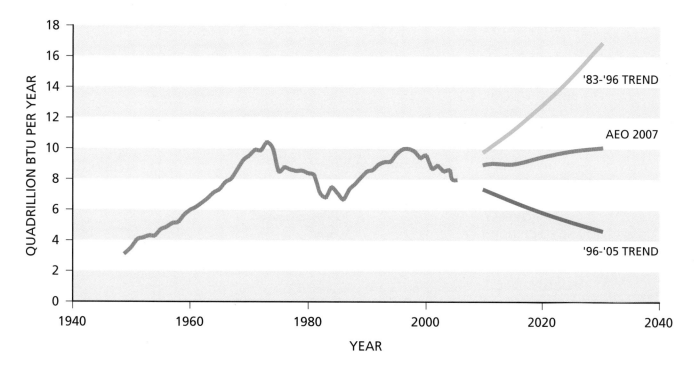

Source: EIA, Table 2.1.d Industrial Sector Energy Consumption, 1949-2005, and *Annual Energy Outlook 2007*.

FIGURE 1-34. *U.S. Industrial Energy Use Scenarios*

current conditions and trends. For example, the energy intensity of the aluminum sector is expected to decrease as secondary smelting, a less energy-intensive process, becomes the dominant technology in the United States. On the other hand, the energy intensity of the petroleum refining industry is expected to increase as liquids from coal come into use (Figure 1-35).

There are significant impediments to greater industrial efficiency. First, U.S.-government-funded energy R&D has fallen at least 70 percent in real terms from its peak in the late 1970s. Second, price volatility makes approval of efficiency projects difficult. Finally, lack of adequate, technically trained human resources impedes implementation of efficiency projects. Figure 1-36

Opportunity	Size (Quadrillion Btu per Year)	R&D Required?
Waste Heat Recovery	0.9	Yes
Industrial Boilers, Heat Recovery from Drying	0.8	Yes
Adoption of Best Practices in Heat and Power Systems and Steam Systems	0.9	No
Other – Requiring R&D	1.4	Yes
Other – Implementing Best Practices	1.1	No

Source: *U.S. Department of Energy,* Energy Use, Loss and Opportunities Analysis: U.S. Manufacturing and Mining, *2004.*

TABLE 1-12. *Approximate Size of Efficiency Technology Opportunities*

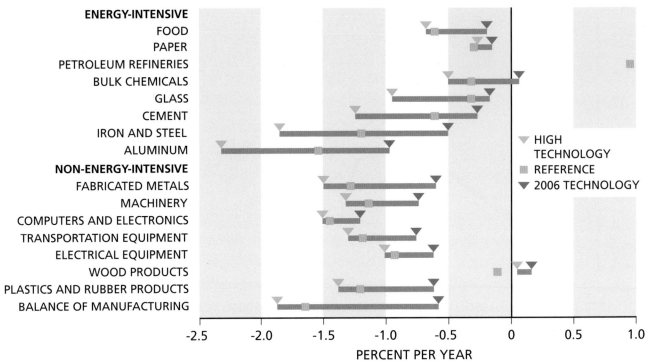

Source: EIA, *Annual Energy Outlook 2007*.

FIGURE 1-35. *Average Change in Energy Intensity in the Manufacturing Subsectors, 2005-2030*

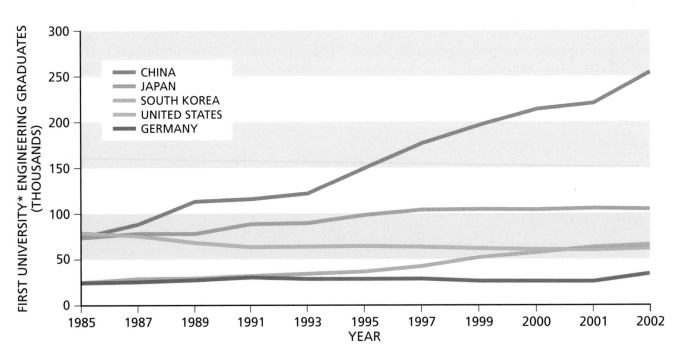

* International equivalent to a bachelor's degree.

Source: "U.S. Manufacturing Innovation at Risk," a study by Joel Popkin and Kathryn Kobe for The Manufacturing Institute and the Council of Manufacturing Associations, February 2006.

FIGURE 1-36. *Engineering School Graduates, by Year*

Facing the Hard Truths about Energy

shows the number of engineering-school graduates per year from several countries.

Industrial energy consumers play an important role in mitigating energy price volatility. Manufacturing provides a quick-acting buffer against supply or demand shocks in the energy industry. However, as demonstrated in Figure 1-37, this role has been reduced as the U.S. capability for fuel switching has fallen over the past decade, in both the power generation and industrial sectors.

CULTURAL/SOCIAL/ECONOMIC TRENDS

This area of investigation is extremely broad. However, after an analysis of the data, the following eight broad findings became apparent. The data analysis relied heavily on the Reference Case projections in WEO 2006 and IEO 2006.

1. Income is the biggest determinant of demand for energy.

Due to the strong influence of income on energy demand, even small changes in assumptions about the Gross Domestic Product (GDP) have major implications for energy growth. Energy projections by the IEA and EIA are highly sensitive to GDP assumptions. In WEO 2006, a 1 percent growth in global GDP results in a 0.5 percent increase in primary energy consumption. This is consistent with the observation that the income elasticity of demand fell from the 0.7 in the 1970s to the 0.4 from 1991-2002 as shown in Figure 1-38. WEO 2006 cites warmer winter weather in the northern hemisphere (which reduced heating-fuel demand) and improved energy efficiency for the reduction in income elasticity for energy as a whole between the two periods.

Assuming that projected economic growth is desired, then to maintain current U.S. energy consumption would require a 45 percent reduction in energy intensity by 2030. To maintain current developing-country energy consumption levels would require a 70 percent reduction in global energy intensity by 2030. Put in perspective, over the last 55 years (1949-2005), U.S. energy intensity has fallen by a little more than half (Figure 1-39). To maintain energy consumption at current levels would require a global reduction in energy intensity of roughly twice that amount.

Aside from structural changes in the economy, the only way to reduce energy is through efficiency and

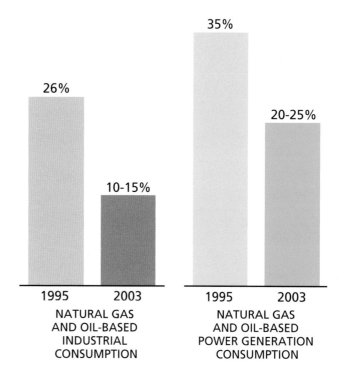

Source: NPC Natural Gas Study, 2003.

FIGURE 1-37. *Fuel Substitution Capability*

conservation. For perspective, businesses and consumers have shown their unwillingness to make efficiency investments with returns of 10 percent. Two-year paybacks for businesses are often cited as the minimum for energy efficiency investments. Consumers often make decisions that imply returns of 50 percent or more. Lack of awareness and know-how are examples of barriers to investments in improved energy efficiency. It is likely that policy action would be required to encourage energy efficiency and conservation.

History suggests that energy-intensity reductions resulting from improved efficiency and structural change will be offset by increased demand for energy services unless policies are put in place to prevent such offsets. For example, technology that could have been used to increase vehicle miles per gallon in light duty vehicles has been used to increase vehicle horsepower and weight. Likewise, improvements in the efficiency (energy use per unit of service) of appliances and buildings have been offset by increased numbers of appliances and building sizes. While policies to promote improved energy efficiency may be more politically palatable than those that restrict demand

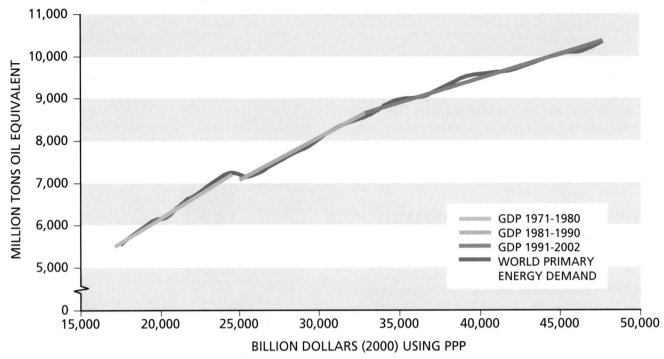

Source: IEA, *World Energy Outlook 2004.*

FIGURE 1-38. *World Primary Energy Demand and GDP, 1971-2002*

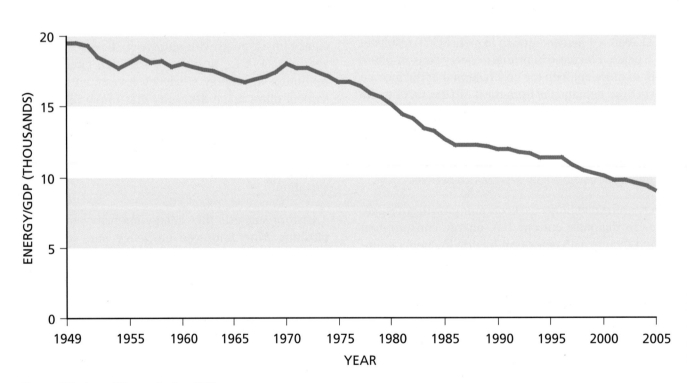

Source: EIA, *Annual Energy Review 2005.*

FIGURE 1-39. *U.S. Energy Intensity*

Facing the Hard Truths about Energy

for energy services, those improving efficiency may not be sufficient to yield significant reductions from baseline projected energy demand.

2. Oil and natural gas demand are projected to increase rapidly in coming decades.

Global oil consumption is expected to increase by 40 percent from 2005 levels by 2030. Global natural gas demand is expected to increase by two-thirds by 2030; U.S. natural gas demand is expected to increase more slowly. The increase in demand for fossil fuels in non-OECD countries will be far more rapid than in OECD countries, both in absolute and percentage terms.

Transportation, industry, and "other" (mostly building heating) are the major sources of oil demand growth in the WEO 2006. Electric power sector demand is expected to decrease by about 1 million barrels per day. Oil demand growth in the transportation sector will exceed growth for all other uses combined. Projected industry and "other" category oil consumption are expected to increase by a large amount as well. These categories are expected to grow by 13 million barrels per day, which compares with a transportation oil consumption growth of around 22 million barrels per day.

Globally, electric generation and industry are the major sources of natural gas demand growth. Natural gas demand for electric generation and industry are expected to double. Natural gas use for building heating is also expected to increase (Figure 1-40).

Perhaps less obvious, electricity use in buildings will indirectly be a major source of natural gas demand growth. Appliances and other "buildings" related energy uses represent the largest component of electricity demand growth, and thus have major impact on the demand for natural gas. A large portion of electric generation growth is expected to be fueled by natural gas.

3. Carbon dioxide from fossil fuel combustion is growing.

Global CO_2 emissions are expected to increase by about half between 2004 and 2030, from around 27 billion tons to 40 billion tons (Figure 1-41). With slow growth in nuclear energy, and with renewable energy growing fast but starting from a low base, the carbon intensity of the global energy economy is projected to increase.

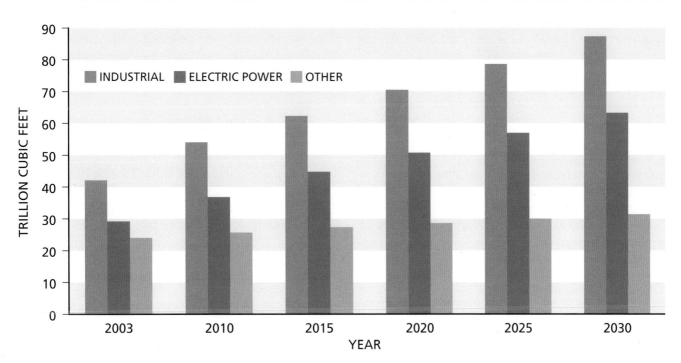

Sources: 2003: Derived from Energy Information Administration (EIA), *International Energy Annual 2003*; Projections: EIA, *International Energy Outlook 2006*.

FIGURE 1-40. *World Natural Gas Consumption by End-Use Sector, 2003-2030*

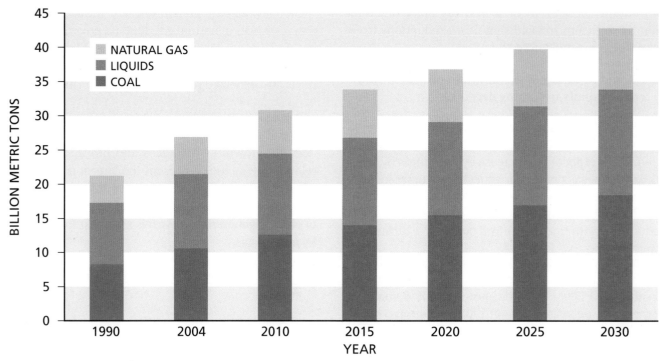

Source: EIA, *International Energy Outlook 2006*.

FIGURE 1-41. *World Energy-Related Carbon Dioxide Emissions by Fuel in the Reference Case*

The biggest contributor to global CO_2 emissions is coal, followed closely by oil and natural gas. Outside China, India, and the United States—all have large coal reserves—natural gas is expected to contribute significantly to the increase in CO_2 emissions.

The electric power sector is expected to be the dominant source of CO_2 emissions in the United States and globally—increasing from 40 percent in 2004 to 44 percent in 2030 worldwide (Table 1-13). The transportation sector, which is dominated by oil, will continue to be responsible for about one-fifth of CO_2 emissions. Yet much of the growth in electricity demand will come from residential and commercial buildings, which are already the largest single-sector source of CO_2 emissions when including the electricity generated that is used in buildings.

4. Keeping China in perspective.

Chinese energy use and GDP are projected to exceed those of the United States some time in the second half of the next decade. Chinese oil demand is projected to increase by twice as much as the U.S. oil demand through 2030 (Figure 1-42). Growth in China's oil demand is often cited as one of the major causes of higher global oil prices.

The fastest CO_2 emissions growth among major countries is occurring in China (Figure 1-43). Chinese emissions growth in 2000-2004 exceeded the rest of the world's combined growth due to increased use of coal and rapidly growing petroleum demand. Chinese CO_2 emissions are projected to pass U.S. emissions late in this decade.

While it is hard to overstate the ever-increasing importance of China in global energy markets and as a carbon emitter, it is important to put these numbers in perspective. The United States has had fast rates of energy and emissions growth for decades. As recently as the last decade (1990-2000), U.S. emissions growth was nearly as fast as China's is today. Even in 2030, China's projected oil demand will be less than the oil demand projected for the United States, both in per capita and absolute terms.

China has made major strides in reducing the carbon intensity of its economy (CO_2 per GDP). China's carbon intensity is roughly equal to that of the United States, and the intensities of both countries are projected to decrease at the same rate.

Nevertheless, while Chinese and U.S. carbon intensity will be similar during the next decade, per capita

Facing the Hard Truths about Energy

	1990	2004	2010	2015	2030	2004-2030*
Power Generation	6,955	10,587	12,818	14,209	17,680	2.0%
Industry	4,474	4,742	5,679	6,213	7,255	1.6%
Transport	3,885	5,289	5,900	6,543	8,246	1.7%
Residential and Services†	3,353	3,297	3,573	3,815	4,298	1.0%
Other‡	1,796	2,165	2,396	2,552	2,942	1.2%
Total	**20,463**	**26,069**	**30,367**	**33,333**	**40,420**	**1.7%**

* Average Annual Growth Rate.
† Includes agriculture and public sector.
‡ Includes international marine bunkers, other transformation, and non-energy use.

TABLE 1-13. *World Energy-Related Carbon Dioxide Emissions by Sector in IEA's World Energy Outlook 2006 Reference Case (Million Metric Tons)*

carbon emissions will still be far lower in China. Likewise, on a per capita basis, U.S. oil demand is 10 times China's, and the United States will still consume 6 times as much per capita as China in 2030 (Figure 1-44).

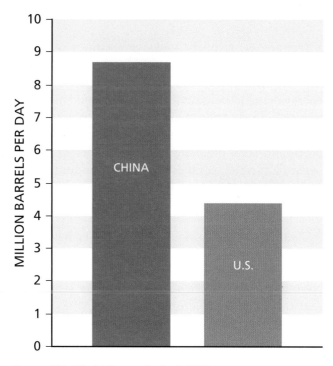

Source: IEA, *World Energy Outlook 2006*.

FIGURE 1-42. *Oil Demand Growth by 2030*

5. New technologies don't necessarily lead to reduced energy consumption.

There are any number of ways that information technologies could be used to reduce energy consumption, including telecommuting, dematerialization (i.e., the paperless office), and energy-efficient digital control systems in cars, buildings, and factories. The rapid penetration of information technologies in the economy has led some observers to predict accelerated reductions in U.S. and global energy intensity.

While the notion that technology development will lead to net reductions in energy use is appealing, is it proven, or even likely? Increased electric-plug loads associated with computers and other types of office equipment, and growing energy demand resulting from increased economic growth fueled by new information technologies, could induce a net increase in energy demand rather than a net decrease.

Based on various studies of information technology energy use, it can be estimated that information technology equipment currently uses about 210 terawatt-hours (210 trillion watt-hours), or about 5 percent of U.S. electricity consumption. This is almost as much electricity as could be saved by 2010 through efficiency measures with a cost of 10 cents or less per kilowatt-hour. In other words, the electricity consumed by information technologies in the United States, most introduced over the last decade, exceeds the

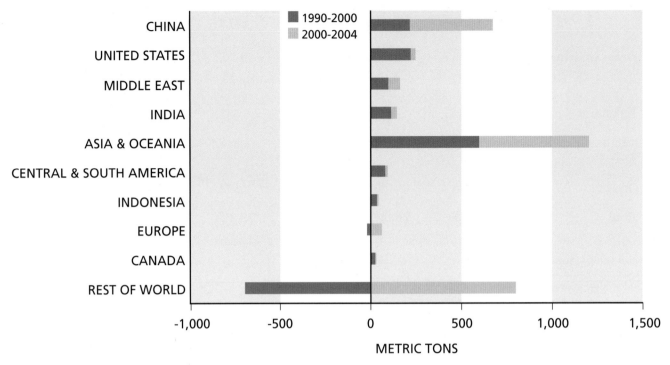

Source: EIA, *International Energy Annual 2004*.

FIGURE 1-43. *Regional Increase in Carbon Dioxide Emissions*

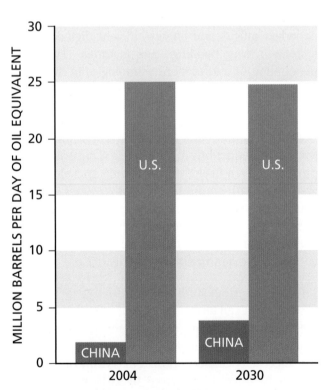

Source: IEA, *World Energy Outlook 2006*.

FIGURE 1-44. *Comparison of Oil Demand Per Capita — 2004 and 2030 Industry*

electricity-savings potential for refrigerators, washers, dryers, televisions, and the multitude of other electricity consuming appliances and equipment.

Technology advances make projecting energy-use trends particularly difficult. If excessive technological optimism causes an under estimation of future energy demand requirements, society could be forced to develop new energy sources hastily, at potentially great financial and environmental costs. Likewise, overly optimistic predictions that information technology (or any other technology) will reduce our reliance on fossil fuels might send the message that addressing energy challenges will not require any hard choices.

There are few historical precedents for new technologies actually reducing energy use (as opposed to just reducing energy intensity). New technologies often create new service demands at the same time that they improve the efficiency of existing service demands—the technology has the potential to reduce energy use, but gets called on for other purposes or allows (and in some cases even encourages) increased demand for new and additional energy services. For example, refrigerators are far more efficient (per cubic foot) than they were two decades ago, but more

Facing the Hard Truths about Energy

households have more than one refrigerator, and refrigerators have become bigger. Likewise, homes are better insulated and air conditioning and heating systems have become more efficient, but at the same time homes have grown in size. And cars, as discussed below, have become far more energy efficient, but that very efficiency has been offset by increased horsepower, size, and weight of vehicles.

In summary, care should be exercised when evaluating the future use of technology—information age or other—as a means of reducing future energy use.

6. Large untapped potential for improved fuel economy in light duty vehicles.

Driven by rising incomes, global light duty vehicle (LDV) ownership rates are expected to increase from 100 vehicles per 1000 persons today to 170 in 2030. As a result, LDVs in use worldwide are expected to double, from 650 million in 2005 to 1.4 billion in 2030. Whereas U.S. and Japanese markets, for example, are expected to increase along with population, vehicle sales are expected to triple in non-OECD countries by 2030.

Vehicle fuel-use efficiency has increased. One recent study found that fuel-use efficiency (energy recovered per unit of fuel consumed) has increased by about 1 percent per year since 1987. This could have resulted in an increase of 0.2 miles per gallon per year. However, gains in efficiency have been offset by increases in vehicle weight, size, power, and accessories. If these factors had instead remained constant since 1987, average fuel economy would be 3-4 mpg higher for both cars and trucks than it is today (Figure 1-45).

Consequently, vehicle fuel economies (miles per gallon) in the United States have stagnated. Low fuel prices, combined with no increase in Corporate Average Fuel Economy (CAFE) standards, have led to U.S. light duty vehicle fleet-wide fuel economy that is essentially flat since the mid 1980s. At the same time, the structure of the CAFE standards allowed increased purchase of light trucks (SUVs, pick-ups, and minivans), which are subject to less-stringent fuel economy requirements. Cars still make up more than 60 percent of total vehicle miles traveled, but light trucks now account for more than half of the light duty vehicle sales in the United States, up from 20 percent in the 1976 to 53 percent in 2003. The period since the mid-1980s stands in stark contrast to the previous decade (1975-85), in which the fuel economy of America's light duty vehicles increased by two-thirds, driven by CAFE standards that increased annually.

There is a lot of uncertainty about business-as-usual trends in fuel economy. AEO 2006 projects that LDV fuel economy in the United States will increase 17 percent, from 24.9 mpg in 2003 to 29.2 mpg in 2030, in spite of an increase in horsepower of 29 percent. WEO 2006, however, projects an increase of just

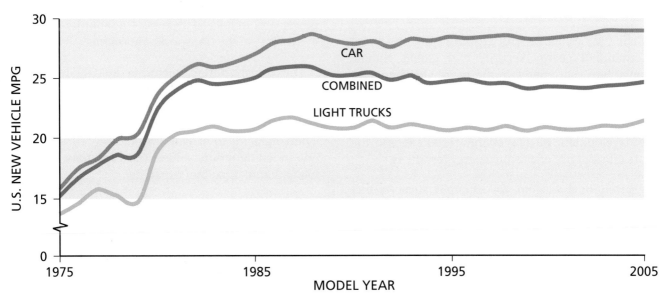

Source: U.S. EPA, *Light-Duty Automotive Technology and Fuel Economy Trends: 1975-2003.*

FIGURE 1-45. *U.S. Car and Light-Truck Fuel Economy*

2.5 percent. Baseline expectations on improved fuel economy make a big difference in terms of how much energy savings we could expect from changes in CAFE standards or from other policies. Higher gasoline prices—if sustained—could result in the purchase of vehicles with better fuel economy, especially if fuel-economy improvements are available with little increase in price or reduced performance.

There are several technologies that could be used without short-changing vehicle performance, including continuously variable transmissions, engine supercharging and turbo charging, variable valve timing, cylinder deactivation, aerodynamic design, the integrated starter/generator, and low-resistance tires. In its 2002 report on fuel economy standards, the National Research Council found that a combination of various technologies could boost LDV fuel economy by one-third, and would be cost-effective for the consumer (would pay back over the life of the vehicles). With much higher gasoline prices, as seen in recent years, that savings potential is even greater. Note that all of these technological improvements could be used to improve other aspects of vehicle performance besides fuel economy.

Realizing such a fuel economy potential will likely require a range of policies to encourage improved fuel economy, including: increasing and/or reforming vehicle fuel economy standards, fuel taxes, and vehicle "feebates" (e.g., fee for low-fuel economy vehicles, rebate for high fuel economy vehicles).

7. Prices matter.

Rising prices, along with growing concerns about international energy security and global climate change have put energy in the news. Policymakers and business leaders want to know how much and when demand will respond to these high prices; and whether new policies and measures might stimulate the development of new energy resources and the more efficient use of existing energy resources.

Conventional wisdom, for example, suggests that there will be little quantity response to higher energy prices, at least in the short run. However, decades of econometric work suggests that over time consumers and businesses do adjust. Based on a meta-analysis by Carol Dahl (2006), which reviewed findings from 190 studies of elasticity conducted from 1990 through 2005, short-run price elasticity appears to range from around -0.1 to -0.3. In the long run, demand for various types of energy is roughly three times as responsive to price

changes. However, demand is far more responsive to income than to price.

Past elasticities are not necessarily indicative of price responsiveness in the future. The magnitudes of all elasticities are influenced by changes in technology, consumer preferences, beliefs, and habits. It is entirely conceivable that a sustained period of high energy prices (for perhaps 5-10 years) could induce far greater percentage changes in the quantity of energy demand.

Elasticities could also be changed by policies. But given the relative importance of income compared to prices, if policies focus only on rising price signals without providing alternatives to current transportation and lifestyle patterns, consumers and businesses may view those policies as more punitive than productive.

8. Fuel-switching capabilities are declining in industry and increasing in transportation.

The ability to substitute fuels in a given sector affects how vulnerable that sector is to supply disruptions and associated price spikes. The ability to substitute fuels during a disruption lessens demand for the disrupted fuel, thereby reducing the size of the shortfall and the associated price spike. Lacking the ability to substitute fuels, prices need to rise to fairly high levels in times of shortage in order to reduce the activity that is generating the demand for fuel.

In the United States, the buildings sectors have very little ability (less than 5 percent) to switch fuel. Fuel-switching capabilities are higher, but falling, in the power and industrial sectors. Capability is low, but increasing, in the transportation sector.

The transportation sector is heavily reliant on petroleum and has little fuel substitution capability. About 5 million light duty vehicles in the United States have flexible fuel capability, representing about 2 percent of the total light duty fleet. By 2030, roughly one in ten light duty vehicle sales will have E-85 flex fuel (ethanol/gasoline) capability.

To make the widespread supply of E-85 economical will require more flex-fuel vehicles, substantial investments in the distribution system, and development of a second-generation feedstock that is not used for food (e.g., cellulosic ethanol). Even then, ethanol's ability to reduce price volatility for motor fuels will be limited unless there is spare ethanol production capacity. Meanwhile, increased reliance on ethanol could result in increased price volatility due to weather factors reducing crop size, transportation bottlenecks, high rail costs, and other local supply and demand factors.

Electric power generation appears to engage in significant short-term fuel switching, especially during times of high natural gas prices. This capability has declined over the last decade, from one-third of power generation gas boilers that were able to use residual fuel oil as a second fuel source in the mid-1990s to about one-quarter now (Figure 1-46). The reasons for the decline in fuel-switching capability include environmental restrictions, costs for additional storage of secondary fuels, and siting and related permitting complications that arise with multi-fuel generation facilities.

In the industrial sector, roughly one-fifth of the natural gas consumed can be switched to another fuel. Protection from highly volatile energy prices for residential and commercial consumers can be had indirectly via the other consuming sectors. To the extent that fuel flexibility and switching in the transportation, power, and industrial sectors mitigates price spikes and volatility, a spillover benefit accrues to the residential and commercial sectors.

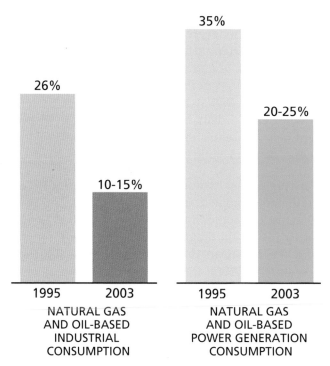

Source: NPC Natural Gas Study, 2003.

FIGURE 1-46. *Fuel Substitution Capability*

RESIDENTIAL/COMMERCIAL EFFICIENCY

Buildings are major consumers of oil and natural gas both nationally and globally, both directly and indirectly through the consumption of electricity generated from oil and natural gas. While most energy consumed in buildings is for traditional uses such as heating, cooling, and lighting, a growing portion is going to new electric devices, many of which were rare or even nonexistent just a few years ago. And, while significant efficiency improvements have been made in building shells, systems, and appliances, the potential energy savings have been partially offset by additional energy service demand requirements that have occurred as a result of increased home sizes as well as new and larger electric devices.

If all achievable, cost-effective energy-efficiency measures were deployed in residential and commercial buildings, anticipated energy use could be reduced by roughly 15-20 percent. The potential for cost-effective energy efficiency improvements depends heavily on the price of energy, consumer awareness and perceptions, and the relative efficiency of available products in the marketplace. These factors are determined in part by government policies.

The major barriers to energy-efficiency investments are low energy prices relative to incomes, due in part to externalities not being included in prices and government subsidies, split incentives (consumers of energy different from those selecting energy consuming facilities or paying for energy), and consumers' lack of information. To the extent that societal benefits from improved efficiency are recognized, government policies to promote energy efficiency are used. To reduce energy consumption significantly below levels associated with the current policy environment will require additional policy related improvements in energy efficiency. These policies should take into account the potential to increase energy-service consumption as a result of less energy consumption.

When energy losses in the generation and distribution of electricity are included, about 40 percent of U.S. energy is consumed in the residential and commercial buildings sectors. Current projections indicate that building energy use will increase by more than one third by 2030. Commercial building energy use is expected to increase by nearly half, due to continued growth in the service economy. Residential energy use is expected to grow at half that rate. The combined energy use growth in residential and commercial buildings is expected to represent about 45 percent of total primary energy growth.[4]

According to AEO 2007, buildings currently represent only about 6 percent of economy-wide petroleum consumption, a share projected to decline to about 4 percent by 2030. The natural gas story is quite different. Buildings consume 55 percent of natural gas and are expected to be responsible for about three quarters of the growth in natural gas consumption through 2030 (including gas used for electricity supplied to buildings). Commercial and residential buildings represent 52 percent and 25 percent, respectively, of overall projected natural gas consumption growth from 2005-2030.[5]

United States Residential/ Commercial Energy Use

The AEO Reference Case is an attempt by analysts at the EIA to predict efficiency improvements given projected energy prices and other factors influencing the penetration of various energy-saving technologies. Energy efficiency savings potential including additional policies, standards, behavioral changes, and technological breakthroughs far exceed the efficiency included in the AEO Reference Cases. Specific estimates of the exact magnitude of this potential vary widely.

Estimates of achievable, cost-effective reductions in building electricity use for commercial and residential buildings in the United States range from 7 to 40 percent below the Reference Case projections. The midrange appears to be around 20 percent for commercial buildings, and slightly less in residential buildings.

EIA (AEO 2007) estimates residential sector energy consumption (not just electricity consumption) would be 24 percent lower than in its Reference Case if "consumers purchase the most efficient products available at normal replacement intervals regardless of cost, and that new buildings are built to the most energy-efficient specifications available, starting in 2007." Energy-efficient building components would include,

for example, solid-state lighting, condensing gas furnaces, and building envelope improvements such as high-efficiency windows and increased insulation.

Similarly, EIA (AEO 2007) estimates that commercial building energy consumption in 2030 would be 13 percent less than projected in its Reference Case if "only the most efficient technologies are chosen, regardless of cost, and that building shells in 2030 are 50 percent more efficient than projected in the Reference Case [including] the adoption of improved heat exchangers for space heating and cooling equipment, solid-state lighting, and more efficient compressors for commercial refrigeration." Table 1-14 lists efficiency improvements that could be achieved in several categories by 2030.

EIA efficiency-potential estimates are on the high end of the residential studies we examined, and on the low to mid range of the commercial estimates (see Figures 1-47 and 1-48). Note, however, that the EIA projections assume that cost is no concern, so inasmuch as the other efficiency potential studies include cost-effectiveness tests, we would expect the EIA estimates to be at the high end of the studies. Furthermore, the other studies are for the most part examining the potential for electricity savings, not energy savings overall.

According to the 2006 McKinsey Global Institute study of energy-efficiency potential, if all energy-efficiency measures with internal rates of return of 10 percent or better are implemented, U.S. residential energy demand could be reduced by 36 percent below its 2020 baseline and commercial energy use could be reduced by 19 percent. Using the same investment criteria, McKinsey estimates global residential building energy demand could be reduced by 15 percent below baseline and global commercial building energy demand could be reduced by 20 percent.[6]

As previously mentioned, most of the studies we examined estimated an efficiency potential of 10 to 20 percent in commercial buildings and 10 to 15 percent in residential buildings beyond business as usual, with the American Council for an Energy-Efficient Economy (ACEEE) studies estimating potentials as high as 35 percent for residential buildings in Florida and 40 percent for commercial buildings in Texas.

At the other extreme, the Electric Power Research Institute (EPRI) developed a supply curve for electric demand-side measures in 2010—including residential

---

4 Energy Information Administration, *Annual Energy Outlook 2007 with Projections to 2030*, Table 2, February 2007, http:// www.eia.doe.gov/oiaf/aeo/excel/aeotab_2.xls.

5 Calculations based on data from *Annual Energy Outlook 2007*, Table 2.

6 McKinsey Global Institute, *Productivity of Growing Global Energy Demand: A Microeconomic Perspective*, November 2006.

Category	Appliance	Efficiency Improvement
Appliance	Refrigerators	22%
	Freezers	8%
Space heating	Electric heat pumps	10%
	Natural gas heat pumps	14%
	Geothermal heat pumps	5%
	Natural gas furnaces	6%
	Distillate furnaces	2%
Space cooling	Electric heat pumps	20%
	Natural gas heat pumps	10%
	Geothermal heat pumps	6%
	Central air conditioners	22%
	Room air conditioners	7%
Water heaters	Electric	3%
	Natural gas	6%
	Distillate fuel oil	0%
	Liquefied petroleum gases	6%
Building shell efficiency	Space heating – Pre 1998 homes	7%
Note: Index includes size of structure in the calculation	Space cooling – Pre 1998 homes	2%
	Space heating – New construction	2%
	Space cooling – New construction	2%

Source: Energy Information Administration, *Annual Energy Outlook 2007,* table 21, http://www.eia.doe.gov/oiaf/aeo/supplement/sup_rci.xls.

TABLE 1-14. *Residential Stock Efficiency Improvements, 2007-2030*

and commercial buildings, and industry.[7] According to the EPRI analysis, by 2010 the United States could reduce electricity use by about 150 terawatt-hours (3.9 percent of total U.S. electricity consumption) with measures costing less than 10 cents per kilowatt-hour and 210 terawatt-hours (5.5 percent) at 20 cents per kilowatt-hour or less. For reference, electricity consumption in 2005 totaled about 3,800 terawatt-hours[8] and the retail price of electricity in 2005 was 9.5 cents per kilowatt-hour for residential, 8.7 cents per kilowatt-hour for com-

mercial, and 5.7 cents per kilowatt-hour for industrial.[9] At these prices, about 50 terawatt-hours (1.3 percent) of electric efficiency improvements could be achieved.

Buildings typically last decades if not centuries. Many of the features of buildings that affect their energy consumption—e.g., solar orientation, windows, tightness, and wall thickness—largely will go unchanged throughout the life of the building. Technologies and practices affecting these long-lived systems will be slow to penetrate the buildings stock and affect overall efficiency.

Building-energy codes typically target only new buildings and major rehabilitations, which is important

---

7   Clark Gellings, Greg Wikler and Debyani Ghosh, "Assessment of U.S. Electric End-Use Energy Efficiency Potential," *The Electricity Journal,* November 2006, Vol. 19, Issue 9, Elsevier Inc, 2006, p.67.

8   Energy Information Administration, Electric Power Annual with data for 2005, November 2006, http://www.eia.doe.gov/cneaf/electricity/epa/epates2.html.

9   Energy Information Administration, Electric Power Annual with data for 2005, November 2006, http://www.eia.doe.gov/cneaf/electricity/epa/epat7p4.html.

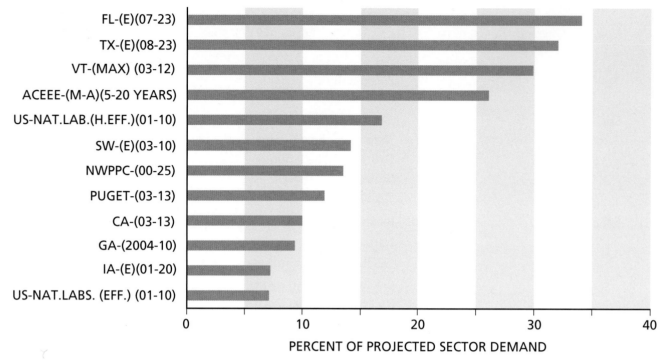

Source: Alliance to Save Energy, 2007.

FIGURE 1-47. *Achievable Potential for Electricity Savings in the Residential Sector (Various Studies)*

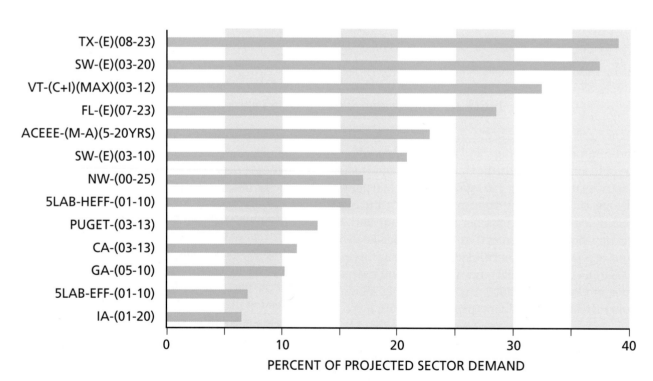

Source: Alliance to Save Energy, 2007.

FIGURE 1-48. *Achievable Potential for Electricity Savings in the Commercial Sector (Various Studies)*

Facing the Hard Truths about Energy

because today's new buildings are tomorrow's existing buildings. New building codes and appliance standards can be bolstered to improve overall building energy use, but to significantly impact building energy use policies that induce significant savings in existing buildings are necessary. Appliance standards, labels and other measures target appliances and other equipment used in existing buildings.

Appliances, heating equipment, and air conditioning facilities are replaced as they wear out. Energy use can be addressed by standards for these applications as the equipment is replaced.

New buildings can be constructed to meet current "best practices" at the time of construction. Since buildings are usually constructed and used by different groups it is likely that standards would be needed to ensure construction that is economically thermally efficient for the areas in which construction takes place.

Translating Efficiency Into Reduced Energy Demand— "Consumption-Based Efficiency"

It is not always clear to what extent efficiency improvements are translated into actual reductions

in energy demand. While the energy efficiency of homes has increased, so have home sizes. The average American home's floor area more than doubled between 1950 and 2000, as did floor area per capita; both square footage per home and per capita have increased by more than half just since the 1980s (see Figure 1-49).[10] Similarly, according to EIA's Residential Energy Consumption Survey (RECS), refrigerator energy use per household was roughly the same in 1993 and 2001, even though energy use per unit virtually halved during that time period.[11] While it is possible that second refrigerators would be commonplace regardless of unit efficiencies, it can at least be said that the demand for new energy services has increased as fast as efficiencies.

The demand for new energy services, such as second (and third) refrigerators and bigger homes, is driven by growing incomes, low energy prices, and to

---

10 National Association of Home Builders (NAHB), "Housing Facts: Figures and Trends 2003," 2003, Washington, DC.

11 EIA, *Residential Energy Consumption Survey 1993*, 1993, Table 5.27, http://eia.doe.gov/pub/consumption/residential/rx93cet6.pdf, & *Residential Energy Consumption Survey 2001*, 2001, Table CE5-1c, http://www.eia.doe.gov/emeu/recs/recs2001/ce_pdf/appliances/ce5-1c_climate2001.pdf; estimated average household site electricity consumption for refrigerators was 5 million Btu in 2001 and 4.7 million Btu in 1993.

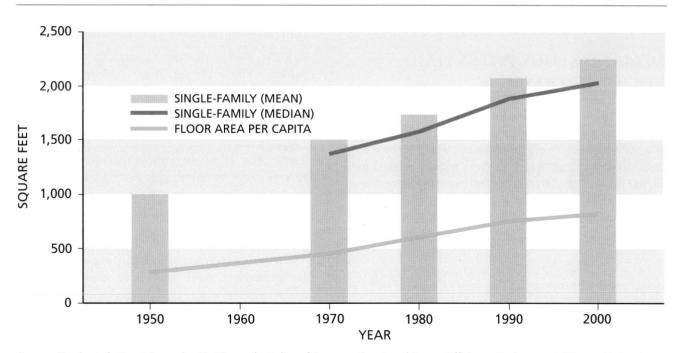

Source: Harris et al., *Don't Supersize Me! Toward a Policy of Consumption-Based Energy Efficiency,* Environmental Energy Technology Division, Lawrence Berkeley National Laboratory, 2006. Original data from National Association of Home Builders.

FIGURE 1-49. *U.S. House Size (Floor Area)*

some extent reduced operating costs due to improved efficiency. Some reductions in demand from energy-efficiency improvements are "taken back" in the form of increased demand for less-costly energy services. For example, efficiency improvements result in lower energy costs for refrigeration, which leads to increased demand for refrigerators. This "snapback" or rebound effect is estimated to be about 10 to 20 percent of the initial energy savings for most efficiency measures, although it varies depending on several factors, including end-use and elasticity of demand.[12]

Some energy-efficiency programs may even be contributing to—or at least not dampening—the increased demand for bigger appliances. The categorization of energy-using products for purposes of standards and labeling development may provide some perverse incentives to purchase products that are bigger, more powerful, or have more amenities. For example, ENERGY STAR label eligibility requirements for refrigerators vary by size—in some cases, the most efficient refrigerator in a larger class (which is therefore eligible for the ES label) may consume more energy than the least efficient in the smaller class (which is not eligible for the label). As a result, the ENERGY STAR label may inadvertently steer consumers toward "more efficient" refrigerators that are larger or have more amenities when the smaller refrigerator with fewer amenities and lower energy consumption might otherwise have been the choice.[13]

DEMAND STUDY POTENTIAL POLICY OPTIONS

From the work that was done by the Demand Task Group, the following list of potential policy actions was developed. The fundamentals supporting the list revolve around factors such as impact related to demand level, understanding of use, and effect on energy security. From this list, the overall study group developed three policies as study recommendations (see Policy Recommendations section below).

1. **Enhance international energy security framework.**

China and India will account for a significant share of future growth in oil and gas demand. The United States should lead the enhancement of an international energy security framework, such as an expanded International Energy Agency, that includes China and India.

2. **U.S. leadership on environmental concerns.**

If policy makers conclude that additional action to reduce carbon dioxide emissions is warranted, then the United States should take a leadership role to develop an effective global framework that involves all major emitters of carbon dioxide. Initiatives may be disjointed without U.S. leadership because some high growth developing countries are not likely to engage in such efforts unless developed countries, and especially the United States, take a clear leadership role.

3. **Areas should be identified where market solutions to support energy efficiency may not be fully effective.**

Policy makers should consider policies that encourage energy-efficiency improvements, including metrics to measure progress.

4. **Raise vehicle fuel efficiency at the maximum rate consistent with available and economic technology.**

Vehicle fuel efficiency standards should be raised. The interests of all concerned parties should be considered when establishing new efficiency standards. Significant gains in efficiency have occurred in the past. The average fuel efficiency of new cars doubled from 1974 to 1985. The Transportation Efficiency Subgroup analysis said "technologies exist, or are expected to be developed, that have the potential to reduce fuel consumption by 50 percent relative to 2005."

5. **The federal government should a) encourage states to implement more aggressive energy efficient building codes and b) update appliance standards.**

Building codes and appliance standards should be updated to reflect currently available technology. New, up-to-date standards should be enforced. Options should be developed for enhancing current incentives to retrofit existing structures for improved energy efficiency.

---

12 Resources for the Future, "Retrospective Examinations of Demand-Side Energy Efficiency Policies," Discussion Paper, 2006.

13 Jeffrey Harris, Rick Diamond, Maithili Iyer, Chris Payne and Carl Blumstein, *Don't Supersize Me! Toward a Policy of Consumption-Based Energy Efficiency*, Environmental Energy Technologies Division, LBNL, 2006 ACEEE Summer Study on Energy Efficiency, p. 7-108.

6. Encourage greater efficiency in the industrial sector.

Foster research, development, demonstration, and deployment of energy efficiency technologies and practices in the industrial sector. The U.S. industrial sector consumes one-third of the energy used in the United States. Technologies exist that could save 15 percent of this energy, but only one-third of this is currently economic. Further research and development is required to implement the remaining potential gain in efficiency. Areas of opportunity include waste heat recovery and boiler/steam efficiency. Make permanent the research and development tax credit is an option to increase industrial energy efficiency.

7. Visible and transparent carbon dioxide cost.

If policy makers conclude that additional action to limit carbon dioxide emissions is warranted, then a mechanism should be developed that establishes a cost for emitting carbon dioxide. The mechanism should be economy-wide, visible, transparent, applicable to all fuels, and durable for the long-term. By establishing a cost (or price), companies will be better positioned to determine how to restrain carbon dioxide emissions. A carbon dioxide cap-and-trade system or a carbon dioxide tax are two possibilities that could reduce emissions and establish a carbon dioxide cost.

8. The U.S. manufacturing industry and national security will be enhanced through a diverse range of fuels to generate power.

Fuel choice for power generation should be fostered to avoid increasing dependence on a single fuel. Reference projections indicate that the United States will be increasingly reliant on LNG imports to satisfy domestic natural gas demand. There are several potential drivers that could result in even higher domestic natural gas demand—e.g., escalating construction costs and greenhouse gas considerations, both of which favor natural gas over coal for new electrical power generation. Relying too heavily on natural gas for power generation could displace energy intensive manufacturing from the United States.

9. Improve energy data collection.

Energy data collection efforts around the world should be expanded to provide data in a consistent and timely fashion. India and China should be encouraged to participate in world energy data collection.

10. Improve energy modeling.

Development and use of economic activity feedback projection techniques should be encouraged to aid in evaluation of critical policies such as carbon constraint.

POLICY RECOMMENDATIONS

Improve Vehicle Fuel Economy

Nearly half of the 21 million barrels of oil products that the United States consumes each day is gasoline used for cars and light trucks. The Reference Case in AEO 2007 projects that gasoline consumption will increase by an average of 1.3 percent per year, totaling an increase of 3 million barrels per day between 2005 and 2030.

The CAFE standards have been the primary policy used to promote improved car and light-truck fuel economy in the United States over the last three decades. The original standards created one economy requirement for cars, and another less stringent one for light trucks to avoid penalizing users of work trucks. At the time, light-truck sales were about one-quarter of car sales. Since then, sport utility vehicles and minivans classified as light trucks have increased their share of the market. Now, these light-truck sales exceed car sales, and the increase at the lower truck fuel economy standard has limited overall fuel economy improvement.

Cars and trucks sold today are more technically efficient than those sold two decades ago. However, the fuel economy improvements that could have been gained from this technology over the last two decades have been used to increase vehicle weight, horsepower, and to add amenities. Consequently, car and truck fuel economy levels have been about flat for two decades, as previously shown in Figure 1-45.

Based on a detailed review of technological potential, a doubling of fuel economy of new cars and light trucks by 2030 is possible through the use of existing and anticipated technologies, assuming vehicle performance and other attributes remain the same as today.[14] This economy improvement will entail

---

14 See in this report, "Transportation Efficiency" section of Chapter 3, Technology. The extent to which technologies translate into reductions in fuel consumption depends on several factors, including costs, consumer preferences, availability, deployment, and timing.

higher vehicle cost. The 4 percent annual gain in CAFE standards starting in 2010 that President George W. Bush suggested in his 2007 State of the Union speech is not inconsistent with a potential doubling of fuel economy for new light duty vehicles by 2030. Depending upon how quickly new vehicle improvements are incorporated in the on-road light duty vehicle fleet, U.S. oil demand would be reduced by about 3-5 million barrels per day in 2030.[15] Additional fuel economy improvements would be possible by reducing vehicle weight, horsepower, and amenities, or by developing more expensive, step-out technologies.

Recommendation

The NPC makes the following recommendations to increase vehicle fuel economy:

- Improve car and light-truck fuel economy standards at the maximum rate possible by applying economic, available technology.

  - Update the standards on a regular basis.

  - Avoid further erosion of fuel economy standards resulting from increased sales of light trucks, or, alternatively, adjust light-truck standards to reflect changes in relative light-truck and car market shares.

Potential Effect: 3-5 million barrels of oil per day in the United States from the increased base in 2030.

Reduce Energy Consumption in the Residential and Commercial Sectors

Forty percent of U.S. energy is consumed in the residential and commercial sectors, including the energy lost while generating and distributing the electricity used. The EIA projects that U.S. residential and commercial energy use will increase almost one-third by 2030.

Significant efficiency improvements have been made in buildings over the last several decades. Improvement areas include the building structure itself; heating, cooling, and lighting systems; and appliances. However, these improvements have been

partly offset by increased building sizes and by use of larger and multiple appliances. Cost-effective energy efficiency building technologies have outpaced current U.S. federal, state, and local policies. If applied, currently available efficiency technology would reduce energy use an additional 15-20 percent.[16]

Buildings typically last for decades. Many of the features of buildings that affect their energy consumption, such as wall thickness, insulation, structural tightness, and windows, will go largely unchanged throughout the life of the building. Technologies and practices affecting these long-lived systems will be slow to penetrate the building stock and affect their overall efficiency, making it important to implement policies early to achieve significant long-term savings.

Major barriers to energy efficiency investments include initial costs, insufficient energy price signals, split incentives (where the consumer is different from the facility provider), and individual consumer's limited information. To reduce energy consumption significantly below the projected baseline will require policy-driven improvements in energy efficiency.

Building Energy Codes

Building energy codes have proved to be a significant policy tool to encourage increased energy efficiency in new buildings, and in buildings undergoing major renovations. Building codes are administered by the 50 states and by thousands of local authorities. To help state and local governments, national model energy codes are developed and updated every few years. Under federal law, states are not obligated to impose energy codes for buildings, although at least 41 states have adopted some form of building energy code.

Adopting a building code does not guarantee energy savings. Code enforcement and compliance are also essential. Some jurisdictions have reported that one-third or more of new buildings do not comply with

---

15 The potential fuel savings of 3 to 5 million barrels per day in 2030 is relative to a scenario where current fuel economy standards remain unchanged through 2030.

16 Baseline projections taken from Energy Information Administration, *Annual Energy Outlook 2007 with Projections to 2030*, Table 2, February 2007, http://www.eia.doe.gov/oiaf/aeo/excel/aeotab_2.xls; savings estimates taken from several studies including *Building on Success, Policies to Reduce Energy Waste in Buildings*, Joe Loper, Lowell Ungar, David Weitz and Harry Misuriello – Alliance to Save Energy, July 2005. "Achievable" used here means that the measures are currently available and the savings can be realized with a reasonable level of effort and with acceptable reductions, if any, in perceived amenity value.

For additional discussion, see the *National Action Plan for Energy Efficiency*, which is available at: http://www.epa.gov/cleanrgy/actionplan/eeactionplan.htm

---

Facing the Hard Truths about Energy

critical energy code requirements for windows and air conditioning equipment, which are among the easiest energy saving features to verify.[17]

Building energy codes typically target only new buildings and major renovations. Additional policies are needed to encourage incremental, significant savings in existing buildings.

Appliance and Equipment Standards

Standards for appliances and other equipment are major policy measures that reduce energy use in existing buildings. These products may not consume much energy individually, but collectively they represent a significant portion of the nation's energy use.[18]

Energy efficiency standards currently do not apply to many increasingly common products, including those based on expanded digital technologies. Product coverage must be continuously evaluated and expanded when appropriate to assure inclusion of all significant energy consuming devices. In addition, industry and other stakeholders have negotiated standards for other products, such as residential furnaces and boilers. Implementing and enforcing expanded and strengthened standards would reduce energy consumption below the levels that will result from current Department of Energy requirements.[19]

Residential and commercial efficiency gains are partially consumed by increased use of the services and products that become more efficient. For example, U.S. house sizes have increased steadily over the years, offsetting much of the energy efficiency improvements that would have resulted had house sizes not swelled. Similarly, household refrigerators have increased in number and size, consuming much of the reduced energy use per refrigerator gained by efficiency standards. Energy efficiency programs should consider steps to avoid increasing the demand for energy services.

Recommendation

The NPC makes the following recommendations to improve efficiency in the residential and commercial sectors:

- Encourage states to implement and enforce more aggressive energy efficiency building codes, updated on a regular basis.

- Establish appliance standards for new products.

- Update federal appliance standards on a regular basis.

Potential Effect: 7-9 quadrillion Btu per year by 2030 in the United States, including 2-3 quadrillion Btu per year of natural gas (5-8 billion cubic feet per day), 4-5 quadrillion Btu per year of coal, and ~1 quadrillion Btu per year (0.5 million barrels per day) of oil.

Increase Industrial Sector Efficiency

The industrial sector consumes about one-third of U.S. energy, and contributes to a large share of the projected growth in both oil and natural gas use globally and in the United States. Worldwide, industrial demand for natural gas is expected to double by 2030. Worldwide, industrial sector demand for oil is expected to increase by 5 million barrels per day, or 15 percent of total oil demand growth through 2030.

The industrial sector is a price-responsive energy consumer. U.S. energy-intensive industries and manufacturers rely on internationally competitive energy supplies to remain globally competitive. In recent years, U.S. natural gas prices have risen faster than those in the rest of the world. As a result, U.S. energy-intensive manufacturers using natural gas as

---

17 From *Building on Success, Policies to Reduce Energy Waste in Buildings*, Joe Loper, Lowell Ungar, David Weitz and Harry Misuriello – Alliance to Save Energy, July 2005, pp. 18-19. For a compilation of compliance studies, see U.S. Department of Energy, *Baseline Studies*, on web site (http://www.energycodes.gov/implement/baseline_studies.stm). Arkansas reports 36 of 100 homes in the study sample did not meet the HVAC requirements of the state energy code.

18 From *Building on Success, Policies to Reduce Energy Waste in Buildings*, Joe Loper, Lowell Ungar, David Weitz and Harry Misuriello – Alliance to Save Energy, July 2005, p. 24

19 For additional savings potential see Steven Nadel, Andrew deLaski, Maggie Eldridge, & Jim Kleisch, *Leading the Way: Continued Opportunities for New State Appliance and Equipment Efficiency Standards*, March 2006, http://www.standardsasap.org/a062.pdf.

a fuel or feedstock have responded by increasing the efficiency of their operations and/or by shifting more of their operations to lower energy cost regions outside the United States.

Across the industrial sector, there are opportunities to increase energy efficiency by about 15 percent.[20] Areas for energy savings include waste-heat recovery, separation processes, and combined heat and power.[21] While 40 percent of that opportunity could be implemented now, further research, development, demonstration, and deployment are required before the remaining savings can be achieved. Providing programs that encourage deployment of energy efficiency technologies and practices will hasten their implementation. Making the federal research and development tax credit permanent is one way to encourage private investment in these areas. However, a lack of technically trained workers can impede the implementation of efficiency projects while the uncertainty from price volatility can make justifying those projects difficult.

---

20 From the *Chemical Bandwidth Study*, DOE, 2004; *Energy Bandwidth for Petroleum Refining Processes*, DOE, 2006; *Pulp and Paper Industry Energy Bandwidth Study*, AIChE, 2006.

See also *Curbing Global Energy Demand Growth: The Energy Productivity Opportunity*, McKinsey Global Institute, May 2007.

21 "Combined heat and power" refers to using the excess heat from generating electricity to meet processing or building heat needs. This combination is frequently called "cogeneration" and results in a substantial increase in efficiency versus generating electricity and heat separately.

Recommendation

The NPC makes the following recommendations to improve efficiency in the industrial sector:

• The Department of Energy should conduct and promote research, development, demonstration, and deployment of industrial energy efficiency technologies and best practices.

• The research and development tax credit should be permanently extended to spur private research and development investments.

Potential Effect: 4-7 quadrillion Btu per year by 2030 in the United States, about equal parts coal, gas, and oil.

Generation of electricity uses a significant amount of energy. In the United States, about 30 percent of primary energy is used by the electric power generating sector. Only modest generation efficiency improvements appear economically feasible in existing plants (2 to 6 percent), as efficiency improvements are incorporated during routine maintenance. The major potential for efficiency improvement comes when existing generation plants are replaced with facilities using updated technology and designs. Retirement of existing facilities and selection of replacement technology and design is driven by economics affected by fuel cost, plant reliability, and electricity dispatching considerations.

Chapter
ENERGY SUPPLY 2

Abstract

World energy resources are plentiful, but accumulating risks threaten continued expansion of oil and natural gas production from conventional sources relied on historically. To mitigate these risks, expansion of all economic energy sources will be required, including coal, nuclear, renewables, and unconventional oil and natural gas. Each energy source faces significant challenges, including technical, environmental, political, or economic hurdles, and each imposes infrastructure requirements for development and delivery.

This chapter examines endowment, resource, and production dynamics; describes the historical and projected energy mix; analyzes diverse public and aggregated proprietary data sources; and considers options for energy infrastructure and delivery.

The outline of the Energy Supply chapter is as follows:

- Supply Summary
- Prospects for Energy Supply
- Analysis of Energy Outlooks
  - Oil and Other Liquids
  - Natural Gas
  - Coal
  - Biomass
  - Non-Bio Alternative Energy Sources
  - Energy Conversion and Delivery Infrastructure
- Access to Resources.

A set of detailed studies on specific supply-related topics supports the analysis in this chapter. These topic papers are included on the CD distributed with this report (a list of all the topic papers can be found in Appendix E). The data used for analyzing energy outlooks are included in the Data Warehouse section of the CD.

SUPPLY SUMMARY

The question of future energy supplies is significant, controversial, and extends beyond oil and gas. Energy supply is a complex system that includes several basic components: (1) the natural endowment or physical store of a particular resource; (2) production or con-

version of the resource to usable form; and (3) delivery of products to consumers. The components function within a larger and changing economic, geopolitical, and technical context. The study takes a comprehensive view that includes each of these elements for fossil hydrocarbons and other energy sources such as biomass, nuclear, and non-bio renewables.

Data Sources

The study considered a diverse set of data that represents the range of opinion about energy supply. These data were collected in the NPC Survey of Global Energy Supply/Demand Outlooks ("NPC Survey of Outlooks"). Figure 2-1 shows the sources of supply forecasts and

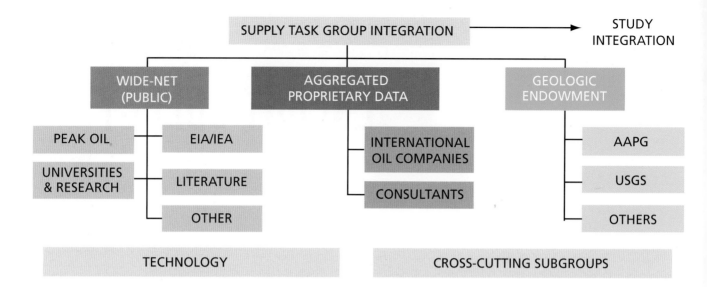

FIGURE 2-1. *Supply Data Sources*

data about the underlying resource base. The comprehensiveness of the data is unique to this study and established an objective basis for the findings.

The data were classified into categories that included quantitative forecasts as well as reports and opinion papers:

- *Public data* are freely available from agencies such as the U.S. Energy Information Administration (EIA) and the International Energy Agency (IEA); academic and research institutions; interest groups; open literature; and foreign governments.

- *Proprietary data* were made available to the study, anonymously and with strict safeguards, by private businesses such as energy companies and industry consultancies.

- *Endowment data* represent expert technical opinion about the physical resource base for hydrocarbons and other sources of energy.

Source data ranged from integrated supply-demand projections through studies of specific elements of the energy system such as biomass and transportation infrastructure. See the Methodology chapter of this report for full details about the techniques used in data collection and analysis.

Resource Endowment

Endowment and recoverable resources are fundamental concepts in any discussion of energy supply.

Endowment refers to the earth's physical store of potential energy sources: tons of coal, cubic feet of natural gas, barrels of oil, etc. The endowment of fossil hydrocarbons is fixed: it can be depleted but not replenished. *Recoverable resources* are a subset of the hydrocarbon endowment—the portion that can be viably produced and converted to fuel and power.

The natural endowment is the foundation of all supply projections. Although there are many estimates for future producible reserves and production, these are often based on the same resource estimates, principally data compiled by the United States Geological Survey (USGS). Other estimates are made by energy companies and non-U.S. governmental agencies. However, public and proprietary assessments are not integrated with each other and may use different methodologies. The wide range of assessments creates uncertainty for policy makers.

Current endowment and resource assessments for oil, gas, and coal indicate very large in-place volumes and resource potential, several times the cumulative produced volumes and current reserve estimates. Renewable resources such as biomass, wind, and solar power add additional potential. However, physical, technical, commercial and other constraints make only a fraction of any endowment available for extraction. The key consideration for all energy sources is converting the resource endowment to economically and environmentally viable production and delivery.

Resources to Production

The United States is the world's largest cumulative oil producer and remains the third-largest daily producer after Saudi Arabia and Russia. However, Figure 2-2 shows that U.S. oil production has declined steadily over the past 40 years. Demand for oil (and natural gas) has grown at the same time, creating a gap with domestic production that is filled by imports. Any continuing production decline for domestic oil will widen the projected gap between supply and consumption over the next 25 years and beyond. Accumulating geological, geopolitical, investment, and infrastructure risks to global oil and natural gas supply may compound the gap.

Supply forecasts are wide ranging and reflect uncertainty at least partly based on recent difficulty in increasing oil production. Forecast worldwide liquids production in 2030 ranges from less than 80 million to 120 million barrels per day, compared with current daily production of approximately 84 million barrels. The capacity of the oil resource base to sustain growing production rates is uncertain. Several outlooks indicate that increasing oil production may become a significant challenge as early as 2015. The uncertainty is based on (1) the rate and timing at which significant quantities of unconventional oil enter the supply mix; (2) industry's ability to overcome increasing risks to supply. Figure 2-3 illustrates potential sources of total liquids supply as depicted in the IEA *World Energy Outlook 2004* (WEO 2004). This figure is an illustrative example of the various components that make up total liquids supply, although the timing and combination of the components may vary.

Public and proprietary supply projections are based on assumptions about underlying factors such as economic growth, energy prices, and resulting demand; carbon constraints; technology; and maximum production volumes and timing. The EIA's low economic growth case, for example, forecasts 50 percent growth in total global energy supply by 2030, while its high economic growth case forecasts 90 percent growth. The EIA, IEA, and consultant reference and high-demand cases result in the highest projected global oil production levels. In contrast, the production maximum (or peak oil) and carbon-constrained cases project the lowest estimates of global oil production. International oil company (IOC) outlooks are considerably higher than the lowest supply cases, but lower than the EIA

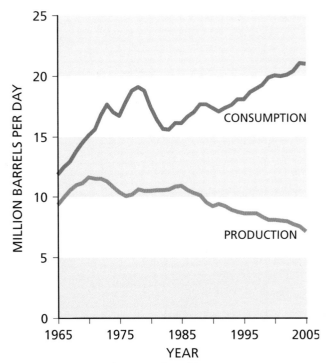

Source: *BP Statistical Review of World Energy 2006.*

FIGURE 2-2. *U.S. Oil Production and Consumption*

and IEA Reference Cases. The distribution of supply outlooks itself raises uncertainties and reflects different assessment of the risks involved in finding, producing, and delivering energy.

The USGS mean assessment indicates that natural gas resources are at least adequate for the increased production anticipated over the study period. However, the increased production will require replacing approximately 50 percent of the existing global natural gas reserve base by 2030.

Coal is a unique energy resource for the United States. Given its vast resource base—by many estimates, the world's largest—and major contribution to electricity generation today, coal is likely to remain a fundamental, long-term component of U.S. energy supply. Many studies forecast growth in coal use for power, plus additional growth through direct conversion of coal to liquids to diversify the fuel supply. However, coal combustion is also the largest source of carbon dioxide emissions from energy production. Adding coal-to-liquids production at scale, as with conversion of most heavy unconventional hydrocarbons, would generate large additional volumes of carbon dioxide. Addressing carbon capture at scale

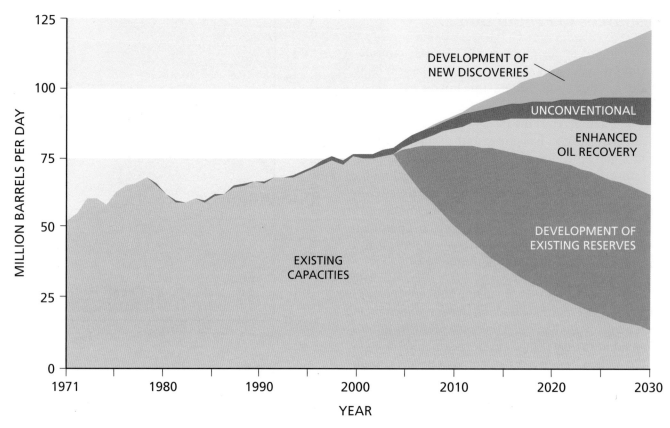

Source: IEA, *World Energy Outlook 2004.*

FIGURE 2-3. *Illustrative Total Liquids Supply*

is therefore a prerequisite for retaining coal as a viable and critical part of the energy supply system.

Understanding the Range of Production Forecasts

This study examined a comprehensive range of global oil production forecasts including integrated supply/demand studies from EIA and IEA (unless otherwise noted, all EIA data referred to in this chapter are from *International Energy Outlook 2006* and IEA data are from *World Energy Outlook 2006*); publicly available projections from a diverse range of other sources; and a unique set of aggregated proprietary forecasts from IOCs and energy consulting groups. The diversity of this range of projections is shown in Figure 2-4, which highlights the EIA reference, the Association for the Study of Peak Oil (ASPO) – France, and the average of the IOC forecasts for 2030. The distribution of production forecasts highlights the effect of assigning different levels of risk and uncertainty to both resource and above-ground factors. This

distribution of outcomes, along with evaluation of assessments of the total resource base, indicates that the key consideration for energy supplies is not endowment but "producibility." Over the next 25 years, risks above ground—geopolitical, technical, and infrastructure—are more likely to affect oil and natural gas production rates than are limitations of the below-ground endowment. The range of outcomes emphasizes the need for proactive strategies to manage the accumulating risks to liquids delivery in 2030.

Explanations for the variance in projections for both conventional oil and natural gas production are widely discussed as part of the "peak oil" debate. As a result, this study sees the need for a new assessment of the global oil and natural gas endowment and resources to provide more current data for the continuing debate.

Diversification

Growing U.S. energy demand requires diversified energy sources that are economically and environmentally sustainable at commercial scale. Coal and

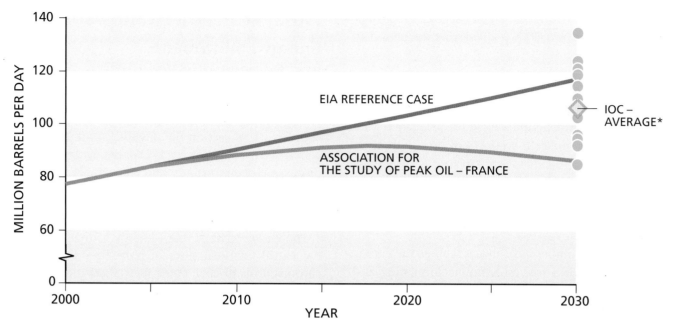

* Average of aggregated proprietary forecasts from international oil companies (IOC) responding to the NPC survey.
  See Analysis of Energy Outlooks, Global Total Liquids Production, later in this chapter
  for identification of other aggregations and outlooks shown here.
Source: EIA, *International Energy Outlook 2006*, and the NPC Survey of Outlooks.

FIGURE 2-4. *Global Total Liquids Forecasts*

nuclear power already play a significant role. Most forecasts expect them to at least retain their relative share of the supply mix. Many forecasts project significant growth for unconventional hydrocarbons, including very heavy oil and bitumen expansion from Canadian oil sands. At a more challenging technical and economic level, many forecasts also predict growing contributions from large-scale conversion of coal to liquids and the eventual development of vast U.S. oil shale resources. All unconventional hydrocarbons face the critical issue of their significant carbon footprint at large-scale implementation.

Biomass and other renewables are playing a growing role as options for transportation fuel or power generation, with high year-to-year growth rates. Biomass includes wood, cultivated crops, or naturally growing vegetation that potentially can be converted to energy sources at commercial scale. First-generation conversion of biomass to fuels is based on corn, sugarcane, soybeans, or other crops that are also food sources. Technically and economically successful, second-generation conversion of plant waste or fuel crops would allow non-food vegetation to be used as feedstock. As with all energy sources,

technical, logistical, and market requirements will need to be met to achieve significant scale.

Energy projections generally show a continuing role for nuclear energy, notwithstanding unique concerns about safety, security, and waste disposal. In a carbon-constrained environment, nuclear energy may become a much larger part of the energy mix. However, the U.S. technical and industrial capability needed to maintain nuclear energy as an option is at risk.

Key Findings

Oil, gas, and coal—the fossil hydrocarbons—are by far the largest sources of energy in industrial economies. While alternative energy sources, particularly biomass and other renewables, are likely to increasingly contribute to total energy supply, hydrocarbons are projected to dominate through at least 2030.

The prospects for hydrocarbon supply are complex. They involve a growing set of global uncertainties ranging from production capabilities through environmental constraints, infrastructure requirements, and geopolitical alignments. Concentration of remaining oil and gas resources in a few countries, for example, challenges whether business-as-usual cases represent the most likely course of events during the period to 2030.

Economically disruptive supply shortfalls of regional, if not global, scale are more likely to occur during the outlook period than in the past. Increased demand will amplify the effects of any short-term events, which are likely to result in stronger reactions than in the past to protect national interests. The new dynamics may indicate a transition from a demand-driven to a supply-constrained system.

While uncertainties have always typified the energy business, the risks to supply are accumulating and converging in novel ways:

- Resource nationalism, bilateral trade agreements, or protectionist policies may remove resources from the market and make them unavailable for general world supply.

- Hydrocarbon resources are becoming more difficult to access and challenging to produce.

- Technology requirements are increasingly complex and demanding.

- Costs of developing and delivering energy are escalating.

- Demands on current and anticipated infrastructure are heavy and growing.

- Human resources may not be adequate to meet projected growth requirements.

- Environmental constraints on energy supply are evolving and indeterminate.

These risks and uncertainties are the basis for understanding supply prospects over the next several decades.

The energy supply system has taken more than a century to build, requiring huge sustained investment in technology, infrastructure, and other elements of the system. Given the global scale of energy supply, its significance, and the time required for substantive changes, inaction is not an option. Isolated actions are not a solution. The study's recommendations address the supply issue as a whole and contribute to building a secure, sustainable energy portfolio.

PROSPECTS FOR ENERGY SUPPLY

Energy Endowment and Recoverable Resources

Endowment and recoverable resource are fundamental concepts in any complete discussion of energy supplies. This section defines these and other concepts used in supply forecasts. For detailed review and discussion of endowment and recoverable resources, see the Endowment and Biomass Topic Papers on the CD included with this report.

The *endowment* of fossil energy sources refers to the earth's physical store of non-renewable hydrocarbons: tons of coal, cubic feet of natural gas, barrels of oil, etc. The total endowment of fossil hydrocarbons is fixed. Some fraction can be developed and depleted, but the endowment cannot be replenished in less than geologic time frames. Renewable resources, such as biomass, represent an additional potential energy endowment, which, in principle, is continuously replenished. *Recoverable resources* are the subset of the total endowment that can be ultimately produced and converted into fuel and power.

Why We Do Endowment Assessments

Hydrocarbon resource assessments fill a variety of needs for consumers, policy makers, land and resource managers, investors, regulators, industry planners, and others involved in energy policy and decision making.

Individual governments use resource assessments to exercise stewardship, estimate future revenues, and establish energy, fiscal, and national security policy. Energy industries and the investment community use resource estimates to establish corporate strategy and make investment decisions. Other interested parties use the estimates in developing their positions and recommendations on energy issues.

Types of Hydrocarbons

Fossil Fuel is a collective term for hydrocarbons in the gaseous, liquid, or solid phase. The global fossil fuel endowment includes the following: coal, crude oil (including condensate), natural gas liquids, and natural gas.

- Coal is the altered remains of prehistoric plants that originally accumulated in swamps and peat bogs. It is organic sedimentary rock that has undergone various degrees of coalification, which determines its current physical properties.

- **Crude Oil** is defined as a mixture of hydrocarbons that exists in a liquid phase in natural underground reservoirs and remains liquid at atmospheric pressure after passing through surface production facilities.

- **Natural Gas Liquids** (NGLs) are those portions of the hydrocarbon resource that exist in gaseous phase when in natural underground reservoir conditions, but are in a liquid phase at surface conditions (that is, standard temperature and pressure conditions: 60°F/15°C and 1 atmosphere).

- **Natural Gas** is a mixture of hydrocarbon compounds existing in the gaseous phase or in solution with oil in natural underground reservoirs at reservoir temperature and pressure conditions and produced as a gas under atmospheric temperature and pressure conditions. Natural gas is principally methane, but may contain heavier hydrocarbons (such as ethane, propane, and butane) and inert compounds.

Hydrocarbon Assessment Terminology

Hydrocarbons In Place

The endowment, or hydrocarbons in place in an accumulation or in all accumulations in the world, is significant because some fraction of the in-place endowment is always the goal for extraction and conversion to resources. In-place estimates have relatively high uncertainty and require assumptions and constraints in the analysis. As an illustration, the following global in-place estimates are based on analyses by Rogner,[1] Schollnberger,[2] and others:

- **Coal:** 14,000 billion short tons (Rogner: grades A-E, several geographical areas not assessed)

- **Oil:** 15,000 billion barrels (Schollnberger: midcase—included conventional, heavy, very heavy, and NGLs; not including oil shales)

- **Gas:** 50,000 trillion cubic feet (Schollnberger: midcase—includes conventional, tight gas, and coalbed methane; not including gas hydrates)

1 Rogner, H-H., Annual Review – Energy Environment 22:217–62: Institute for Integrated Energy Systems, University of Victoria, 1997.

2 Schollnberger, W.E., 1998b, Projections of the world's hydrocarbon resources and reserve depletion in the 21st century: Houston Geological Society Bulletin, November, p. 31-37.

While these volumes can only be estimated within wide ranges, they indicate the fossil hydrocarbon endowment is large compared to past produced volumes and current reserve estimates. However, only a fraction of the total hydrocarbon endowment can ever be technically converted into recoverable resources and producible reserves. While continuing technical advances are likely to increase this fraction as they have in the past, economic, political, and environmental factors will be important in determining the likely size of the recoverable resource base.

Resources and Reserves

Resources and reserves are the strategically important elements of the hydrocarbon endowment remaining to be produced. Figure 2-5 shows various classifications of reserves and resources.

- **Resources** are those quantities of the endowment estimated, as of a given date, to be potentially recoverable from known or undiscovered accumulations. Resources are not considered commercial at the time of estimation.

- **Reserves** are those estimated quantities of the endowment anticipated to be commercially recoverable from known accumulations from a given date forward. Reserves must satisfy four criteria: they must be *discovered, recoverable, commercial,* and *remaining* based on the development technologies currently applied.

Reserves and Total Resource Growth

Growth in estimated reserves or resources occurs in almost all hydrocarbon systems in the world. Many analysts consider it to be the most important source for potential additional reserves in mature petroleum regions such as the United States. Many factors can increase the estimated ultimate recovery from known accumulations, including improved: (1) data as a field matures, (2) recovery techniques, (3) imaging for well placement, and (4) completion efficiency. Additions to reserves from growth are volumetrically significant, as most additions to world reserves in recent years are from growth of reserves in known accumulations rather than new discoveries.

The importance of reserves growth to estimating available future oil is the subject of considerable debate. One challenge stems from the fact that not all countries report reserves in the same way. For example, the percentage and rate of conversion of

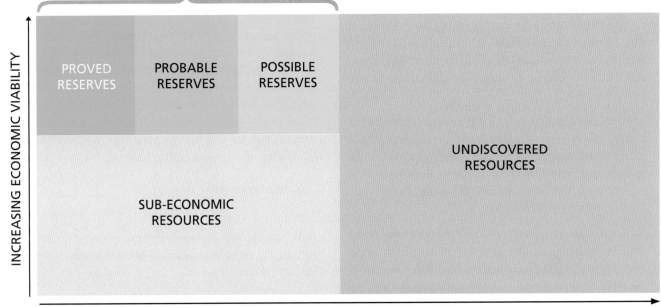

DISCOVERED (IDENTIFIED) RESOURCES

INCREASING ECONOMIC VIABILITY

PROVED RESERVES

PROBABLE RESERVES

POSSIBLE RESERVES

UNDISCOVERED RESOURCES

SUB-ECONOMIC RESOURCES

INCREASING GEOLOGIC UNCERTAINTY

Source: McKelvey, V.E., "Mineral Resource Estimates and Public Policy," *American Scientist*, 1972.

FIGURE 2-5. *Example of a McKelvey Diagram, Used to Illustrate the Technical Distinction Between Resources and Reserves*

reserves, and, therefore, the predicted amount of field growth, depends significantly on the reference point. In some cases, the reference point is proved reserves (often referred to as P1). In other cases, the basis is proved plus probable reserves (P1 + P2). The different reference points yield different results for reserves growth.

Oil fields today are also generally smaller and developed more quickly, completely, and with better technology than in the past. This situation raises the possibility that the growth patterns of older fields may no longer be reliable predictors for new development and estimates of future oil.

Undiscovered Resources

Undiscovered resources consist of potential recovery from accumulations that are postulated to exist on the basis of geologic knowledge and theory. There are many aspects of resource endowment that must be present for hydrocarbons to form and be preserved. In a comprehensive resource assessment, each of these aspects is examined and measured, but a great deal about these aspects remain uncertain. Examination

of *known accumulations*, together with an analysis of how many have already been discovered in a hydrocarbon province, are used to project numbers and sizes of those which may remain to be discovered. The larger and more obvious potential accumulations are generally drilled first, and usually the largest discoveries are made early in the life of a basin.

Table 2-1 shows the USGS 2000 reserve and resource assessment for conventional oil and gas. Between the reference date of that study (1/1/96) and the end of 2005, approximately 275 billion barrels of conventional oil have been produced. Uncertainty around future additions from growth and undiscovered volumes provides a range of about 2 trillion barrels between low and high estimates.

Conventional and Unconventional Reserves and Resources

Until the 1990s, virtually all estimates of the global oil and gas endowment focused on *conventional* reserves and resources, defined as oils, NGLs, and gas expected to be economically produced using conventional technology and distributed in nature as discrete

Facing the Hard Truths about Energy

	P95	Mean	P5
Oil & Natural Gas Liquids (Billion Barrels)			
Undiscovered and Reserves Growth	776	1,669	2,767
Cumulative and Remaining Reserves		1,676	
	2,452	**3,345**	**4,443**
Natural Gas (Trillion Cubic Feet)			
Undiscovered and Reserves Growth	4,096	8,856	14,770
Cumulative and Remaining Reserves		6,545	
	10,641	**15,401**	**21,315**

Note: P95 refers to a 95 percent probability that the resource size will exceed the estimate, while P5 indicates a 5 percent probability that the resource size exceeds the estimate—thus P95 represents the low end of an assessment and P5 the high end. USGS provides a range of outcomes for reserves growth and undiscovered resources. No range is provided for cumulative production and proved reserves.

Source: United States Geological Survey, 2000.

TABLE 2-1. *Global Resource Estimates for Conventional Oil and Natural Gas*

accumulations. More recent estimates of the endowment include significant additional potential from *unconventional* resources.

In most contemporary definitions, the primary differences between conventional and unconventional petroleum liquids are API gravity and viscosity, i.e., the density of the liquid and how easily it flows. For natural gas, the primary delimiter is the reservoir in which the accumulation is located. Viscosity is the basis of the following definitions:

- **Conventional Oil:** Petroleum found in liquid form (with gravity of greater than 20°API) flowing naturally or capable of being pumped at reservoir conditions without further processing or dilution.

- **Unconventional Oil:** Heavy oil, very heavy oil, oil sands, and tar sands (bitumen) are all currently considered unconventional oil resources. These compounds have a high viscosity, flow very slowly

(if at all) and require processing or dilution to be produced through a well bore.

- **Continuous Resources:** The USGS uses the term *continuous resources* to define those resources that may be economically produced but are not found in conventional reservoirs. Continuous accumulations are petroleum accumulations (oil or gas) that have large spatial dimensions and indistinctly defined boundaries, and which exist more or less independently of the water column. Because they may cover hundreds, or even thousands, of square miles, continuous accumulations may occur across a wide range of stratigraphic environments, each of which may have widely varying reservoir properties. Or they may exist in their source rock, never having migrated into a carrier bed or reservoir.

Table 2-2 provides global resource estimates for various types of unconventional oil and gas.

Previous Estimates—Results, Methodology, Differences, and Challenges

Many organizations conduct endowment and resource estimates, for a variety of purposes and with varying methodologies. Figures 2-6 and 2-7 show various global conventional oil and gas endowment estimates plotted against the date of the assessment. Most estimates before 1958 were relatively low, smaller than 2 trillion barrels of oil. Since 1958, both the number and range of estimates have grown.

	Heavy Crude Oil	Tar Sands (Bitumen)	Coalbed Methane	Tight Gas
Oil (Billion Barrels)	761	794		
Natural Gas (Trillion Cubic Feet)			8,225	4,024

Sources: Oil – BGR (Bundesanstalt für Geowissenschaften und Rohstoffe [Federal Institute for Geosciences and Natural Resources]) *Reserven, Ressourcen und Verfügbarkeit von Energierohstoffen [Availability of Energy Reserves and Resources 1998]*, Germany, 1998. Natural Gas – Rogner, H-H., "World Energy Assessment – Energy and the Challenge of Sustainability," United Nations Development Programme, 2000.

TABLE 2-2. *Global Resource Estimates for Unconventional Oil and Natural Gas*

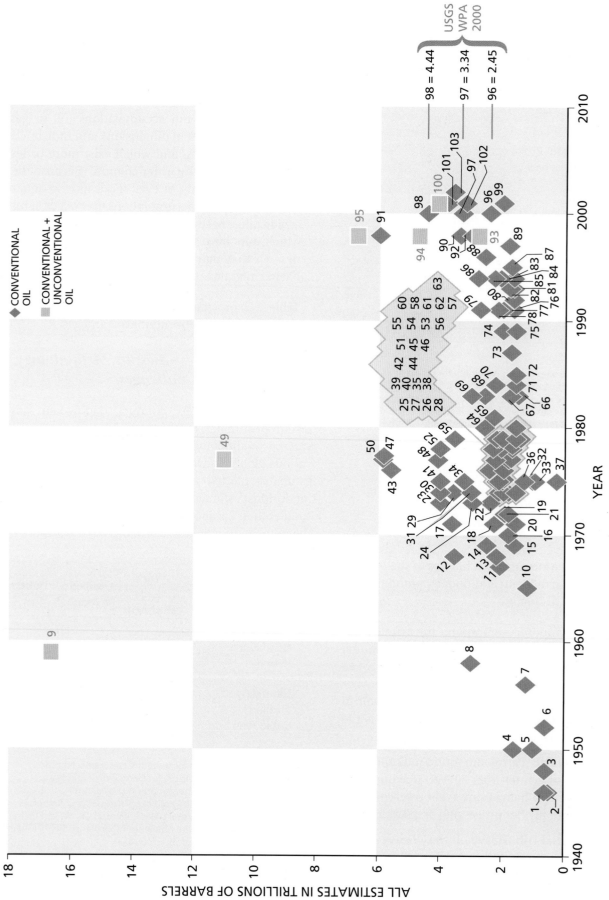

FIGURE 2-6. *World Oil Resource Estimates, 1940 – Present*

Source: Ahlbrandt, Thomas S., and Klett, T.R., "Comparison of methods used to estimate conventional undiscovered petroleum resources: World examples," *Natural Resources Research*, 2005.

Facing the Hard Truths about Energy

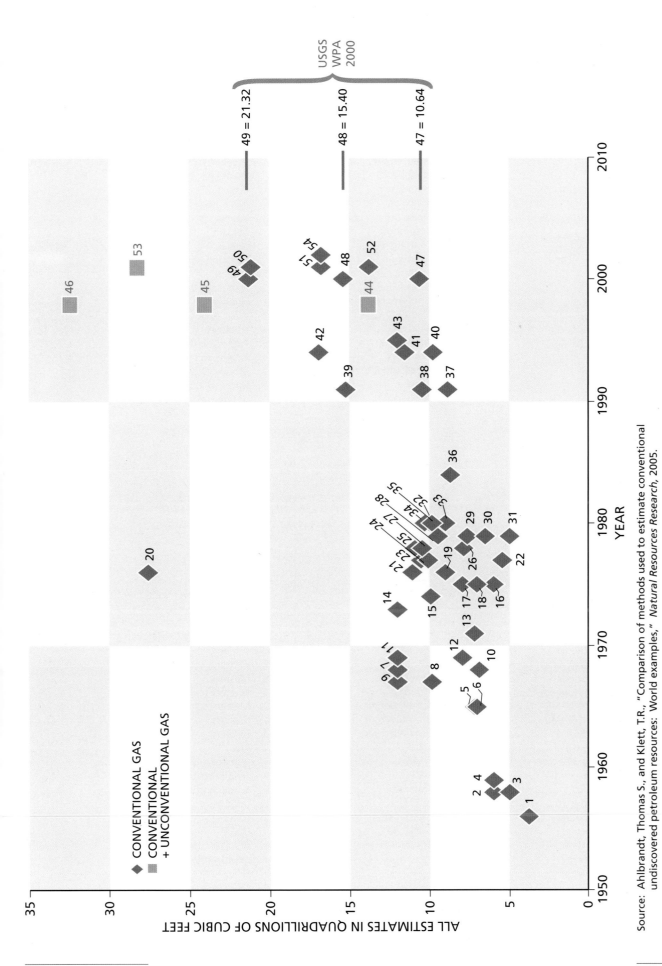

FIGURE 2-7. *World Natural Gas Resource Estimates, 1950 – Present*

Source: Ahlbrandt, Thomas S., and Klett, T.R., "Comparison of methods used to estimate conventional undiscovered petroleum resources: World examples," *Natural Resources Research*, 2005.

Legend for Figure 2-6

Conventional Oil/Conventional + Unconventional Oil References

1	Duce	54	Moody
2	Pogue	55	Nehring (H)
3	Weeks	56	Nehring (L)
4	Levorsen (and up)	57	Halbouty
5	Weeks	58	Halbouty
6	Pratt	59	Halbouty
7	Hubbert	60	Meyerhoff
8	Weeks	61	Nehring (H)
9	Weeks	62	Nehring (L)
10	Weeks	63	De Bruyne
11	Ryman	64	World Energy Conference
12	Weeks (H)	65	Halbouty
13	Weeks (L)	66	Masters
14	Hubbert (H)	67	Masters
15	Hubbert (L)	68	Masters
16	Moody	69	Odell and Rosing
17	Weeks (H)	70	Masters (H)
18	Weeks (L)	71	Masters (L)
19	Bauquis	72	Martin
20	Warman	73	Masters
21	Warman	74	Bookout
22	Hubbert	75	Campbell
23	Odell	76	Campbell
24	Schweinfurth	77	Masters
25	Hubbert (H)	78	Masters
26	Hubbert (L)	79	Masters
27	Kirkby, Adams (H)	80	Campbell
28	Kirkby, Adams (L)	81	Campbell
29	Parent, Linden	82	Laherrere
30	Parent, Linden (H)	83	Campbell
31	Parent, Linden (L)	84	Masters
32	MacKay, North (H)	85	Masters
33	MacKay, North (L)	86	Masters
34	Moody, Esser (H)	87	Campbell
35	Moody, Esser	88	MacKenzie
36	Moody, Esser (L)	89	Campbell
37	Moody, Geiger	90	BP
38	Moody, Geiger	91	Odell (H)
39	Moody, Geiger	92	Odell L)
40	National Academy of Science	93	Schollnberger
41	Odell and Rosing	94	Schollnberger
42	Barthel, BGR	95	Schollnberger
43	Grossling (H)	96	USGS
44	Grossling (L)	97	USGS
45	Folinsbee	98	USGS
46	Klemme	99	Deffeyes
47	Seidl, IIASA (H)	100	SHELL
48	Seidl, IIASA (L)	101	SHELL (H)
49	Styrikovich	102	SHELL (L)
50	Styrikovich	103	Edwards
51	World Energy Conference		
52	IFP (4 estimates >4 TBO)		
53	Klemme		

Legend for Figure 2-7

Conventional Gas/Conventional + Unconventional Gas References

1	MacKinney
2	Weeks (H)
3	Weeks (L)
4	Weeks
5	MacKinney
6	Weeks
7	Ryman
8	SHELL
9	MacKinney
10	Weeks
11	Hubbert (H)
12	Hubbert (L)
13	Weeks
14	Hubbert
15	Parent, Linden (and up)
16	Adams and Kirkby (H)
17	Moody, Geiger
18	National Academy of Science
19	Barthel, BGR (and up)
20	Grossling (H)
21	Grossling (L)
22	International Gas Union
23	Parent, Linden (H) (and up)
24	Parent, Linden (L)
25	Desprairies (H)
26	Desprairies (L)
27	McCormick, AGA
28	Bois
29	Meyerhoff
30	Nehring (H)
31	Nehring (L)
32	Parent, Linden (H) (and up)
33	Parent, Linden (L)
34	Schubert
35	World Energy Conference
36	Masters
37	Masters
38	Masters
39	Masters
40	Masters
41	Masters
42	Masters
43	Riva
44	Schollnberger
45	Schollnberger
46	Schollnberger
47	USGS
48	USGS
49	USGS
50	CEDIGAZ (H)
51	CEDIGAZ (L)
52	SHELL
53	SHELL
54	BGR

Resource estimates as seen in Figures 2-6 and 2-7 are snapshots in time. They represent only what has been assessed: particular parts of the world (basins, plays, regions, or countries); specific commodities (oil, natural gas, conventional, unconventional); and data available at the time. Assessing additional types of resources or additional parts of the world can greatly change the estimates. Resource estimates are one basis of forecasting. Other important factors and risks can also significantly shape forecasted production profiles over time.

Finally, comprehensive assessments built from global, detailed geological studies are very limited. While the USGS survey of resources in 2000 is the most comprehensive U.S. agency assessment and the basis of many forecasts, the strategic importance of endowment and resource estimates emphasize the ongoing need for comprehensive, up-to-date data. For a detailed discussion of the hydrocarbon resource endowment, see the Endowment Topic Paper on the CD included with the report.

Primary Energy Mix

Energy forecasts generally show that fossil fuels will dominate the total energy mix, although their share may decline from today's 85 percent to slightly more than 75 percent in 2030. In several forecasts, gas and coal are expected to increase their share. Oil's share of the total primary energy mix is generally forecast to decrease, even as absolute oil volumes grow, principally for transportation use. While renewable energy, gas-to-liquids, coal-to-liquids, and coal-to-gas grow rapidly from a low base, they remain a smaller share of the energy mix in 2030. In any case, the enormous scale of global energy means that a prospective 10 percent decline in fossil fuel share will require a major reallocation of investment, infrastructure, and technical effort.

Historical Energy Consumption

Figure 2-8 shows that global primary energy consumption has grown just over 2 percent per year since 1980. U.S. primary energy consumption has grown just over 1 percent per year since 1980, as shown in Figure 2-9. Most demand forecasts include historical energy mix and consumption patterns as inputs to their projections.

Projected Energy Consumption

Energy forecasts are typically based on macro-economic inputs and historical factors that drive global energy consumption. Reference Cases generally use business-as-usual assumptions that do not consider (1) potential global supply disruptions resulting from geopolitical events, (2) technology breakthroughs that could substantially enhance supply or reduce demand, and (3) significant shifts in energy policies. In addition, most outlooks make separate forecasts for various scenarios that would materially change outcomes, such as carbon constraints or significant price changes. The Energy Demand chapter of this report provides an extensive discussion of demand outlooks that supplements the summary in this section.

Fossil fuels are projected to dominate the total global energy mix, contributing approximately 75 percent of global energy supplies in 2030 compared with some 85 percent today (Figure 2-10). Most business-as-usual outlooks show that total energy demand in 2030 will be 40 to 70 percent higher than the 2005 level of 425 quadrillion Btu. These forecasts assume the global fossil energy system will provide supply and infrastructure required to meet the increased demand.

Outlooks that assume no further restrictions on carbon dioxide emissions generally do not include significant carbon capture and sequestration (CCS). These forecasts show a significant increase in global carbon dioxide emissions by 2030. In the case of carbon-constrained energy use, projected reduction in carbon dioxide emissions is achieved through reduced energy consumption, fuel switching, and carbon capture and sequestration.

Gas and coal are generally expected to increase their share of the total primary energy mix, while the oil share continues to decrease even as oil volumes in most cases continue to grow. Figure 2-11 projects four EIA and IEA cases for global energy consumption to 2030. Crude oil continues its trend towards becoming primarily a source of transportation fuels. Renewable energy, as well as gas-to-liquids, coal-to-liquids, and coal-to-gas grow rapidly from a low base, but their shares of the total mix remain relatively small.

Carbon constraints without nuclear energy and CCS increase the demand for natural gas. However, in some carbon-constrained cases, nuclear power increases substantially as a share of total energy, although it remains flat in reference forecasts. The biomass share of total energy expands dramatically in several constrained cases, with the biggest impacts occurring after 2030.

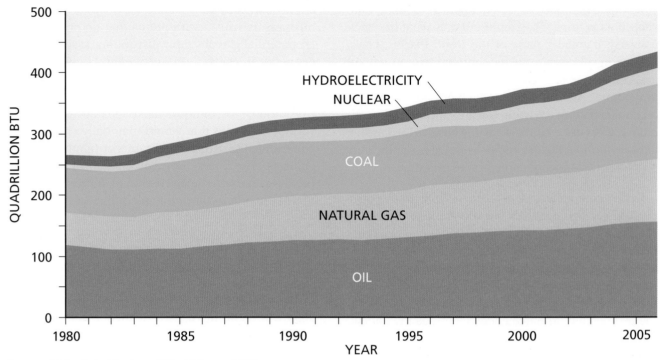

Source: *BP Statistical Review of World Energy 2007.*

FIGURE 2-8. *Global Primary Energy Consumption, 1980-2006*

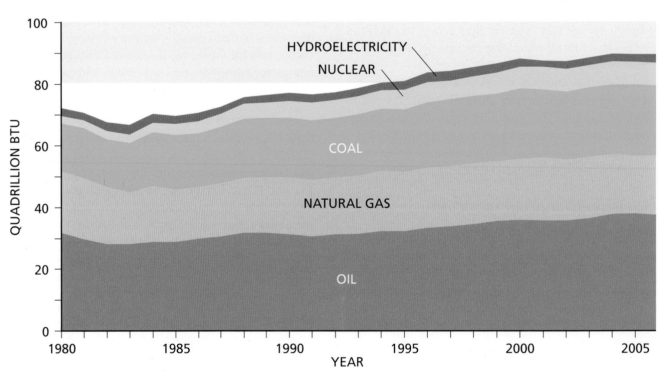

Source: *BP Statistical Review of World Energy 2007.*

FIGURE 2-9. *U.S. Primary Energy Consumption, 1980-2006*

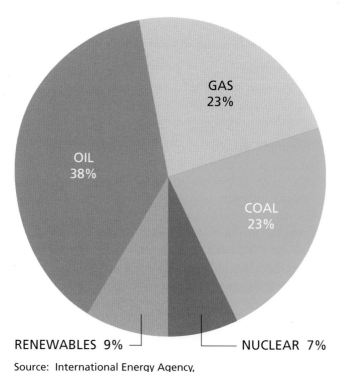

Source: International Energy Agency,
World Energy Outlook 2006.

FIGURE 2-10. *Global Energy Consumption Shares in 2005*

Oil and Natural Gas Supply

Oil

Total energy supply forecasts are wide-ranging, based largely on variations in oil demand outlooks and differing views on the deliverability of oil. Some views of future oil production consider lower limits on the available recoverable oil resource while others extrapolate historical successes in expanding the recoverable resource base. Current endowment and resource assessments for both oil and gas indicate large in-place volumes and development potential. The gas resource base is more than adequate to meet the increased gas production typically anticipated by energy outlooks over the study period. However, this will require replacing 50 percent of existing gas reserves by 2030.

There is more uncertainty about the capacity of the oil resource base to sustain growing production rates. The uncertainty is based on (1) the rate and timing at which significant quantities of unconventional oil enter the supply mix, and (2) the ability of the oil industry to overcome growing supply-development risks.

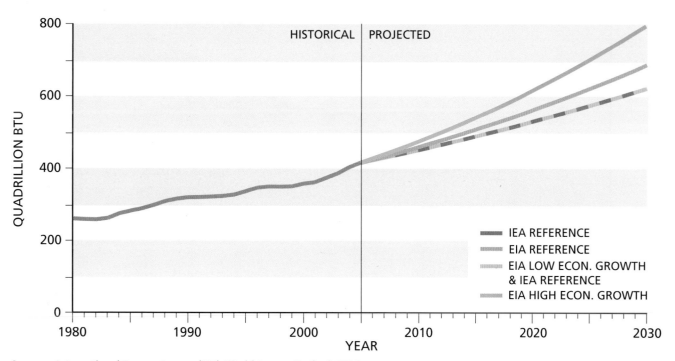

Sources: International Energy Agency (IEA) *World Energy Outlook 2006;*
and Energy Information Administration (EIA) *International Energy Outlook 2006.*

FIGURE 2-11. *Projected Global Energy Consumption*

The finite nature of the oil endowment and the prospect that production will reach a peak and eventually decline contribute to the debate about oil supply. The timing of the decline is subject to interpretation because:

- The underlying decline rate in currently producing fields is not universally well-reported. Many observers think that 80 percent of existing oil production will need to be replaced by 2030—in addition to the volumes required to meet growing demand. Figure 2-12 is an illustrative example showing various components of total liquids supply as depicted in the IEA World Energy Outlook 2004. Resource components such as existing production capacity, booked reserves, enhanced oil recovery, etc., contribute to virtually all projections of liquids supply, although the combination and timing of components may differ.

- Opinions differ about the world's estimated ultimately recoverable oil resource and whether fields can continue to increase production if more than half of today's estimated ultimately recoverable resources (URR) has already been produced.

- The increased cost of producing oil (both conventional and unconventional including alternative liquids) raises concerns about the timing and scale of major energy development.

- Timing of development for alternative liquid supplies at scale is uncertain.

Supply outlooks reflect uncertainty about oil supplies, at least partly based on recent difficulties in increasing production. Forecast global liquids production in 2030 ranges from less than 80 million to 120 million barrels per day, compared with current daily production of approximately 84 million barrels.

Conventional oil is forecast to contribute the largest share of global liquid supply, principally through increased production in Saudi Arabia, Russia, Venezuela, Iran, and Iraq. Unconventional oil such as Canadian and Venezuelan heavy oil and U.S. oil shale is also

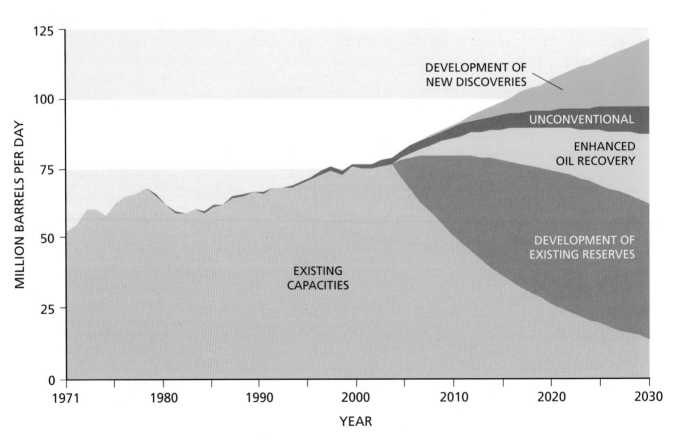

Source: IEA, *World Energy Outlook 2004.*

FIGURE 2-12. *Illustrative Total Liquids Supply*

Facing the Hard Truths about Energy

likely to play a growing role in liquids supply. However, most forecasts project that unconventional oil, together with coal-to-liquids (CTL) and gas-to-liquids (GTL), is unlikely to exceed 10 million barrels per day globally by 2030.

Natural Gas

Most outlooks project that natural gas production to 2030 will grow faster than it has historically, ranging from 400 billion to 500 billion cubic feet per day. The EIA high-production cases, for example, are at the upper end of the range, with a projected doubling of production from today's 250+ billion cubic feet per day. Figure 2-13 shows the EIA and IEA projections for natural gas production.

While there is some concern about the gas resource base relative to projected demand growth, most outlooks consider it more than adequate to meet demand. However, nearly two-thirds of natural gas resources are concentrated in four countries, Russia, Qatar, Iran, and Saudi Arabia, which are projected to show the biggest growth in production. Since these countries are relatively distant from likely consuming regions, global gas supply chains will be needed to connect produc-

ers and markets—similar to the trading system that has been developed over decades for oil. In North America, major new additions to gas resources are possible, given expansion of unconventional U.S. gas production and development of infrastructure to transport Arctic gas. Generally, production growth in resource-owning countries, creation of a global gas supply chain, and very large infrastructure investments are all elements of risk in matching projected gas supply to demand.

Coal

The global coal endowment is considerably larger than either the oil or gas endowment, with only a small portion of the resource base having been produced to date. The United States, Russia, China, India, and Australia hold over three quarters of the world's proved coal reserves. As other fossil fuels become relatively more costly or difficult to secure, these large resource owners may increase domestic coal production and use. However, the same constraints that apply to other resources may also apply to coal development globally and in the United States:

• Environmental constraints including carbon management, water use, land use, and waste disposal.

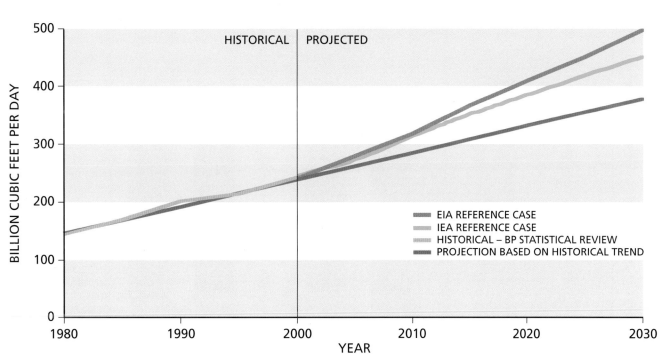

Sources: Energy Information Administration (EIA), *International Energy Outlook 2006;* International Energy Agency (IEA), *World Energy Outlook 2006;* and *BP Statistical Review of World Energy 2006.*

FIGURE 2-13. *Projected Global Natural Gas Production*

- Limits on transport and delivery infrastructure development within local markets.

These environmental and infrastructure limitations are potentially more severe for coal than for other conventional fossil fuels.

Business-as-usual energy outlooks, without significant environmental constraints, generally show a 50 to 60 percent increase in global coal production between 2005 and 2030. Most coal production growth will occur in rapidly expanding Asian economies, with China and India accounting for nearly 80 percent of the annual increment. Figure 2-14 shows projected growth in coal production in business-as-usual cases without carbon constraints.

In alternative policy/carbon constrained cases that do not consider carbon CCS, coal production is generally flat-to-declining from today's levels, as energy demand is met by fuels with a lower carbon impact. Where CCS is considered, the balance between growth in natural gas demand, biomass energy sources, and coal provides for growth in coal production and use.

Most technology development for new uses of coal, such as coal-to-liquids and CCS, addresses the technical, environmental, and economic barriers to increasing coal use. The delivery infrastructure needed for expanding coal use appears to receive less attention.

Biomass

Biomass refers to wood, cultivated crops, or natural vegetation that potentially can be converted to energy. As with coal, biomass is an abundant, indigenous resource for the United States and some other major centers of energy demand. Accordingly, biomass could be seen as an important option to reduce risks related to supply security. First-generation biomass conversion to fuels has been based on crops such as sugarcane, corn, and soybeans, which are also food sources, giving rise to concerns about crop competition among food, animal feed, and fuel use. Second-generation conversion technologies such as cellulosic ethanol seek to address these concerns by using plant waste as a feedstock. See the Biomass section later in this chapter for a discussion of potential sources of biomass energy.

Numerous studies have assessed the potential of agriculture to produce both energy and food for the

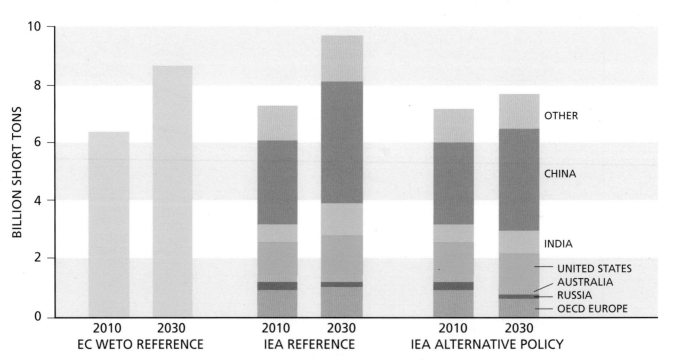

Sources: European Commission, *World Energy Technology Outlook 2050* (EC WETO), 2006; and International Energy Agency (IEA), *World Energy Outlook 2006*.

FIGURE 2-14. *Projected Growth in Global Coal Production without Carbon Constraints, 2010 to 2030*

Facing the Hard Truths about Energy

world. While conclusions vary, most estimate that 250 to 500 exajoules (approximately 238 to 476 quadrillion Btu) of biomass energy could be produced while still feeding a growing global population. These estimates represent a potentially substantial contribution to a 2030 global energy demand projected at about 740 exajoules, or 702 quadrillion Btu, in the EIA *International Energy Outlook 2007* (IEO 2007) Reference Case. Meeting both food and large-scale fuel demand would require successfully developing and deploying second-generation crop production and conversion technology. Most business-as-usual forecasts (EIA, IEA, European Commission, and aggregated proprietary outlooks) suggest that biomass will meet 5 to 10 percent of total energy demand in 2030, comprising less than 5 million barrels per day of total global liquids production. Other forecasts that are not business as usual show substantially higher biofuels production.

As with any large-scale energy source, technical, logistical, and market requirements will need to be met for biofuels to achieve their potential. Milestones along this development path will include: investments in rail, waterway, and pipeline transportation; scale-up of ethanol distribution; and technology deployment for cellulosic ethanol conversion. The time frames required in many cases to move technology from concept to full-scale application may make such sources available only later in the outlook period. For a detailed discussion of biomass, see the Biomass Topic Paper on the CD included with the report.

Nuclear

Nuclear power faces unique controversy based on concerns about safety, security, and management of the nuclear fuel and waste cycle. In addition, the capital intensity of nuclear generation increases the risk profile for investors. Accordingly, nuclear power's current 5 to 6 percent of the total energy mix is not projected to increase over the study timeframe, unless nuclear generation is promoted for policy objectives such as limiting carbon dioxide emissions or enhancing energy security. Figure 2-15 shows projected global growth in the installed nuclear power base.

Non-Bio Renewables

Hydroelectric generation has historically been the dominant non-bio source of renewable energy, providing vast amounts of electricity at very low marginal

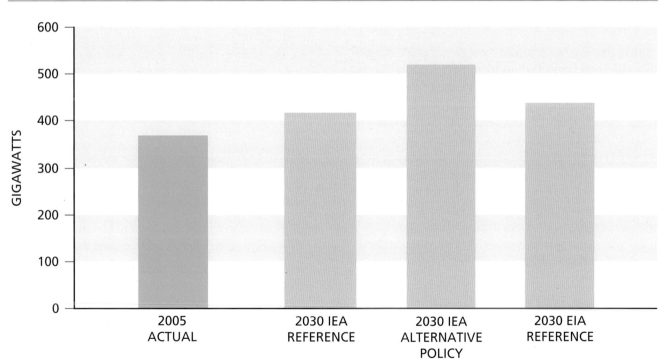

Sources: Energy Information Administration (EIA), *International Energy Outlook 2006;* and International Energy Agency (IEA), *World Energy Outlook 2006.*

FIGURE 2-15. *Projected Global Installed Nuclear Power Base*

cost of production. Most hydroelectric resources have been tapped in industrialized nations, while there may be limited additional opportunities in industrializing and economically developing nations. Wind and solar energy, which have shown significant growth in recent decades, are forecasted to grow several times faster than overall energy demand, starting at their current base of less than 2 percent of global energy supply. Geothermal presents more limited opportunities for new supplies and is not expected to outpace global energy supply growth.

Non-bio alternative and renewable energy sources require unique technologies that tap natural energy flows in different ways. Collectively, however, they have several common characteristics, in addition to mainly producing power rather than fuels: (1) high initial capital costs of construction or fabrication and installation; (2) low operating costs and minimal fuel or feedstock expenses; and (3) possible economies of scale that have not been fully developed. Some of these technologies require energy storage solutions to offset highly variable power production rates. As costs have risen for developing and converting fossil resources to power and fuel, non-fossil options have become more economically competitive and attractive for their potential renewable and environmental benefits. However, large-scale development of these energy options raises concerns about their potential ecological impacts.

Most forecasts of future energy supplies suggest that the total contribution from new renewable and alternative energy sources will remain small for the next two decades since they start from a relatively small base. Although the potential contribution of solar and wind power, waves, tides, and geothermal energy is vast, the economic cost of harnessing most of these sources at scale has been high, relative to other sources such as fossil fuels, hydro, and nuclear. However, the cost differential continues to decline. As with any energy source, resolution of ecological, technical, and commercial issues will favor some technologies rather than others.

Energy Conversion and Delivery Infrastructure

Finding and developing resources are two steps in the energy supply chain. Converting the resources to usable products and delivering them to consumers are equally essential steps that rely heavily on conversion, storage, and transportation infrastructure. However, the total requirements for new infrastructure to 2030 are difficult to assess with any certainty, since energy outlooks generally do not directly account for infrastructure development.

Energy outlooks typically assume supply infrastructure for any energy source will be built if it is economically viable, without regard to potential constraints on financing, permitting, and building. In addition to these potential constraints, the United States faces the issue of maintaining its refining and manufacturing capability, a contentious problem familiar in other industrial sectors. New energy sources will add their own infrastructure demands. Finally, much of the projected increase in global oil and gas trade is likely to move through narrow sea lanes, raising a security challenge for this part of the transportation system. Taken together, infrastructure issues add additional, often unrecognized, risks to prospective energy supply.

ANALYSIS OF ENERGY OUTLOOKS

Oil and Other Liquids

Key Observations—Oil and Other Liquids

- *While crude oil will remain a primary energy source throughout the study time frame and beyond, the capacity of the production and delivery system to increase supply is subject to multiple, increasing risks.*

- *The global in-place oil endowment is very large, but the recoverable resource and the rate at which it can be produced are subject to considerable uncertainty. Forecasted oil production rates vary widely: some rely heavily on OPEC to meet rising demand; others on contributions from unconventional oil and alternative liquids; a third set of forecasts project a production plateau or peak.*

- *As production from existing oil fields declines, future oil supply is likely to rely increasingly on:*

  - *Growth from existing accumulations through use of new technology, better knowledge of reservoir characteristics, or enhanced oil recovery*

  - *Production of unconventional resources such as oil sands or oil shale*

  - *Exploration discoveries, many from new frontiers such as the Arctic and ultra-deepwater*

  - *Conventional oil from hydrocarbon provinces where access is currently restricted.*

Alternative liquids such as biofuels, gas-to-liquids, and coal-to-liquids will also contribute materially to fuel supply.

- *U.S. oil production is generally projected to rise modestly, at best, or decline somewhat during the study time frame. With limited growth from conventional oil sources, the ability to meet expected demand growth will rely increasingly on heavier and unconventional domestic supplies, ultra-deepwater basins, and alternative fuels.[3]*

- *Few projections of domestic supply assume changes in access to U.S. onshore and offshore basins currently under drilling moratoria or subject to significant development restrictions. The time required to explore and develop newly released areas means that production from these areas would appear only later in the study time frame.*

- *Oil production growth after 2015 appears subject to increasing risks as both subsurface and above ground issues become more challenging. The risks include:*

  - *Production declines of many of the world's maturing fields*

  - *Increasingly restricted access to resources*

  - *Unprecedented investment requirements under uncertain fiscal regimes.*

The risk of not meeting forecasted demand over the study time frame also increases dramatically without sustained technology development and the pursuit of all economically viable fossil and alternative liquid fuel sources.

Crude Oil Endowment

Ancient biomass was converted to oil over millions of years as it was exposed to high temperature and high pressure deep in sedimentary layers. Migration of the oil from source rocks into porous formations at accessible depths in the earth's crust creates the opportunity to locate and produce oil from this endowment.

The global conventional and unconventional oil in place endowment has been variously estimated at 13 trillion to 15 trillion barrels. These barrels represent the estimated total volume of liquid hydrocarbons

---

3   The U.S. Energy Information Administration defines *conventional production* to include crude oil (including lease condensates), natural gas plant liquids, other hydrogen and hydrocarbons for refinery feedstocks, alcohol and other sources, and refinery gains. *Unconventional production* includes liquids produced from energy crops, natural gas, coal, oil sands, and shale.

generated and retained in geologic formations over time. Since oil generates very slowly, the current endowment is relatively fixed and is considered a non-renewable resource.

Recoverable resources are the portion of the estimated in-place endowment thought to be technically recoverable from their geologic setting. Recoverable resource assessments have generally grown as new technology, or political and economic factors, made more of the in-place endowment recoverable. Based on geological and geophysical data, these assessments require judgments about finding and development costs, extraction efficiencies, oil prices, and other factors. Generally, about one-third of the oil in place is currently assumed to be ultimately recoverable. This assumption yields an estimated 4.5 trillion barrels or more of conventional and unconventional ultimately recoverable oil.

Unconventional Oil Endowment and Resource Development

The global endowment of unconventional oil in place is large, as much as 7 trillion barrels (Figure 2-16). Recovery factors vary widely but are expected to be lower than for conventional oil due to technical challenges and huge capital requirements associated with extraction. Current public and proprietary assessments of URR are similar: 1.5 trillion barrels estimated by Bundesanstalt für Geowissenschaften und Rohstoffe (BGR) and an average 1.7 trillion barrels estimated by IOCs. The estimates are uncertain, but likely to grow as new technologies emerge. Development of heavy oil and oil shale has lagged that of conventional oil because it is more expensive and technically difficult to bring liquids on-line from these sources. Nonetheless, unconventional oil will likely play an increasing role in meeting future energy needs.

Unconventional oil has a much different global distribution than conventional oil. Very heavy oil in Venezuela, oil sands in Canada, and oil shale in the United States account for more than 80 percent of unconventional resources, while conventional oil resources are mainly in the Middle East, West Africa, and Russia. Factors that particularly affect unconventional supplies include technology development, environmental impact, geopolitical climate, capital and operating costs, and material and human resource availability. Uncertainty about each of these factors is a major consideration in projecting future energy supply.

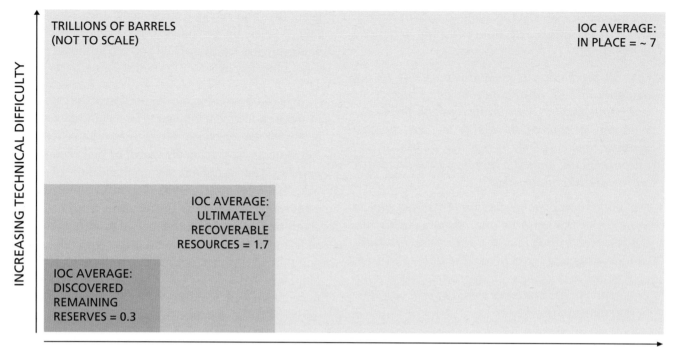

TRILLIONS OF BARRELS
(NOT TO SCALE)

IOC AVERAGE:
IN PLACE = ~ 7

INCREASING TECHNICAL DIFFICULTY

IOC AVERAGE:
ULTIMATELY
RECOVERABLE
RESOURCES = 1.7

IOC AVERAGE:
DISCOVERED
REMAINING
RESERVES = 0.3

INCREASING GEOLOGIC UNCERTAINTY

Source: NPC Survey of Outlooks.

FIGURE 2-16. *Global Unconventional Oil Endowment*

Conventional Oil Endowment and Resource Development

Conventional oil and natural gas liquids have historically received the greatest development attention. The IEA estimates between 6 and 7 trillion barrels of conventional oil and NGL in place, while other estimates are somewhat higher (Figure 2-17). About 1 trillion barrels of the conventional oil endowment have been produced since the late 19th century.

The USGS assessment published in 2000 is one of the few comprehensive, publicly available resource assessments for conventional oil. Many outlooks provided to this study include USGS estimates in their projections after adjusting to reflect newer or proprietary information. For example, EIA will routinely adjust estimated recoverable resources to reflect cumulative production or evolving knowledge that has not been included in USGS assessments.

The USGS mean estimate of ultimately recoverable global conventional oil plus NGL is 3.345 trillion barrels at the beginning of 1996. The estimates range from 2.5 to 4.4 trillion barrels, expressed in statistical terms as P95 and P5 estimates, respectively. P95 refers to a 95 percent probability that the resource size will exceed the estimate, P5 indicates a 5 percent probability that the resource size exceeds the estimate. By comparison, IOCs responding to the NPC data survey provided an average projection of 3.5 trillion barrels. The IOC most-likely estimates for ultimately recoverable global conventional oil range from 2.8 to 4.0 trillion barrels. While the USGS and proprietary ranges are statistically different, Figure 2-18 allows approximate comparison.

After taking into account the approximately 1.0 trillion barrels that have been produced to date, the estimated USGS range of remaining, ultimately recoverable global conventional oil and NGL is 1.5 to 3.4 trillion barrels. A higher URR for conventional oil and NGL would sustain oil production growth for a longer time or faster rate, assuming adequate investment and access to the resources. However, the opposite is true if the actual URR is at the lower end of the range. This uncertainty, combined with above-ground risks that could hinder production, fuels the debate about supply outlooks and has a material impact on policy and investment decisions.

Facing the Hard Truths about Energy

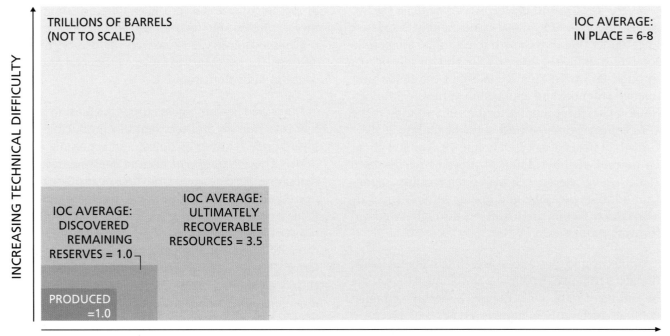

Source: NPC Survey of Outlooks.

FIGURE 2-17. *Global Conventional Oil and NGL Endowment*

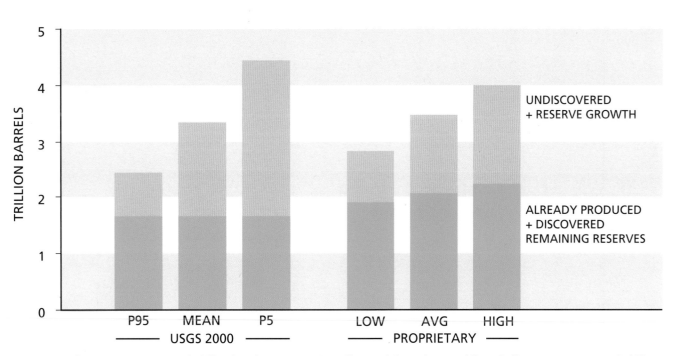

Note: P95 refers to a 95 percent probability that the resource size will exceed the estimate, while P5 indicates a 5 percent probability that the resource size exceeds the estimate – thus P95 represents the low end of an assessment and P5 the high end.
Source: NPC Survey of Outlooks.

FIGURE 2-18. *Conventional Global Oil and NGL Ultimately Recoverable Resource Estimates*

Reserve Growth and *Undiscovered Resources* are two categories of the USGS 2000 assessment with greatest uncertainty. Reserve Growth refers to the increase in reserves in oilfields. Reserve Growth typically occurs through improved knowledge about the field's productive potential and application of new technology. Reserve Growth accounted for 0.7 trillion barrels of the USGS mean estimated URR at the beginning of 1996. Growth in fields discovered before 1995 added about 65 percent of this volume to proved reserves from 1995 to 2004.[4] Reserve Growth often requires significant additional capital and energy input, especially as recovery factors are increased through enhanced recovery processes.

Undiscovered Resources accounted for an additional 0.9 trillion barrels in the USGS mean case at the beginning of 1996. Only 18 percent of this estimated volume, or about 17 billion barrels per year, has been discovered through exploration in the decade following.[5] Exploration discoveries have shown a declining trend over the past several decades, partly as a result

of restricted access to promising hydrocarbon provinces. Significant technology advances, access to unexplored basins, or discovery of very significant fields will be necessary to replace produced resources over the study time frame.

Discovered Remaining Reserves is the portion of URR that is technically and economically producible in the future under current technical and economic conditions. The *BP Statistical Review 2006* estimates that Remaining Reserves grew from 0.9 to 1.2 trillion barrels from 1996-2005, primarily through reserve additions to fields discovered before 1995. The current estimate of reserves is one indicator of how much oil production capacity could be developed in the near to medium term. The quality of reserve additions and undisclosed estimating methods for countries that hold most remaining reserves are significant uncertainties in making supply forecasts.

Globally, conventional oil reserves are concentrated in the Middle East (Figure 2-19). The seven countries with the largest conventional oil reserves account for more than 70 percent of the world total. Saudi Arabia holds approximately 20 percent of conventional reserves, equal to 75 years of production at 2005 rates.

---

4   K. Chew and P.H. Stark, "Perspectives on Oil Resource Estimates," IHS Energy – 2006.

5   Ibid.

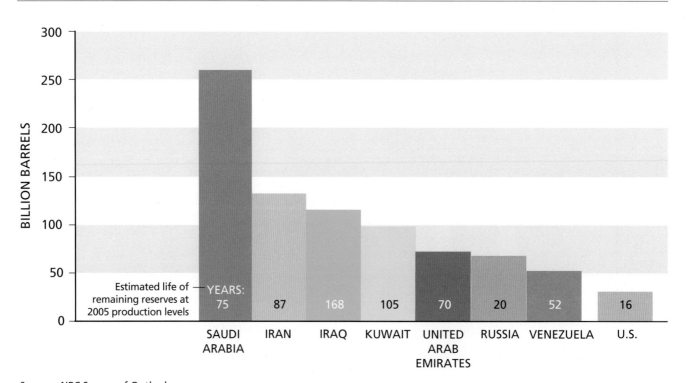

Source: NPC Survey of Outlooks.

FIGURE 2-19. *Large Holders of Discovered Remaining Reserves*

Facing the Hard Truths about Energy

The United States has 31 billion barrels of reserves, 16 years of production at 2005 rates. The estimated life of remaining reserves was calculated by dividing reserves numbers provided to the NPC study by the 2005 production volumes reported in EIA IEO 2007.

The reserves-to-production (R/P) ratio is often used to describe how effectively a country or region has developed oil resources that are currently economically and technically recoverable. High ratios may indicate opportunities for further development and additional rate capacity. Low ratios may indicate that a country has fully developed its available accumulations and production is in decline. Alternately, low R/P ratios may mean that known accumulations have not been fully delineated in order to add them to more certain reserve classifications. The R/P ratio does not by itself indicate remaining production capacity in a field or region. Investment and technology often allow R/P ratios to remain stable over many years even as annual production rates remain unchanged or increase.

Estimates of remaining reserves are not adequate indicators of how much oil remains to be produced under future conditions or potential long-term production capacity. The additional components of URR should be considered for these purposes. Resource size will determine how much oil is likely to be produced in the long term, while the distribution and nature of the oil will determine the likely production rate.

Global Total Liquids Production

Conventional oil will remain the largest source for liquid fuel supply in the near to intermediate term, with forecasts almost unanimously predicting at least modest growth in conventional oil supply for the next 5 to 10 years. However, there are great uncertainties

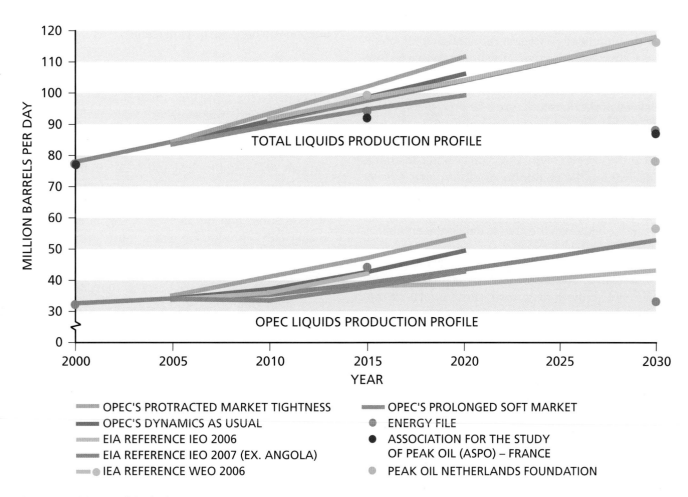

FIGURE 2-20. Projected Global and OPEC Total Liquids Production

about long-term forecasts of oil and total liquid production rates, ranging from business-as-usual cases that show few constraints, to alternative scenarios constrained by the resource base, environmental concerns, or geopolitical issues.

The EIA IEO 2007 Reference Case projects total liquids production of 118 million barrels per day (MB/D) in 2030, with similar estimates in the IEA Reference Case (116 MB/D), the IOC Average (107 MB/D), and Consultant Average (115 MB/D). Higher and lower forecasts include:

- EIA IEO 2007 Low Price: 134 MB/D

- EIA IEO 2007 High Price: 103 MB/D

- Peak Oil Netherlands and Association for the Study of Peak Oil (ASPO) – France: 78-88 MB/D.

The lower production figures in specific cases are driven by carbon constraints, investment constraints, higher oil prices, geological challenges, or other issues. The highest demand projections for 2030 assume favorable development policies in resource-holding countries, technology advances, investment, infrastructure, project completion, and personnel.

Several projections in Figure 2-20 show that total liquids production may not increase after 2015. The lowest total liquids forecasts in 2030 are consistent with a URR at the low end of the USGS range and constraints to developing the conventional oil resource base or alternatives. This set of forecasts projects that liquids production will reach a maximum within the study time frame, although the precise date is uncertain.

Forecasts for declining production are based on various above- and below-ground factors, including: declines in volumes discovered; conventional oil production peaks and subsequent declines in countries such as the United States and the United Kingdom; and anticipated oil production plateaus in countries such as Russia and China. The discussion of peak oil forecasts later in this chapter considers these views more fully.

The production rate for unconventional oil is an additional uncertainty in projected total liquids supply. In the EIA IEO 2007 Reference Case, for example, Canadian oil sands and Venezuelan heavy oils supply 5.2 MB/D in 2030, assuming sustained investment in development. Forecasts that include constraints on development project lower supplies from unconventional sources (Figures 2-21 and 2-22).

Conventional Oil Production

All forecasts project that a few countries, where resources are concentrated, will supply most conventional oil, although specific contributions vary. Geographic concentration generally creates more uncertainty in supply availability or deliverability due to infrastructure, resource, and geopolitical risks; increases the market power of resource holders; and enhances the global role of national oil companies (NOCs).

The EIA and IEA have somewhat different views on the balance of conventional oil supply between OPEC and non-OPEC countries (Figure 2-23). The IEA expects non-OPEC conventional oil production to decline after 2015, with OPEC increasing its share of conventional oil production from 42 percent in 2005 to 52 percent in 2030. The EIA projects that non-OPEC conventional oil production (including Angola) will increase through 2030. In the EIA IEO 2007 Reference Case, OPEC is expected to increase production to meet growing demand, but its share of conventional oil production will only rise to 47 percent.

Non-OPEC Production

Estimates for non-OPEC total liquids production vary significantly. Some forecasts indicate that production of non-OPEC conventional oil will decline in the next decade. Other forecasts show production growth through 2030 (Figures 2-24 and 2-25). In the EIA IEO 2007 Reference Case, non-OPEC output rises through 2030. Russia and other Caspian region producers provide about half the increase. Angola is included in non-OPEC production, since most forecasts were completed before it joined OPEC.

By comparison, the IOC Average and all peak oil cases show that non-OPEC production peaks within the outlook period. The IEA WEO 2006 Reference Case shows that non-OPEC production may not grow after 2010 due to high decline rates of currently producing fields and rising costs. The IEA Reference Case also shows that only Russia, Central Asia, and Latin America achieve significant increases in conventional oil production through 2030.

U.S. Production

The United States is the third-largest oil producing country in the world, after Saudi Arabia and Russia. The United States produced 5.2 MB/D of conventional crude oil in 2005, but its production is at best rising

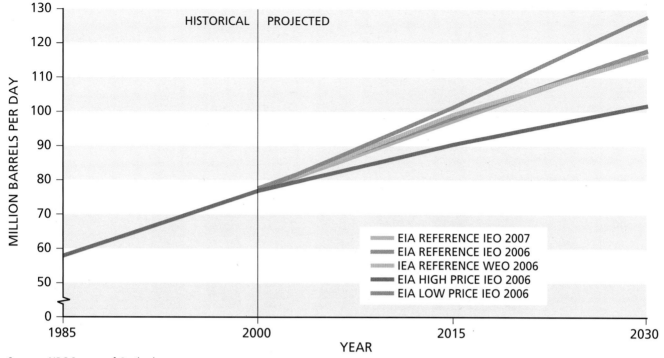

Source: NPC Survey of Outlooks.

FIGURE 2-21. *Projected Global Total Liquids Production*

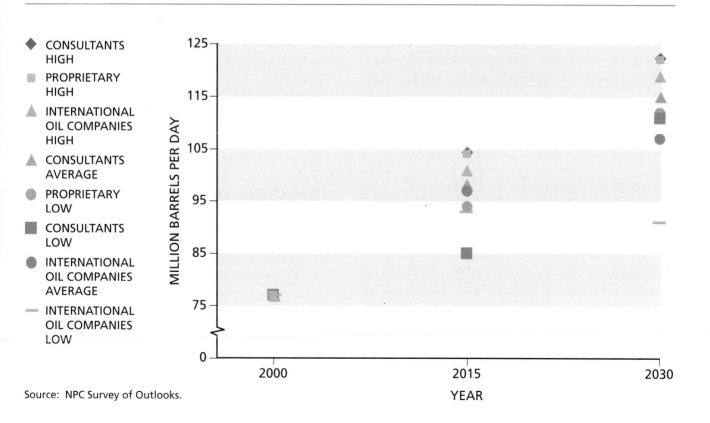

Source: NPC Survey of Outlooks.

FIGURE 2-22. *Projected Global Total Liquids Production — Proprietary Aggregated Cases*

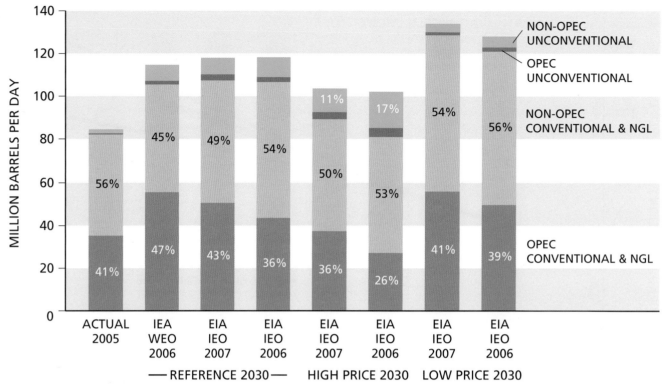

Source: NPC Survey of Outlooks.

FIGURE 2-23. *OPEC and Non-OPEC Total Liquids Production Shares, 2005-2030*

slightly in absolute terms while declining as a share of domestic demand. This production volume is a subset of the conventional production shown in Figure 2-26. Total conventional production is comprised of crude oil, including lease condensates, natural gas plant liquids, other hydrogen and hydrocarbons for refinery feedstocks, alcohol and other sources, and refinery gains.

Existing fields, which are maturing onshore and offshore, in Alaska and the lower-48 states, are generally not seen as having the potential to reverse existing declines. The EIA Annual Energy Outlook 2007 (AEO 2007) includes cases showing U.S. conventional crude oil production ranging between 5.25 MB/D and 6.04 MB/D in 2030. An AEO 2007 case that simulated access to the Arctic National Wildlife Refuge (ANWR) sees U.S. crude oil production rising to 6.03 MB/D in 2030, which is about 0.8 MB/D higher than the 2005 rate. By comparison, the IEA Reference Case forecasts U.S. production dropping about 1 MB/D by 2030.

Increasing domestic total liquids production more than marginally would depend on access to basins that have both substantial undeveloped liquid resources

and exploration potential and a significant contribution from unconventional oil. Access issues are discussed later in this report. Figure 2-26 shows how substantial production from unconventional sources would affect North American oil imports. Unconventional production is greatest in the EIA High Oil Price case, where imports in all years are below the 2005 level.

Production from Other Large Non-OPEC Countries

Of the other large non-OPEC producers, Russia will be a critical supply source. All forecasts show Russian production rates increasing from just under 10 MB/D currently to a range of 11 to 13 MB/D by 2030 (Figure 2-27).

Production from two primary sources of U.S. supply, Mexico and Canada, could be headed in opposite directions. Future Mexican production (Figure 2-28) is uncertain. Some forecasts see modest increases, despite recent production declines at a major field. Other forecasts, including the EIA IEO 2007, indicate lower Mexican production in 2015 and 2030 than in 2005. Conventional oil production from Canada is not expected to be material, but expanded development

Facing the Hard Truths about Energy

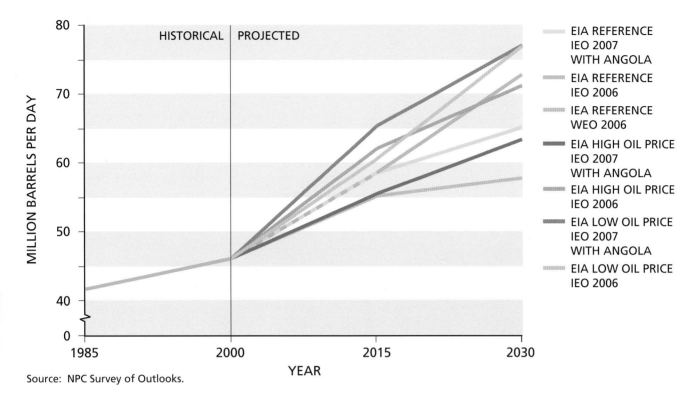

Source: NPC Survey of Outlooks.

FIGURE 2-24. *Projected Non-OPEC Total Liquids Production*

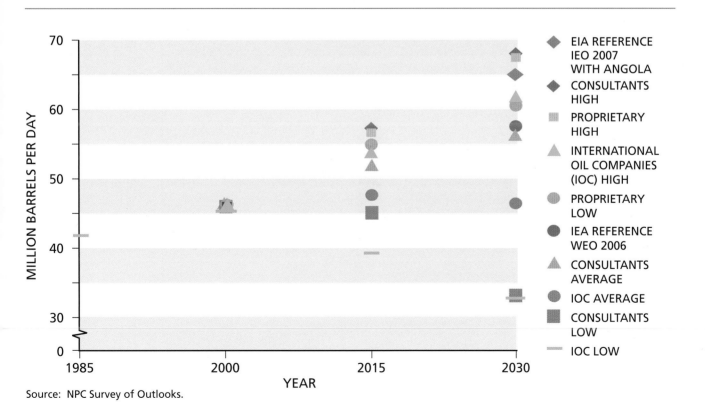

Source: NPC Survey of Outlooks.

FIGURE 2-25. *Non-OPEC Total Liquids Production — Proprietary Aggregated Cases*

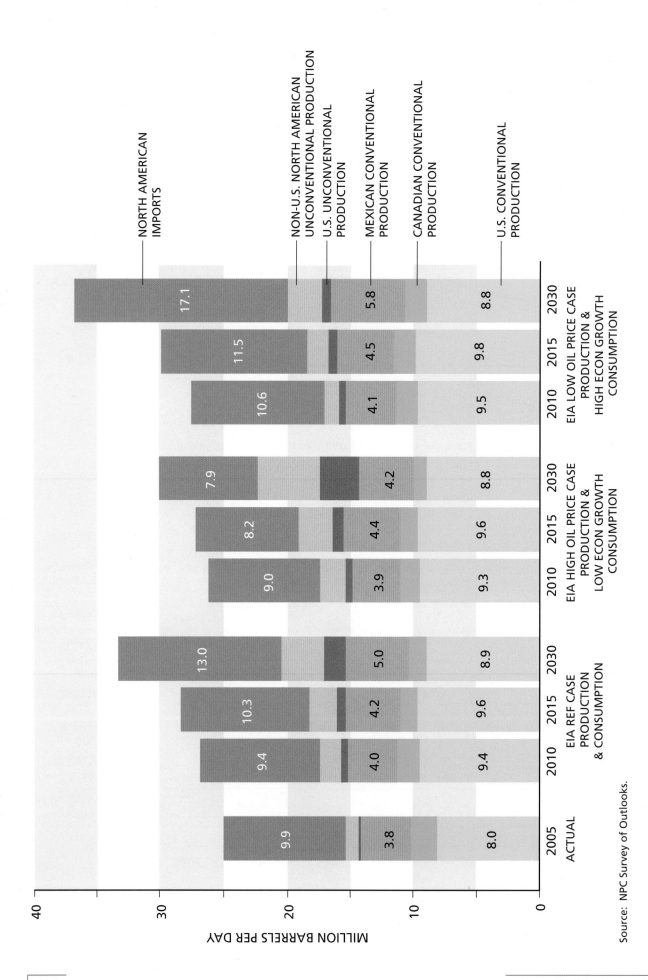

FIGURE 2-26. *North American Production and Imports*

Source: NPC Survey of Outlooks.

Facing the Hard Truths about Energy

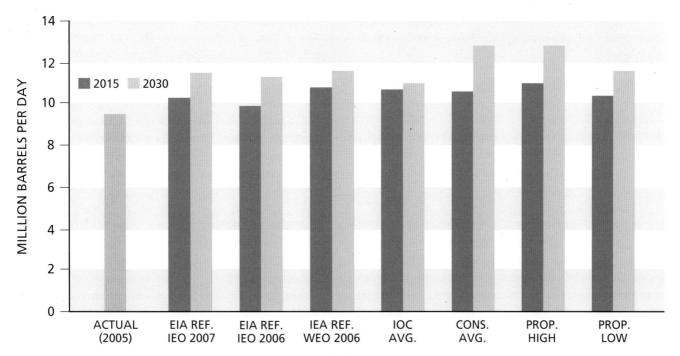

Note: IOC = International Oil Companies; CONS. = Consultants; and PROP. = Proprietary.
Source: NPC Survey of Outlooks.

FIGURE 2-27. *Russian Total Liquids Production Outlooks*

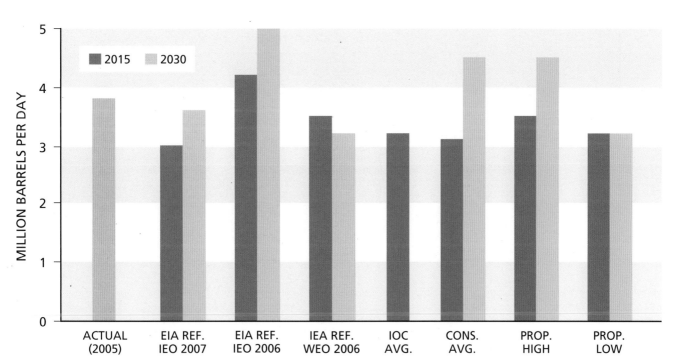

Note: IOC = International Oil Companies; CONS. = Consultants; and PROP. = Proprietary.
Source: NPC Survey of Outlooks.

FIGURE 2-28. *Mexican Total Liquids Production Outlooks*

of Canadian oil sands is forecast to bring considerable unconventional production into North American supply (Figure 2-29).

OPEC Oil Production (Excluding Angola)

Almost all long-term forecasts expect production to increase rapidly in OPEC countries. This is especially true of the Middle East, where resources are much larger and production costs generally lower than in other regions. Several forecasts suggest that OPEC is capable of raising total liquids production by 20 MB/D above present levels. The IOC Average case forecasts OPEC production at about 44 MB/D by 2030. The EIA IEO 2007 Reference Case, excluding Angola, projects 53 MB/D. The IEA Reference and Consultant Average cases indicate OPEC production above 50 to 55 MB/D (Figures 2-30 and 2-31). The range of projected OPEC total liquids production, relative to projected global production is shown in Figure 2-32.

Saudi Arabia continues to be the largest OPEC producer in every forecast. The IEA assigns the kingdom a vital role in supplying the global oil market. The IEA WEO 2004 considers timely Saudi Arabian investment in oil-production capacity to be a major determinant of future supply trends. Saudi Arabian production in the IEA case rises from 10.6 MB/D of conventional oil and NGL to 17.3 MB/D by 2030. As Figure 2-33 shows, the IEA has the highest forecast for Saudi Arabia's total liquids production in 2030.

In addition to projected Saudi Arabian production, significant conventional oil production increases from Iraq, Iran, Venezuela, and Nigeria will be needed to meet projected global demand in 2030. Among these producers, the near-term prospects for oil production in Iraq remain very uncertain. Nonetheless, the projected production increases for 2015 differ by a relatively small 0.5 MB/D, from 0.9 to 1.4 MB/D more than in 2005. By 2030, the difference between forecasts expands to 2.3 MB/D. IEA projects Iraqi production as growing to 6 MB/D in 2030, double its current share of OPEC conventional oil production. (Figure 2-34)

Forecasts show a wide range for total Iranian liquids production. The difference between production forecasts for 2015 is 1.5 MB/D, with some showing a drop in production and others showing flat production, or growth of almost 1 MB/D. By 2030, the differences broaden to 1.6 MB/D, with the highest production forecast at more than 6 MB/D. (Figure 2-35)

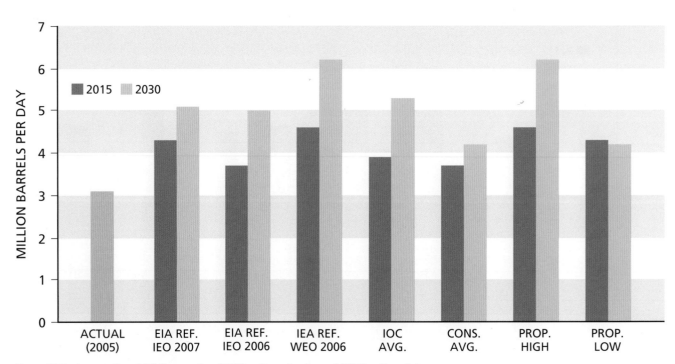

Note: IOC = International Oil Companies; CONS. = Consultants; and PROP. = Proprietary.
Source: NPC Survey of Outlooks.

FIGURE 2-29. *Canadian Total Liquids Production Outlook*

Facing the Hard Truths about Energy

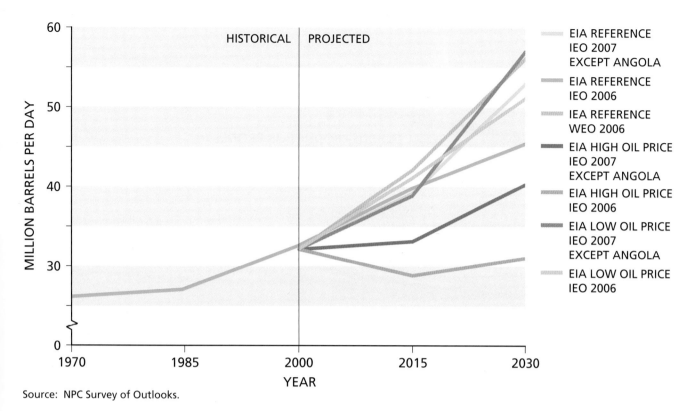

Source: NPC Survey of Outlooks.

FIGURE 2-30. *Projected OPEC Total Liquids Production*

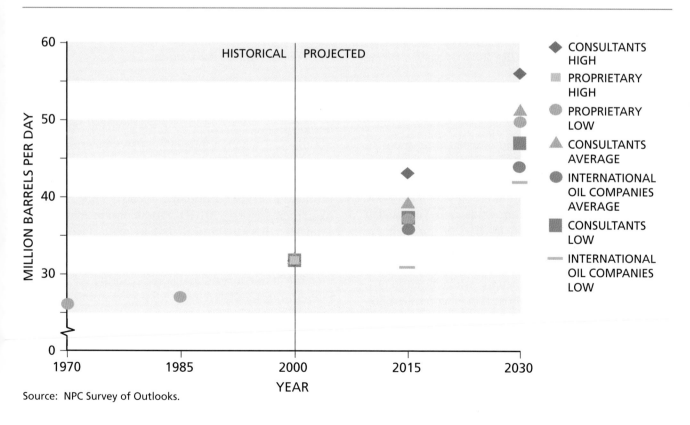

Source: NPC Survey of Outlooks.

FIGURE 2-31. *Projected OPEC Total Liquids Production — Proprietary Aggregated Cases*

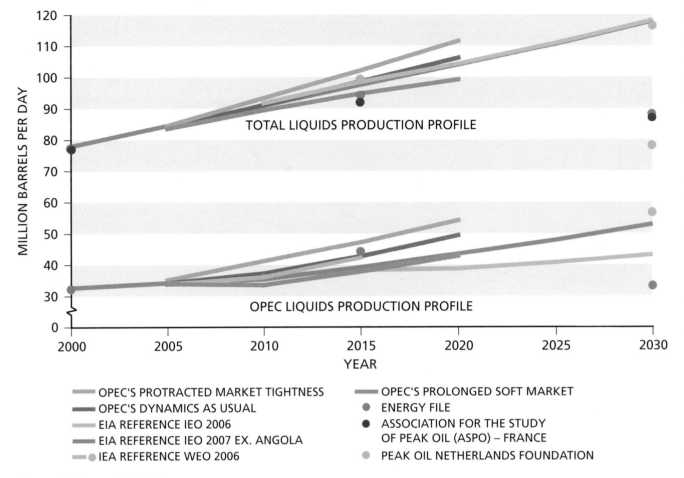

FIGURE 2-32. *Projected Global and OPEC Total Liquids Production*

Legend

OPEC'S PROTRACTED MARKET TIGHTNESS
OPEC'S DYNAMICS AS USUAL
EIA REFERENCE IEO 2006
EIA REFERENCE IEO 2007 EX. ANGOLA
IEA REFERENCE WEO 2006

OPEC'S PROLONGED SOFT MARKET
ENERGY FILE
ASSOCIATION FOR THE STUDY OF PEAK OIL (ASPO) – FRANCE
PEAK OIL NETHERLANDS FOUNDATION

Source: NPC Survey of Outlooks.

Unconventional Liquids Production

Unconventional liquids are projected to grow to about 10 percent of total liquids production by 2030 (Figure 2-36). The EIA IEO 2007 Reference Case shows total unconventional liquids production above 10 MB/D, with Canadian oil sands and Venezuelan heavy oil comprising the major part of the increase. Commercial considerations and the relative immaturity of production technologies for unconventional liquids lead to much uncertainty about the availability and timing of these fuels. Oil sands projects in Alberta will be pivotal to forecasted growth in Canadian total liquids production, if they overcome infrastructure, environmental, and cost challenges. While all forecasts expect growth, the range between them widens to 2 MB/D by 2030.

Most forecasts project that Venezuelan production will increase from 2005 levels. Venezuela's national oil company, Petroleos de Venezuela (PDVSA), projects the

highest growth, expecting to more than double its total liquids production capacity to 5.8 MB/D by 2012.[6] The IEA forecast, which is lower than PDVSA's, expects new production from both extra-heavy oil projects in the Orinoco area and conventional oil fields. Forecasted production in 2015 compared to 2005 ranges from flat to an increase of 0.6 MB/D. Production in 2030 ranges from 0.5 to 2.3 MB/D more than in 2005. (Figure 2-37)

The EIA Reference Case expects the remaining increase in unconventional liquids production to come mainly from: biofuels derived from agricultural products (16 percent); gas-to-liquids (11 percent); and coal-to-liquids (23 percent). Indicative of this trend, the United States has announced a production goal for ethanol and other unconventional fuels of 2.3 MB/D by 2017, up from about 0.4 MB/D in 2006 and 0.5 MB/D in 2012.

---

6   http://www.pdvsa.com/index.php?tpl=interface.en/design/home.tpl.html

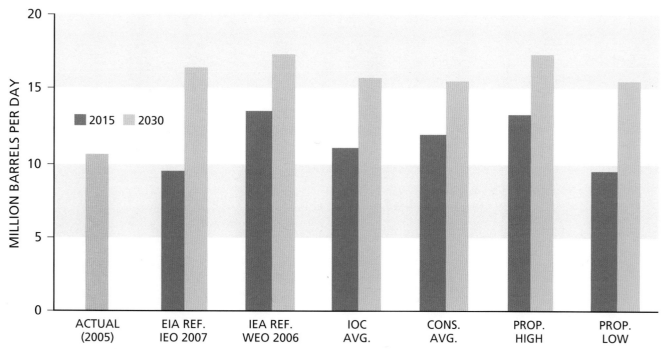

Note: IOC = International Oil Companies; CONS. = Consultants; and PROP. = Proprietary.
Source: NPC Survey of Outlooks.

FIGURE 2-33. *Projected Saudi Arabian Total Liquids Production*

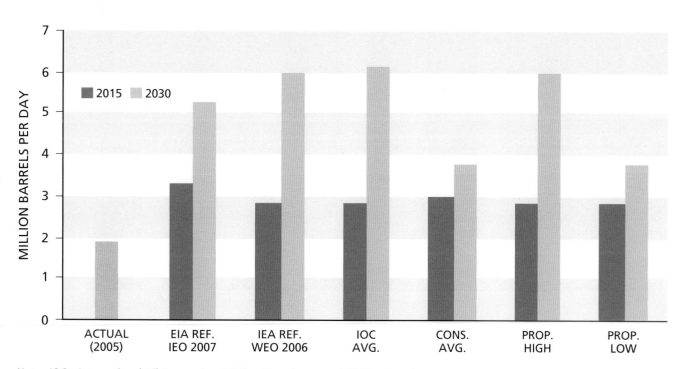

Note: IOC = International Oil Companies; CONS. = Consultants; and PROP. = Proprietary.
Source: NPC Survey of Outlooks.

FIGURE 2-34. *Projected Iraqi Total Liquids Production*

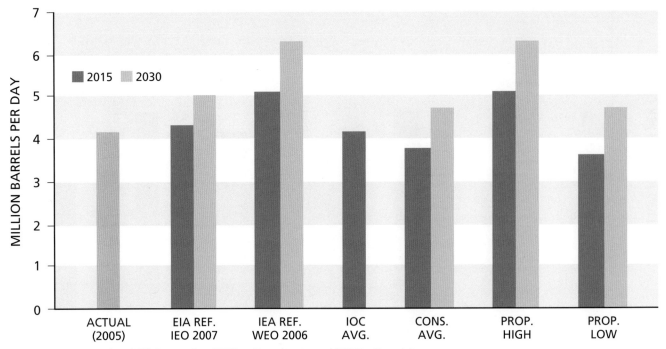

Note: IOC = International Oil Companies; CONS. = Consultants; and PROP. = Proprietary.
Source: NPC Survey of Outlooks.

FIGURE 2-35. *Projected Iranian Total Liquids Production*

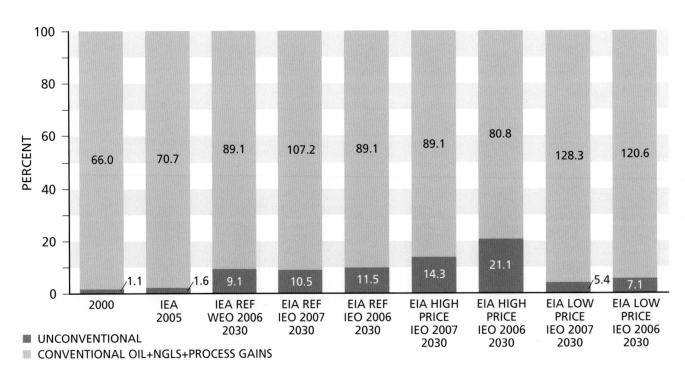

Note: Units shown in million barrels per day.
Source: NPC Survey of Outlooks.

FIGURE 2-36. *Projected Global Conventional and Unconventional Total Liquids Production*

Facing the Hard Truths about Energy

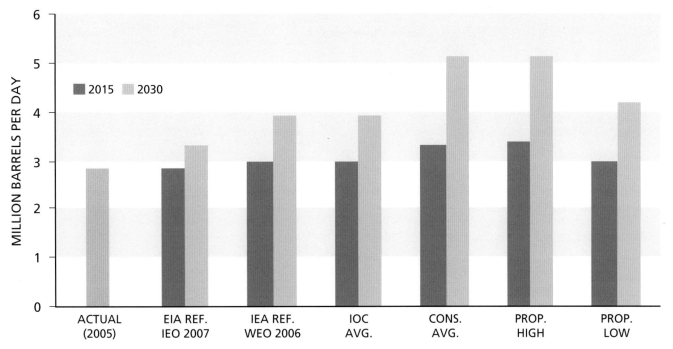

Note: IOC = International Oil Companies; CONS. = Consultants; and PROP. = Proprietary.
Source: NPC Survey of Outlooks.

FIGURE 2-37. *Projected Venezuelan Total Liquids Production*

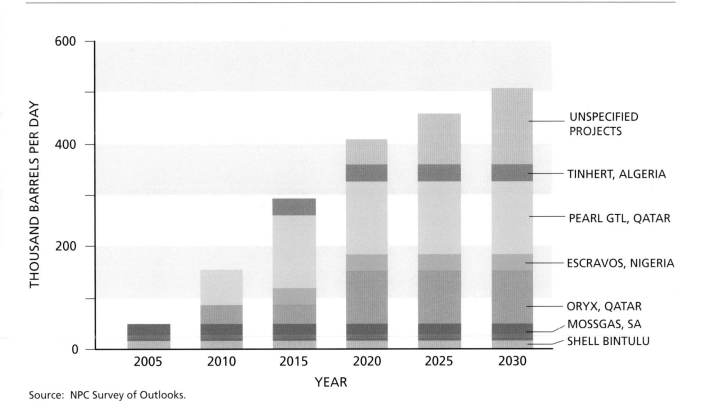

Source: NPC Survey of Outlooks.

FIGURE 2-38. *Projected Gas-to-Liquids Plant Capacity Based on Current Projects*

Production Source	Current Production Forecasts 2005-2030 (Million Barrels per Day)	Access	Investment	Infra-structure	People and Equipment	Environ-ment	Geopolitics
Conventional Non-OPEC	35-75		X	X			X
Russia	10+	X	X	X			X
Conventional OPEC	30-55	X	X	X	X		X
Saudi Arabia	10-17+						
Unconventional Crude	1-10		X	X	X	X	
Heavy	1-10						
Shale Oil	<1						
Alternatives	1-5						
Biofuels	1-3		X	X	X		
Gas-to-Liquids	~1			X			
Coal-to-Liquids	~1		X			X	
Production Growth	2005-2030 Expected Growth (Million Barrels per Day)						
Saudi Arabia	+5-7		X		X		
Iraq	+4		X	X	X		X
Canada	+2			X	X		
Venezuela	+2	X	X	X	X		X
Nigeria	+2		X				X
Iran	1-2	X	X	X	X		X
Kuwait	1-2		X		X		
UAE	1-2		X		X		
Libya	1-2		X		X		

Note: An X in any column means that the matter is problematic or open to question for that resource type or country.

TABLE 2-3. *Oil Production Challenges*

GTL and CTL plants typically convert natural gas and coal to liquid fuels. The product is usually about 70 percent ultra-clean diesel fuel and 25 percent naphtha for chemical feedstock.

In the past ten years, several world-scale GTL plants have been developed or announced. However, given recent cost increases, several large projects (e.g., in Qatar) have been cancelled or postponed in 2006 and 2007. All forecasts received for the study project that GTL will grow quickly from a very low base, but not enough to significantly affect oil product or natural gas markets. Several estimates for GTL capacity growth show only 0.5 MB/D of GTL fuels being produced worldwide through 2030, mainly clean diesel and naphtha (Figure 2-38). In this event, GTL would provide only about 1 percent of global middle distillate fuel requirements. By comparison, EIA IEO 2007 shows stronger GTL production growth to 1.2 MB/D in 2030, with Qatar as the primary source. For further discussion, see the Gas-to-Liquids Topic Paper.

For a further discussion of coal-to-liquids, see the Coal section of this chapter and the Coal-to-Liquids Topic Paper on the CD that accompanies this report.

Oil Supply Challenges

The forecasts and data received for this study lead to the conclusion that oil supply increasingly faces above-ground challenges in addition to geological and technical hurdles. The challenges include access, geopolitics, investment requirements, commercial and trade regimes, infrastructure, and workforce availability. Table 2-3 is a snapshot of above-ground challenges that affect the resource types and sources of projected oil supplies to 2030. The prospects are likely to be further complicated since the challenges change with place, resource, and time.

Peak Oil

Concerns about the reliability of production forecasts and estimates of recoverable oil resources are the basis of

warnings about future oil supplies and the deliverability of oil. The concerns are compounded by the challenges some companies face in adding new reserves to replace those already produced. The warnings are strongly expressed in a set of forecasts known collectively as *peak oil*. The term derives from the *Hubbert's Peak* analysis of U.S. oil production written by M. King Hubbert.

Peak oil forecasts project that oil supply will not grow significantly beyond current production levels and therefore may not keep pace with projected global demand; a peak and decline in oil production is inevitable and may be near-at-hand. The conclusions lead to calls to develop additional resources to increase supply, accelerate the use of unconventional resources as substitutes for oil, and moderate demand in order to bridge the forecast supply shortfalls. Such actions generally converge with the recommendations of this study.

The forecasts reviewed for this study that do not consider new policies such as carbon constraint show considerable agreement until 2015 (Figure 2-39). After 2015, views about supply trends diverge, with peak oil forecasts providing the lower bound. The divergent views of oil supply after 2015 fuel growing concern about the

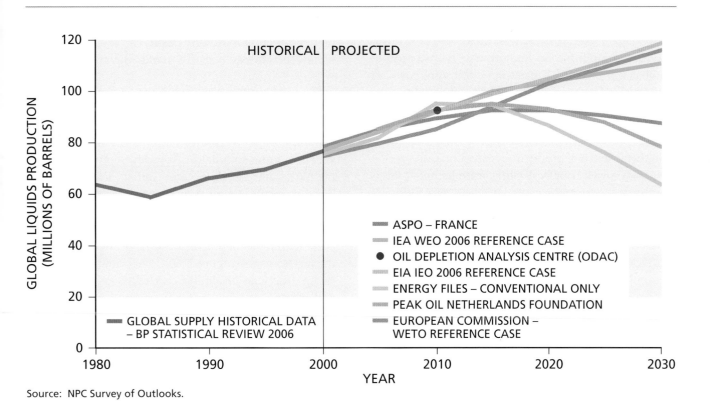

Source: NPC Survey of Outlooks.

FIGURE 2-39. *Global Total Liquids Production — Reference Forecasts 2000-2030*

deliverability of the resource base and the uncertainty regarding timing and volume of future supplies.

Peak oil forecasts emphasize various physical limitations to raising production rates, including: reserve estimates that are lower than reference cases; limited future development opportunities; and insufficient volumes from unconventional production over the study time frame. These forecasts generally consider oil supply independently of demand and point to supply shortfalls. Such views contrast with forecasts and economic models that expect market forces to provide incentives for developing global hydrocarbon and other resources to meet fuel needs through at least 2030.

Peak oil forecasts use several indicators to support the case for an imminent peak in global production. One leading indicator is the difficulty of adding new reserves to make up for produced volumes, especially through exploration. However, companies and countries use different methods to estimate recoverable resources and what they term reserves. The lack of transparency and consistency in this reporting confuses the situation and is a concern in all forecasts.

A second indicator is the growing number of countries that show a historical peak in their oil production. Many forecasts rely on the shape of production curves in countries that have displayed a peak to extrapolate future production rates for that country and to develop forecasts for countries whose production has not peaked. The extrapolations are based on the observed physical behavior of most oilfields. This method raises considerable debate, since many factors affect production from a field, basin or country.

In the absence of production restrictions, oil production from a well usually declines from its initial levels. As other wells are incorporated in a field, oil production rises to a given rate at the field level and then declines. Production costs generally increase throughout the development of the field as the productivity of wells decreases. This well and field production profile is often extrapolated to represent producing basins, countries and the world. If a fixed or slowly growing resource base is also assumed, forecasted global production would inevitably follow a similar pattern of decline.

Peak oil forecasts point to the importance and dominance of large fields, since they have produced most of the world's oil. In general, large fields are among the first to be found, and have economically attractive scales and production costs. Production from such

large reservoirs is usually considered conventional oil that did not require technology to stimulate oil flow during the early stages of production.

Views of an impending peak in liquids production are usually countered by expectations for new discoveries, additions to the resource base, new technologies, and greater operating experience that change the production profile of new and existing producing fields. Production rates are not fixed and can be influenced by these and other factors such as costs and price.

Peak oil forecasts are concerned about the ability to extend and apply experience from mature areas to less produced areas. As a hydrocarbon province matures, production transitions from large reservoirs to smaller, less prolific, and possibly higher-cost reservoirs. In the United States, for example, production from smaller and mature reservoirs dominates supplies. Peak oil forecasts assume that remaining smaller reservoirs will not compensate for declines in the larger reservoirs, resulting in declining conventional oil production in the near future. However, the North Sea has seen the evolution away from larger, depleted fields to smaller fields that can be brought online using existing infrastructure. North Sea production has actually been sustained for many years at significantly higher levels than was generally thought likely in the 1980s and early 1990s. Production growth from 1990 to 2000 shows how production in mature basins can revive as a result of new technology, price, or market dynamics.

As conventional oil development moves to smaller reservoirs in regions where access remains feasible, the industry is increasingly turning to frontier resources, deep and ultra-deepwater fields, and unconventional very heavy and sour fields. New developments include the Alaskan Arctic, deepwater Gulf of Mexico, offshore West Africa and Brazil, and Alberta oil sands. Frontier and unconventional resources in North America have compensated for declines in United States oil production, keeping total liquids production nearly flat over the last 15 years (Figure 2-40). This view of sustained North American production is challenged by expected and announced decreases in production from the Cantarrell field in Mexico, the fourth largest producer in the world and source of most of Mexico's production in recent decades. Peak oil forecasts argue that development of smaller reservoirs will not be able to reverse Mexico's decline.

Although production growth from frontier and unconventional resources will require long lead times

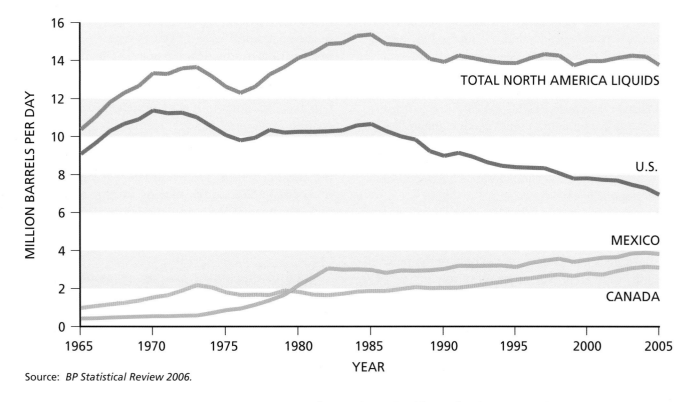

Source: *BP Statistical Review 2006.*

FIGURE 2-40. *North American Liquids Production*

and very large investments, there is considerable agreement about continued growth in the supply of unconventional oil and alternative liquids. However, peak oil forecasts do not see these resources as offsetting declines in existing conventional oil production.

A country's oil production profiles are the sum of the production profiles of the fields in that country, just as fields are the sum of profiles of individual wells. The overall decline rate of a field is a combination of the decline from existing wells and the production volumes from new wells. In addition, changes in production technology and the use of enhanced recovery techniques can reduce expected declines.

Figure 2-41 shows typical production profiles as they evolve over time. The curves can apply at different scales from individual oil wells to fields, countries, or larger regions. Wells and fields vary in their stage of development: some may be declining, some at a production plateau, while others may be ramping up production. The global production profile is the aggregate of the profiles from all individual fields with diverse profiles.

While most fields have production profiles shaped like Part A of Figure 2-41, many have other more

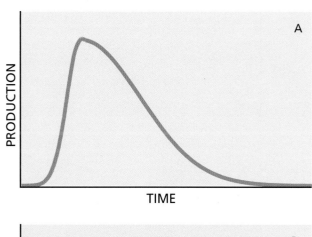

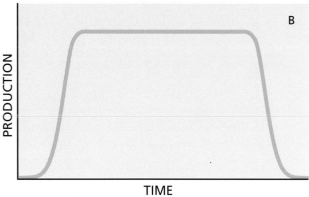

FIGURE 2-41. *Typical Oil Production Profiles*

general profiles. For example, where downstream bottlenecks constrain production, the profile may plateau as in Part B. Historically, technology advances have increased the recovery factors, or percent of resources, recovered from a reservoir. Technical advances, such as enhanced oil recovery (EOR), will continue to improve recovery factors and thus modify production profiles for individual wells and fields. For a complete discussion of production profiles and potential technology effects, see the Conventional Oil section in the Technology chapter of this report.

Figure 2-41 is illustrative. It demonstrates that managing the shape and duration of the production profile is a central issue not only in the peak oil debate but in all prospects for oil supply.

Investment

The IEA WEO 2006 Reference Case estimates that the global oil industry will need a total investment of about $4.3 trillion between 2005 and 2030, or about $164 billion annually, to meet projected demand. Most of the projected investment will be in the upstream sector, largely devoted to maintaining existing production capacity. The IEA investment figure is substantially higher than prior years, partly based on sharp increases in unit capital costs. Other causes for the higher projection include the cost of developing remote, technically challenging, or deeper reservoirs, or oil in smaller accumulations. Additional capital will be needed to minimize production declines at the world's largest, aging fields. A recent OPEC study showing strong correlation between exploration and production (E&P) investment and oil production rates suggests that projected capital requirements are likely to increase.

Much of the world's existing oil production will need to be replaced by 2030. Figure 2-42 is an illustrative example of the various resource components that contribute to total liquids supply. These components contribute to virtually all liquids supply projections, although the combination and timing of the components may differ. Maintaining current oil supply levels will require slightly more than half the $4.3 trillion

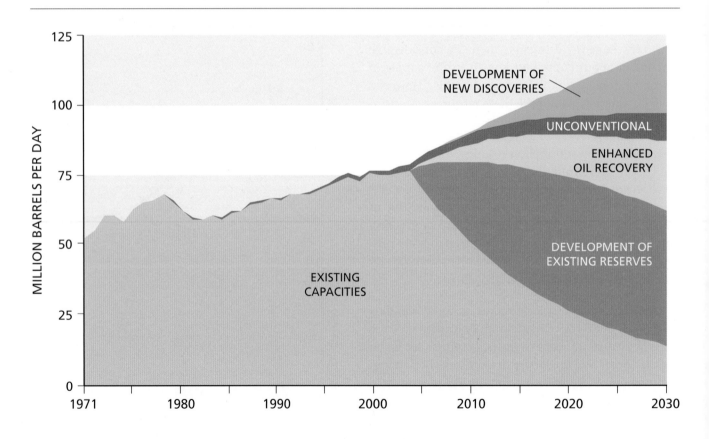

Source: IEA, *World Energy Outlook 2004.*

FIGURE 2-42. *Illustrative Total Liquids Supply*

Facing the Hard Truths about Energy

investment. The remaining investment will be needed to expand supply to meet projected demand and build or replace infrastructure. Financing this investment is likely to be a major undertaking, with enormous requirements in individual countries and regions. For example, projected investment in China alone is about $350 billion, or half the total for Middle Eastern countries. Of the total global investment, more than half is expected to be in developing countries.

Geopolitics

Oil is currently a fungible commodity traded in global markets. Changes in oil trading patterns are expected during the study's time frame, based on evolving relationships between importing and exporting countries and regions. Global redistribution of infrastructure and manufacturing capability will also change commodity and product trade flows. These changes are likely to have important and uncertain geopolitical dimensions. For example, the IEA reports that OECD countries imported 17.9 million MB/D from OPEC producers in 2003, or 57 percent of OPEC's petroleum exports. The IEA Reference Case shows these exports rising by 3.2 MB/D at the end of the study time frame, with slightly more than 40 percent of the increase supplied from the Persian Gulf. The projection assumes that the existing OECD–OPEC trading relationship can be reliably extrapolated. If this is not case, the availability of supply becomes a more uncertain and pressing issue. Such geopolitical factors apply to all energy forecasts and are fully addressed in the Geopolitics chapter of this report.

Natural Gas

Key Observations—Natural Gas

- *Most forecasts project that global natural gas production will grow rapidly to meet increasing demand.*

- *Current estimates of recoverable natural gas resources are sufficient to sustain the large, anticipated increase in production over the study time frame, providing above-ground issues and challenges do not become major constraints.*

- *As gas production in OECD countries lags demand growth, these demand centers will require major additional infrastructure to ensure delivery by pipeline and liquefied natural gas (LNG).*

- *Growth in global natural gas trade is expected to occur at a faster pace than historically, with the largest new supply volumes originating in Russia and the Middle East.*

- *Additions to LNG supply capacity are capital intensive, complex, and face development uncertainty. Growing risks in the investment climate for LNG and for long-distance natural gas pipelines may delay or reduce supply availability.*

- *North American and U.S. natural gas production is likely to lag projected demand growth over the study time frame, requiring significant growth in LNG imports. The wide range of projected U.S. LNG import requirements raises uncertainty about whether these requirements will be met, particularly at the higher estimates.*

- *Unconventional natural gas is expected to make up an increasingly important share of U.S. gas production*

- *Development of Arctic natural gas resources, both in the United States and Canada, could contribute significantly to North American gas supply if major infrastructure is developed*

- *Increased access to restricted and moratoria areas on U.S. offshore and onshore public lands could increase natural gas supplies available to the United States.*

- *Natural gas demand in a carbon-constrained world is likely to be significantly higher than in a business-as-usual future, increasing the importance of timely supply and infrastructure development.*

Global Natural Gas Endowment and Technically Recoverable Resources

In 2000, the USGS estimated that remaining recoverable conventional gas resources totaled about 12,000 trillion cubic feet (TCF). This is the mean estimate in a range from 8,000 to 19,000 TCF. This gas volume is equivalent to about 2 trillion barrels of oil, or double the total amount of oil produced globally to date. Many gas supply forecasts base their projections on the USGS estimate, which is somewhat higher than proprietary estimates aggregated for this study. For example, the IOC aggregated mean for total recoverable resources is 12,000 TCF, with a range of 11,300 to 13,900 TCF. The IOC range for remaining recoverable resources is 8,000 to 12,000 TCF, with a mean of 10,300 TCF. The USGS recoverable resource assessments do not include unconventional gas, which may represent a significant addition to gas supplies over the next 25 years. Similarly, the assessments do not include natural gas hydrates, a potentially significant resource that is not currently considered technically recoverable and is unlikely to be developed over the study time frame.

About 3,000 TCF of natural gas has already been produced (Figure 2-43). The projected supply of natural gas to 2030 ranges from 3,100 to 3,650 TCF. Thus, current mid-range estimates of conventional, global, technically recoverable resources are considerably greater than combined historical and projected production. Indeed, mid-range projections expect less than 50 percent of USGS-estimated conventional gas reserves to be produced by 2030. If IOC mean or low-range estimates prove more accurate, global gas production will exceed 50 percent of the technically recoverable resource by 2030. Whether or not global natural gas production reaches a plateau during the study time frame, the possibility becomes greater within the next 50 years, unless a major technical breakthrough allows economic production of significant volumes of unconventional gas and gas hydrates.

Nearly 83 percent of technically recoverable natural gas resources are in the Middle East, Non-OECD Europe,

Asia/Oceania, and Africa (Figure 2-44). The overall distribution of resources is becoming more remote from major natural gas markets, with the exception of Russia, a major gas consumer as well as resource holder.

Current proved reserves of natural gas are concentrated in a few countries, with Russia, Iran, Qatar, and Saudi Arabia comprising more than two-thirds of the global total (Figure 2-45). Of the 12 largest resource owners, 11 are outside the OECD, comprising more than 75 percent of global gas reserves. Such concentration raises issues about risks and the costs of developing and producing the reserves to meet growing gas demand.

U.S. Technically Recoverable Gas Resource

The 2003 NPC study, *Balancing Natural Gas Policy*, estimated that about 1,450 TCF of technically recoverable resource remain in the United States. Technical advances may add an additional 400 to 500 TCF by 2030 (Table 2-4).

The technically recoverable domestic gas resource is subject to numerous restrictions. About 162 TCF of the U.S. onshore recoverable natural gas resources

Sources: U.S. Geological Survey, 2000; and Rogner, H-H., "An Assessment of World Hydrocarbon Resources," Institute for Integrated Energy Systems, University of Victoria, 1997.

FIGURE 2-43. *Global Natural Gas Endowment*

Facing the Hard Truths about Energy

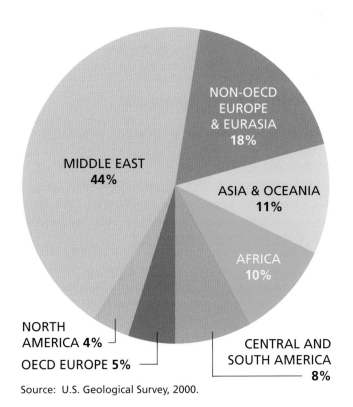

Source: U.S. Geological Survey, 2000.

FIGURE 2-44. *USGS Estimated Natural Gas Resource Shares, 2000*

lie beneath federal lands that are restricted beyond standard lease terms or are entirely off limits. This estimate was developed by government studies conducted in accordance with the U.S. Energy Policy and Conservation Act of 2000 and the Energy Policy Act of 2005. The restricted areas range from Alaska to the Rockies, the Gulf Coast, and Appalachia. Approximately 92 TCF of U.S. offshore technically recoverable natural gas resources are also currently off limits for leasing and development. Of these, almost 86 TCF of natural gas are in the federal U.S. Outer Continental Shelf (OCS) moratoria areas (Table 2-5). Resource estimates for all restricted areas are very uncertain, since the last seismic data acquisition or drilling in some cases occurred 25 to 40 years ago.

In aggregate, access is restricted to 76 percent of U.S. technically recoverable natural gas resources. About 66 percent of domestic resources (882 TCF) are on state, tribal, and private lands, predominantly in onshore tight gas and shale formations. The technical challenges to developing domestic gas resources are compounded by urban growth, competing land use, and changing public values that increasingly constrain existing and new natural gas development.

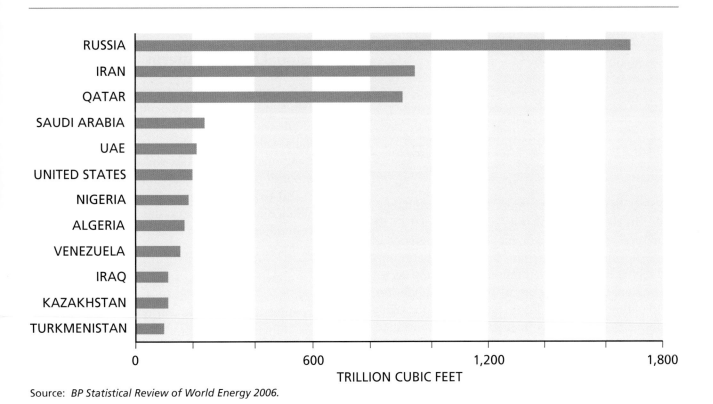

Source: *BP Statistical Review of World Energy 2006.*

FIGURE 2-45. *Largest Natural Gas Reserve Holders, 2005*

	Current Technology	2015 Technology	2030 Technology
Lower-48 Onshore	764	839	1,006
Lower-48 Offshore	384	415	486
Alaska	303	331	395
Total U.S.	1,451	1,585	1,887

Source: National Petroleum Council, *Balancing Natural Gas Policy,* 2003.

TABLE 2-4. *U.S. Natural Gas Resource Base (Trillion Cubic Feet)*

Moratoria Areas	Resources
Gulf of Mexico	22
Alaska	9
Atlantic	37
Pacific	18
U.S. Federal OCS	**86**
Great Lakes	5
State Waters	1

Sources: Department of the Interior (MMS and USGS) and Interstate Oil and Gas Compact Commission.

TABLE 2-5. *U.S. Offshore Natural Gas Resources in Moratoria Areas (Trillion Cubic Feet)*

The United States has almost 290,000 marginal gas wells.[7] In 2005, marginal wells accounted for 1.7 TCF of natural gas per day, or more than 9 percent of domestic onshore production. Increasing operational and regulatory costs and diminishing pipeline access to markets may contribute to premature abandonment of these wells and loss of gas production. When marginal wells and fields are prematurely abandoned, the associated oil and gas resources may never be recovered due to economics, lease termination, and related issues—thus widening the gap between projected gas demand and domestic supply.

Global Natural Gas Production

Global gas production to 2030 is forecast to grow faster than the historical rate since 1980 of about 50 billion cubic feet per day per decade. The EIA and IEA 2006 Reference Cases project growth rates of 2.4 percent and 2.0 percent, respectively. Both rates are higher than the growth rates for coal and oil over the study time frame (Figure 2-46).

The proprietary forecasts aggregated for the study show average gas production of about 450 billion cubic feet per day in 2030, a value very similar to the IEA Reference Case. The upper and lower limits are approximately 425 and 500 billion cubic feet per day (Figure 2-47).

The highest projected natural gas production in 2030 is 530 billion cubic feet per day. This forecast requires a high supply of gas to balance energy demand, since it also projects that oil production in 2030 will be below today's level (Figure 2-48). Most Alternative Policy cases in Figure 2-48 also project gas production above 400 billion cubic feet per day, as the energy mix increasingly favors lower carbon fuels that reduce carbon dioxide emission levels.

Regional Supply Patterns

Regional supply patterns for natural gas are shifting. Forecasts show that production and exports from the Middle East, Non-OECD Europe (Russia), and Asia (Australia) will increase substantially over the next 25 years, although in total Asia will probably remain a net importer of natural gas (Figure 2-49). The United States and OECD Europe are likely to increase their dependence on gas imports, since most projections show continued growth in demand but flat or declining production in these regions.

Most growth in natural gas production is expected to occur in exporting countries. Transporting the gas to consuming regions will require substantially increased investment in production and transportation infrastructure, particularly:

- Liquefaction plants in producing countries and regasification terminals in consuming countries for LNG.

- Long-distance, high-capacity natural gas pipelines.

---

7   Interstate Oil and Gas Compact Commission (IOGCC), *Marginal Wells: Fuel for Economic Growth* (2006). The IOGCC defines marginal wells as those producing 60 thousand cubic feet or less of natural gas per day. The Internal Revenue Service defines marginal wells as producing 75 thousand cubic feet or less of natural gas per day.

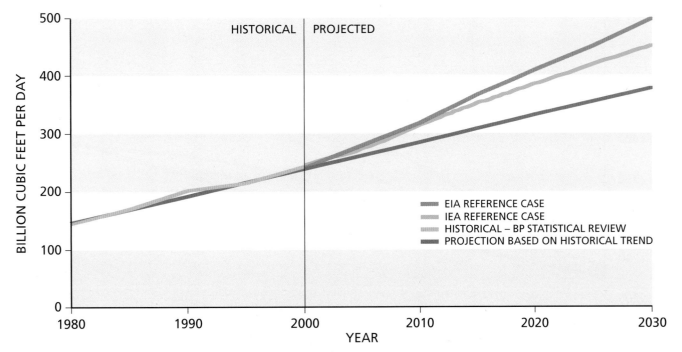

Sources: Energy Information Administration (EIA), *International Energy Outlook 2006;* International Energy Agency (IEA), *World Energy Outlook 2006;* and *BP Statistical Review of World Energy 2006.*

FIGURE 2-46. *Projected Global Natural Gas Production*

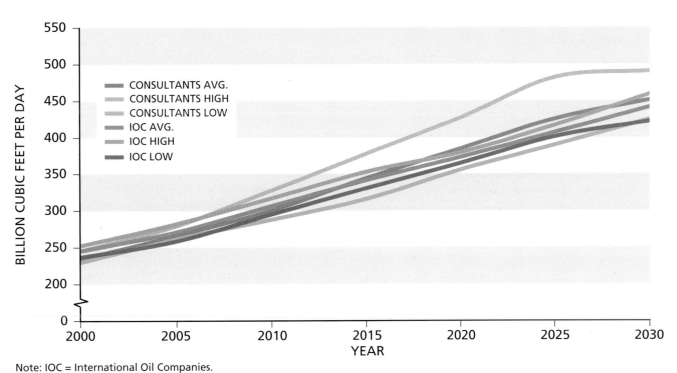

Note: IOC = International Oil Companies.
Source: NPC Survey of Outlooks.

FIGURE 2-47. *Projected Global Natural Gas Production — Proprietary Aggregated Data*

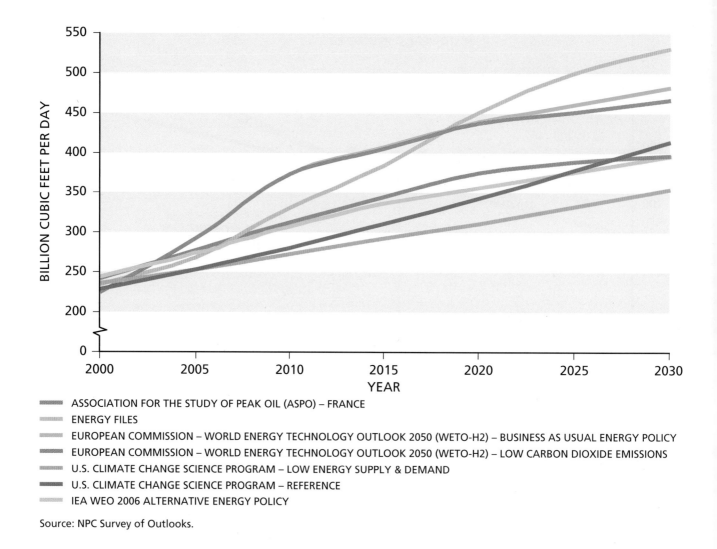

Source: NPC Survey of Outlooks.

FIGURE 2-48. *Projected Global Natural Gas Production — Public Data*

Figures 2-50, 2-51, and 2-52 show the increasing importance of imports in the main OECD demand regions that were traditionally supplied from indigenous sources. Domestic supply in North America is expected to decline and then, possibly, to reach a plateau as unconventional resources (e.g., tight gas, coalbed methane, and shale gas) supplement domestic conventional gas production. Most forecasts assume that pipeline supplies from Alaska and the Mackenzie Delta will reach North American markets in the study time frame. However, projected demand growth will ultimately be met by increasing LNG imports.

Domestic production in Europe is expected to be flat or declining, with pipeline imports increasing dramatically, primarily from Russia and the Caspian region. LNG imports will also play a growing and more significant role in meeting Europe's gas requirements.

Unlike other major consuming areas, Asia Pacific is expected to see a significant increase in domestic production of natural gas. Much of this growth will be traded between producing countries such as Indonesia and Australia and consuming countries such as Japan and China. The region will also need greater supplies of LNG to meet about 30 percent of projected regional demand. Long-distance gas pipelines to Russian, Caspian, and Middle East supplies are also a potential option.

North American Gas Production

Natural gas production in the United States has been relatively flat over the past 35 years, while

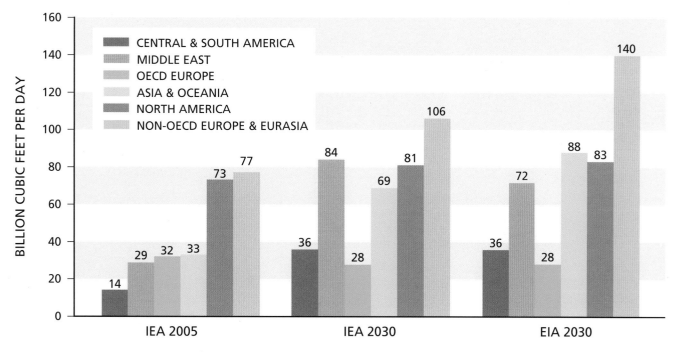

Sources: International Energy Agency (IEA), *World Energy Outlook 2006;* and Energy Information Administration (EIA), *International Energy Outlook 2006.*

FIGURE 2-49. *Projected Regional Natural Gas Production (Regional Data)*

demand has been growing over most of that period (Figure 2-53). Since the mid-1980s, most of the growing gap between domestic production and consumption has been filled by increased gas pipeline imports from Canada. Since 2003, LNG imports from several other countries have also grown, making a small but increasingly important contribution to U.S. gas supply.

For North America as a whole, natural gas production has been largely sufficient to meet demand over the past 35 years (Figure 2-54). Growing integration of the pipeline systems of Canada, the United States and Mexico has allowed regional trade flows to develop and balance the gas markets in each of the countries. Beginning in 2004, the region has imported larger quantities of LNG, with the LNG contribution reaching about 2 percent of North American supply by 2006.

EIA projections show some potential for maintaining a slow growth rate in North American natural gas production (Figure 2-55). The IEA concurs with this outlook, also projecting a North American natural gas production growth of about 0.4 percent per year. Both forecasts assume growing success in exploiting unconventional natural gas resources in North

America and completion of two major pipelines to bring Arctic gas to market centers from Alaska and the Mackenzie Delta. The risks and challenges associated with these potential supply sources are discussed below.

Over the next 25 years, it will be an increasing challenge to avoid declining conventional gas production rates in the United States. The 2003 NPC natural gas study identified such contributing factors as accelerating decline rates, decreasing size of new conventional discoveries, and higher finding and development costs for deeper and more technically challenging gas accumulations.

The forecasts analyzed for the current study largely agree that domestic conventional gas production will decline over the forecast period, assuming that restricted onshore and offshore areas will not be developed. The balance of natural gas supply to the United States over the next 25 years is generally expected to be met by a combination of three elements:

• Increased domestic production of unconventional gas (basin-centered gas, tight gas, shale gas, coalbed methane)

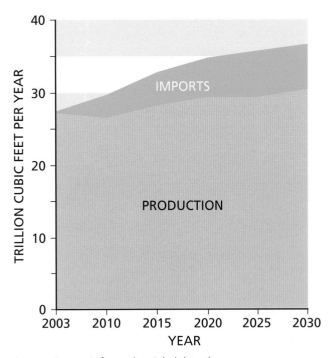

Source: Energy Information Administration,
International Energy Outlook 2006.

FIGURE 2-50. *North American Natural Gas Production and Imports*

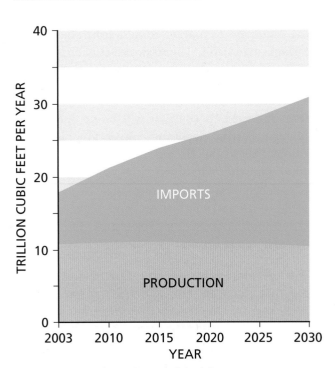

Source: Energy Information Administration,
International Energy Outlook 2006.

FIGURE 2-51. *OECD Europe Natural Gas Production and Imports*

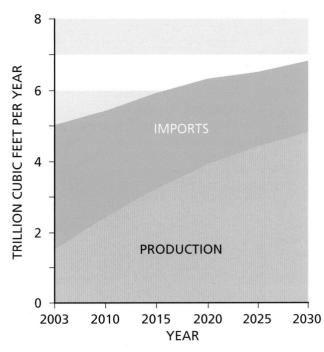

Source: Energy Information Administration,
International Energy Outlook 2006.

FIGURE 2-52. *OECD Asia Natural Gas Production and Imports*

- Arctic gas resources from Alaska and the Canadian Mackenzie Delta, both of which require development and massive new infrastructure to bring gas to market

- Increased LNG imports.

Each of these elements may be subject to risks that make development slower or less significant than the forecasts assume.

Unconventional gas typically costs more to develop than conventional gas, requires different production technologies, has a different environmental impact, and produces at lower rates. Therefore, maintaining or increasing investment in unconventional gas will be essential to growing supply. In addition, many unconventional gas resource basins are located in areas at some distance from demand centers. For example, the Rocky Mountain and San Juan basin regions contain very significant resources of tight gas, coalbed methane, and basin-centered gas. Growth in production capacity in these regions proportionate to the resource size will require new pipeline capacity to bring the gas to markets in the Midwest, Northeast, and West Coast.

Facing the Hard Truths about Energy

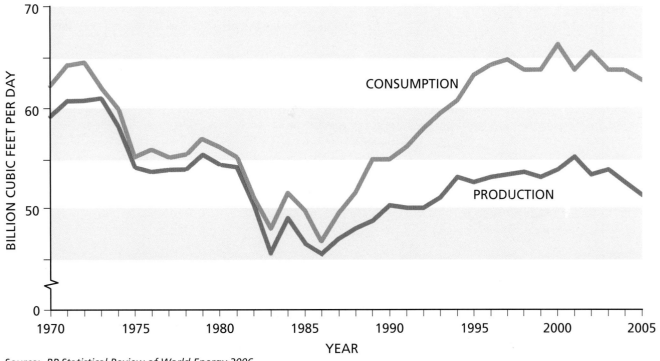

Source: *BP Statistical Review of World Energy 2006.*

FIGURE 2-53. *U.S. Natural Gas Production and Consumption, 1970-2005*

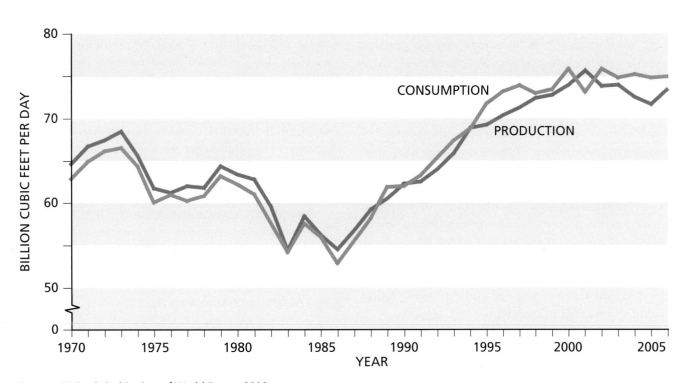

Source: *BP Statistical Review of World Energy 2006.*

FIGURE 2-54. *North American Natural Gas Production and Consumption, 1970-2005*

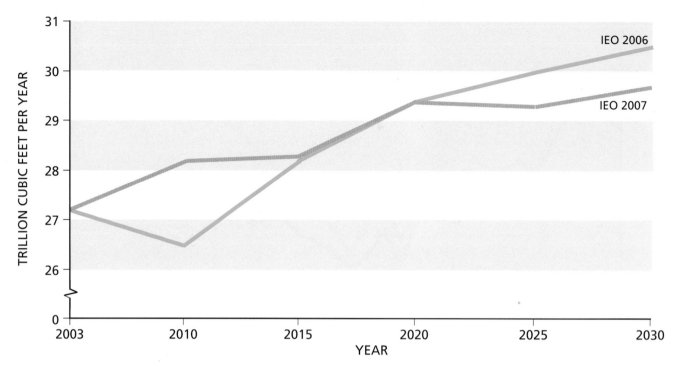

Source: Energy Information Administration, *International Energy Outlook 2006* and *2007*.

FIGURE 2-55. *Projected North American Natural Gas Production*

Most forecasts assume that Arctic gas from the United States and Canada will contribute significant volumes to North American supply, perhaps 6 to 8 billion cubic feet per day by around 2020. Huge stranded gas resources exist in the Arctic regions, but bringing gas to markets will require construction of new high-capacity, long-distance pipelines through Arctic terrain. Companies and agencies involved in proposed development of these pipelines have thus far not resolved complex issues involving regulatory frameworks, fiscal regimes, local communities, and environmental impacts. The investment required for these pipeline projects is huge, amounting to tens of billions of dollars. If the issues cannot be resolved, there is a significant risk that the investments may not be made in the timeframe of this study. If Arctic gas is not developed, North America and the United States would require significantly higher LNG imports.

Gas Supply Challenges

Considerable uncertainty surrounds the growth of natural gas production from mature areas as well as the timing of new projects in specific countries and regions. Table 2-6 summarizes various challenges

that may constrain gas production. They include restricted access to resources; uncertain investment and fiscal frameworks; requirements for high-capacity, long-distance infrastructure; shortages of skilled people; escalating costs and possible shortages of vital equipment; geopolitical tensions; development policies of major gas resource holders; and the time required to develop and deploy new technology. The challenges are dynamic and will have different combinations in time and place over the time frame of the study.

Considering investment alone, the IEA WEO 2006 Reference Case estimates that the required investment in natural gas supply will amount to $3.9 trillion over the next 25 years. This figure includes large capital investments in Russia, Qatar, Iran, Nigeria, and Australia to increase exports.

Russia, the largest regional supplier to Europe, will be challenged to meet European demand growth while initiating exports to Asia and supplying its large and growing domestic market. The IEA projects that the Middle East and Africa will provide more than two-thirds of global inter-regional exports. At the same time, the Middle East will see increased

		Access	Investment	Infra-structure	People and Equipment	Geopolitics
Large Producers	*Current Production (Billion Cubic Feet per Day)*					
Russia	~100	X		X		X
United States	~ 50	X	X	X		
Indonesia	~ 10		X			
Production Growth	*2005-2030 Expected Growth (Billion Cubic Feet per Day)*					
Russia	+ 30	X		X		X
Qatar	+ 15				X	
Iran	+ 15	X	X	X	X	X
Nigeria	+ 10		X			
Australia	+ 10		X			

Note: An X in any column means that the matter is problematic or open to question.

Source: NPC Survey of Outlooks.

TABLE 2-6. *Natural Gas Supply Challenges*

domestic demand. It will also need natural gas to maintain pressure or enhance recovery in its oil fields.

Liquefied Natural Gas (LNG)

Key Observations—LNG

- *LNG trade is projected to grow faster than historical or future global gas and energy demand.*

- *The natural gas reserve base can support the projected expansion of LNG supply over the next 25 years.*

- *The global LNG market has many new entrants.*

- *Major uncertainties surround the scope and pace of liquefaction development in key supply countries.*

This section summarizes a full discussion in the LNG Topic Paper included on the CD distributed with this study.

Liquefied natural gas is a means of delivering natural gas from the wellhead to the market. Cooling the gas to such low temperatures that it converts to liquid reduces its volume, making it economical for transport over long distances by specialized ship. Since natural gas is in many cases too far from markets to be economically or practically transported by pipeline, liquefaction provides a way to link remote gas to markets.

Despite its rapid growth in recent years, LNG remains a relatively small contributor to total internationally traded gas. It comprises about 22 percent of the total gas trade and supplies only 7 percent of global gas demand. Pipeline gas still dominates international trade, notably supply to Western Europe from Russia, North Africa and Norway, and supply to the United States from Canada. By region, LNG trade in the Pacific Basin and Asian markets is almost double the size of Atlantic Basin and Mediterranean markets. However, the Atlantic Basin market has grown much faster than the Pacific market over the past ten years, growing by 12 percent per year compared to 5.5 percent per year in the Pacific market.

Global LNG Forecasts

All forecasts agree that global LNG growth is very likely to accelerate over the next 25 years. In the IEA WEO 2006 Reference Case, LNG trade grows by 6.6 percent per year between 2004 and 2030, from around 9 billion cubic feet per day to 46 billion cubic feet per day. The expected LNG contribution grows more than three times faster than a projected 2 percent per year increase in world natural gas demand. The IEA also projects that LNG will account for 70 percent of the increase in gas trade by 2030. LNG would then comprise half the internationally traded gas by 2030, compared to around 22 percent in 2004. The IEA identified key trends in the changing pattern of LNG supply:

- The Middle East and Africa account for over 70 percent of the increase in gas exports by 2030, mainly to supply Europe and North America.

- Russia will begin supplying gas to Asian markets by LNG.

- Australia and the Middle East will supply LNG to China.

- Venezuela is projected to emerge as an important supplier to North America and Europe.

The EIA IEO 2006 provides a less detailed view of LNG developments to 2030. Discussion of LNG and gas trade developments in this outlook includes the following main points:

- Increasing concentration of natural gas reserves in Russia and the Middle East make these regions the most likely sources of supply growth.

- African natural gas production is expected to grow strongly through 2030, mainly for exports.

- Central and South America will have a surplus of gas, with Peru and Venezuela potentially joining Trinidad as LNG exporters.

- Russia, Norway, Equatorial Guinea, and Peru are likely to be new LNG exporting countries over this period.

- China, Canada, Mexico, Germany, Poland, Croatia, Singapore, and Chile are potential new LNG importing countries.

- The reliance of OECD countries on gas supplies from other regions will increase from 22 percent in 2003 to over 33 percent in 2030.

U.S. LNG Forecasts

Figure 2-56 shows projected LNG imports to the United States over the next 25 years. Depending on the forecast, LNG grows from about 2.5 percent of U.S. supply to 16 to 18 percent by 2030.

The EIA Annual Energy Outlooks provide a detailed look at factors specific to the U.S. gas market that may drive growth. The 2006 and 2007 Reference Case projections for LNG imports to the United States are similar. The main difference between the forecasts is that the

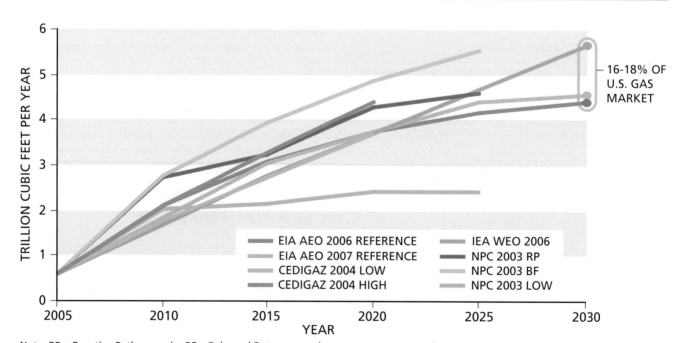

Note: RP = Reactive Path scenario; BF = Balanced Future scenario.
Sources: Energy Information Administration (EIA), *Annual Energy Outlook 2006* and *2007*; Cedigaz, *LNG Trade and Infrastructures*, February 2004; International Energy Agency (IEA), *World Energy Outlook 2006*; and National Petroleum Council (NPC), *Balancing Natural Gas Policy*, September 2003.

FIGURE 2-56. *Projected U.S. LNG Imports*

Facing the Hard Truths about Energy

2007 update is slightly lower in the early years, because of slower development of upstream LNG projects, and slightly higher in the later years, especially after 2020.

The EIA AEO 2006 Reference Case projects that U.S. LNG imports will grow by 8 percent per year to 2030. Two factors drive the rapid increase: (1) a domestic gas production profile that begins to decline after 2020 and only increases by 0.5 percent per year over the entire period to 2030; and (2) pipeline imports from Canada. A high rate of LNG imports is needed to balance the market, despite slow demand growth of 0.7 percent per year. The Reference Case assumes that high natural gas prices in the United States and the availability of import infrastructure will attract LNG to the U.S. market. However, LNG imports may be affected after 2015, as world natural gas prices rise, attracting LNG to other markets. It should be noted that this projection does not integrate U.S. requirements for LNG into a global market balance where LNG competes against indigenous gas to find the best economic opportunities.

The AEO 2006 includes several sensitivity cases built around: high or low oil price paths; high or low adoption of new technology favoring indigenous gas production and lowering gas prices; and high or low

LNG supply based on the uncertainty of upstream developments in the LNG supply chain. Figure 2-57 shows the range of outcomes from these cases, which by 2030 range from more than double to only 30 percent of the Reference Case. The range between the various high and low cases is close to 23 billion cubic feet per day of natural gas delivered to the U.S. market, indicating the scope of very different outcomes according to the assumptions made.

LNG Trade and Infrastructure

Global natural gas supply patterns are shifting, as domestic production in major demand centers of North America and Western Europe fails to keep pace with growing demand. The growing LNG trade is expected to play a pivotal role in meeting this increasing demand. In North America, for example, LNG imports are expected to grow to around 20 percent or more of gas supply by 2030, compared to about 2 to 2.5 percent in recent years. The natural gas resource and reserve base in current and potential LNG exporting countries appears more than adequate to support a high growth rate. However, such growth will require a much stronger LNG supply and delivery infrastructure than currently available.

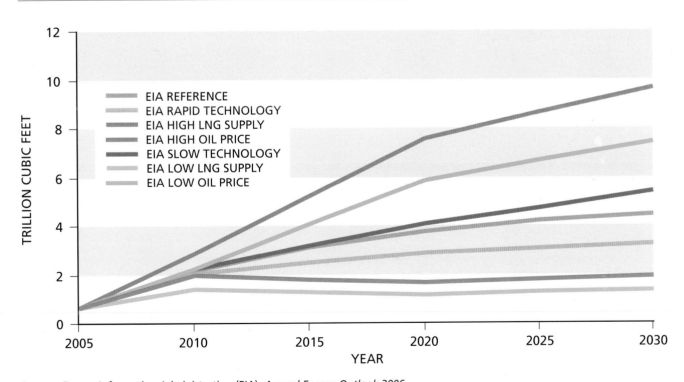

Source: Energy Information Administration (EIA), *Annual Energy Outlook 2006*.

FIGURE 2-57. *Projected U.S. LNG Imports — Alternative Cases*

LNG terminal and distribution infrastructure in the key markets of North America, Western Europe, East Asia, and South Asia is being developed at a scale that will support the expected increase in LNG imports. Uncertainty and risk are now more concentrated in upstream export projects. Less than expected or slower development of export projects could lead to tighter global supply, higher prices, and potential shortages, perhaps for extended periods.

Coal

Key Observations—Coal

- *The global coal endowment is large (Figure 2-58) but national and local issues such as infrastructure limitations, environmental regulation, energy security, and coal conversion activities will determine how extensively coal is used in future global, regional, and national energy markets.*

- *Most business-as-usual energy forecasts expect an increasing demand for coal.*

- *Coal is the major feedstock for power generation growth. Future regulation of carbon dioxide emissions or carbon capture and sequestration will affect the direction of growth.*

- *China, India, and the United States have significant indigenous resources and are the largest coal consumers during the study time frame.*

- *International and U.S. coal transportation infrastructure will need additional capacity in order to meet projected demand.*

Global Coal Endowment & Resources

There are few independent estimates of the global coal endowment and resources. Almost all forecasts evaluated in this study use a World Energy Council assessment of the global coal resource base. World Energy Council assessments are based on self-reported, individual-country submissions that vary widely in quality. U.S. information on coal reserves and resources is extensive but outdated, since it is based on a Bureau of Mines 1974 study that used pre-1971 geological assessments and technology assumptions.[8]

---

8 U.S. Bureau of Mines, Compiled by U.S. Geological Survey, "Coal Resources of the United States," 1974.

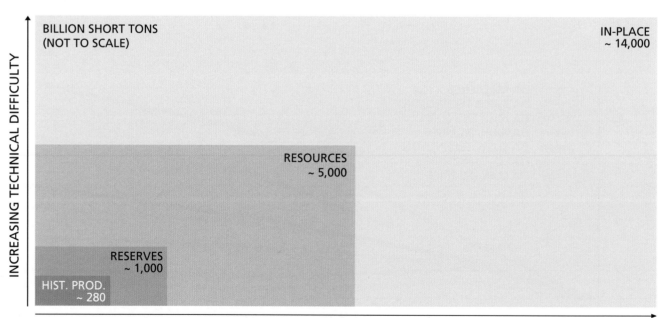

Sources: (1) 1800 to 1980: Bernardo F. Grossling, "World Coal Resources," Financial Times Businesss Information, London, 1981; 1981 to 2005: Energy Information Administration, *International Energy Annual.* (2) World Energy Council, "Survey of Energy Resources," 2004. (3) Rogner, H-H., "Annual Review – Energy Environment," Institute for Integrated Energy Systems, 1997.

FIGURE 2-58. *Global Coal Endowment*

Facing the Hard Truths about Energy

About 280 billion short tons of coal have been produced globally to date, a small portion of the total coal resource base of approximately 5,000 billion short tons.[9] While coal resource estimates clearly suggest many years of supply, resources are not equally distributed among consuming centers, which may create significant trade and regional supply issues.

Global proved coal reserves are approximately 1,000 billion short tons.[10] This figure suggests a reserves-to-production ratio of about 150 years, making coal much more abundant in these terms than oil or gas. Given potential risks and constraints on other fossil fuel resources, countries with substantial indigenous coal resources such as China, India, and the United States, can see benefits to increasing coal use in their domestic energy mix (Figure 2-59).

Table 2-7 shows the five countries that hold over 75 percent of global proved coal reserves. The United States holds 27 percent of these reserves, the Russian Federation 17 percent, China 12.6 percent, India 10.2 percent, and Australia 8.7 percent.

Coal varies by chemical and physical properties that reflect its maturity from peat to anthracite. These properties are described by referring to the coal's rank. Low rank coals such as lignite and subbituminous have high moisture levels and low carbon content, resulting in low energy content. Higher rank coals such as bituminous and anthracite are characterized by less moisture and higher carbon and energy content. Lignite is

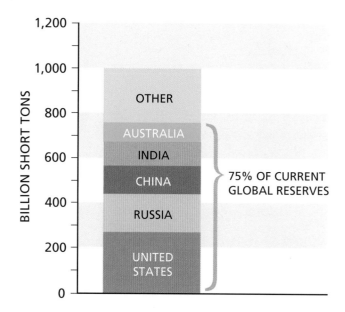

Note: Global coal reserves are approximately 1.0 trillion short tons. Reserves data are available from limited sources and are generally self-reported by individual countries. Quality and vintage of estimates will vary.

Source: World Energy Council, 2004 Survey of Energy Resources.

FIGURE 2-59. *Estimated Global Coal Reserves*

at the bottom and anthracite is at the top of the coal rank scale. The quality of indigenous coal supplies varies between countries (Figure 2-60). This variation will affect end uses and environmental impacts. Global reserves are about evenly split between anthracite/bituminous coal and lignite/subbituminous coal.

U.S. Coal Resource Base

Coal is the most abundant fossil energy source in the United States. Figures 2-61 and 2-62 show regional

---

9 Grossling, B.F., "World Coal Resources", 2nd Edition, Financial Times Business Information, London, England, 1981; and Rogner, H-H., "Annual Review – Energy Environment," Institute for Integrated Energy Systems, University of Victoria, 1997.

10 World Energy Council, "2004 Survey of Energy Resources."

	United States	Russia	China	India	Australia
Estimated Coal in Place	3,968	6,600	5,572		
Identified Resources	1,731			279	479
Proved Amount in Place	493	220	1,110	132	118
Proved Recoverable Reserves	**271**	**173**	**126**	**106**	**87**

Sources: EIA, *Annual Energy Review 2006*; IEA, "Russia Energy Survey," 2002; Cui Mingxuan (ed.), "China Energy Development Report 2006," 2006; India, Ministry of Coal, 2006; Geoscience Australia, "Australia's Identified Mineral Resources," 2007.

TABLE 2-7. *Major Coal Resource Owners (Billion Short Tons)*

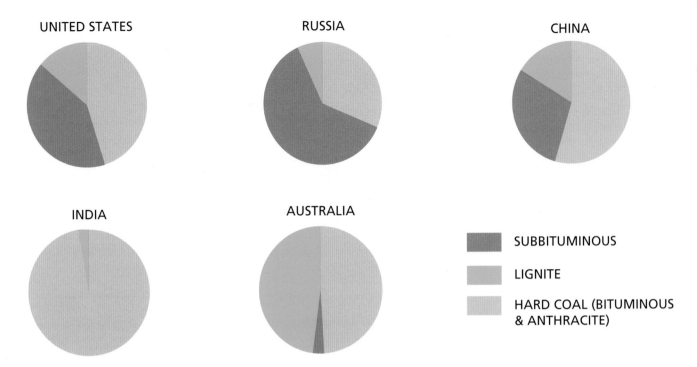

UNITED STATES   RUSSIA   CHINA

INDIA   AUSTRALIA

- SUBBITUMINOUS
- LIGNITE
- HARD COAL (BITUMINOUS & ANTHRACITE)

Source: World Energy Council, 2004 Survey of Energy Resources.

FIGURE 2-60. *Coal Rank Distribution in Large Resource Countries*

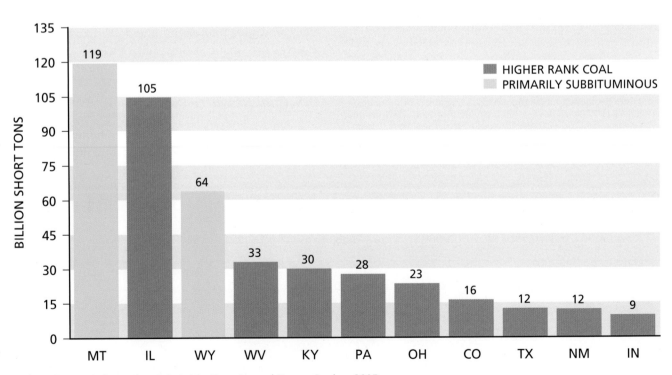

HIGHER RANK COAL
PRIMARILY SUBBITUMINOUS

Source: Energy Information Administration, *Annual Energy Review 2005.*

FIGURE 2-61. *U.S. Coal Demonstrated Reserve Base by Key State*

Facing the Hard Truths about Energy

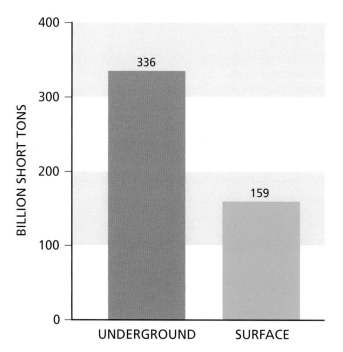

Source: Energy Information Administration,
Annual Energy Review 2005.

FIGURE 2-62. *U.S. Coal Demonstrated Reserve Base by Mining Method*

distribution, rank, and extraction methods for U.S. coal resources. The EIA Annual Energy Review 2005 indicates that demonstrated U.S. coal reserves, equivalent to proved amount in place, amount to 493 billion short tons. Figure 2-63 shows the U.S. coal resource pyramid, which identifies known and estimated coal resources.

The EIA reports three mining regions: Appalachian, Interior, and Western. The Western region contains 47 percent of the reserve base, followed by Interior with 32 percent, and Appalachian with 21 percent. Of the 234.5 billion tons of Western reserves, about 77 percent are subbituminous coal; 13 percent are lignite; the remaining 10 percent are bituminous coal. The Western region contains all U.S. subbituminous reserves and 68 percent of U.S. lignite reserves, primarily in Montana and North Dakota. The bituminous coal is dispersed through the western states, with the largest reserves, in descending order, in Colorado, Utah, Wyoming, and New Mexico.

Approximately 92 percent of the Interior region's 158 billion short tons of reserves are bituminous coal, while the remainder is lignite. About 40 percent of the bituminous reserves are located in Illinois. The lignite reserves are located primarily in Texas, Louisiana,

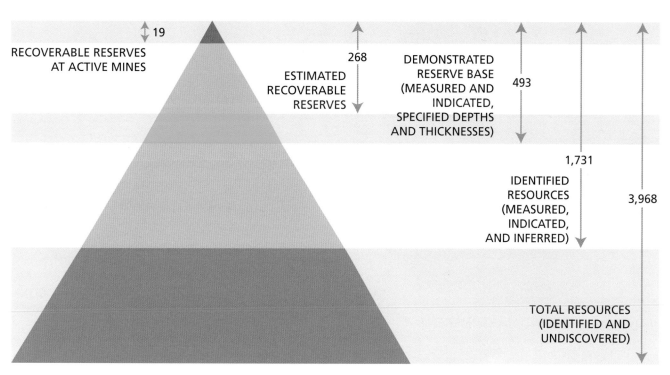

Sources: Energy Information Administration 2004; and United States Geological Survey 1974.

FIGURE 2-63. *U.S. Coal Resources and Reserves Pyramid (Billion Short Tons)*

and Mississippi. In the Appalachian region, 92 percent of the reserves are bituminous coal and 7 percent are anthracite. Nearly all the anthracite is located in Pennsylvania.

Coal is critical to future energy security in the United States. The foundation for coal resource estimates is more than 30 years old and should be updated to account for new technologies, better subsurface information, and improved understanding of recovery efficiencies. The U.S. National Academies has found that current U.S. reserve estimates may be overstated and recommends that USGS undertake a new assessment of domestic coal reserves and resources.[11]

Total U.S. Coal Production and Disposition

The United States is self-sufficient in coal production, virtually matching estimated consumption through the study time frame. EIA forecasts total U.S. coal production to increase an average of 1.6 percent

---

11 U.S. National Academies – Board on Earth Sciences and Resources (BESR), "Coal: Research and Development to Support National Energy Policy," 2007.

per year from 2005 through 2030, in order to meet increasing domestic demand. The primary consumer of coal in the United States is the power industry, using 92 percent of the 1.128 billion short tons burned in 2005. The EIA AEO 2007 forecasts that power generation will decrease to 89 percent of coal consumption by 2030, although total volume is increasing significantly (Figures 2-64 and 2-65). If implemented at scale, new energy applications, such as CTL and coal-to-gas (CTG) would consume an increasing share of coal production later in the study time frame, although this is likely to remain small relative to total consumption.

Most forecasts received by the study project relatively low CTL production volumes in the United States (Figure 2-66). Forecasting organizations such as the EIA may make widely varying estimates of U.S. coal consumption for CTL and CTG conversion, depending on the date of their forecast. Between the 2006 and 2007 Annual Energy Outlooks, the EIA decreased its forecast for CTL and CTG coal consumption from 190 million to 112 million short tons per year in 2030 (Figure 2-67). The variation in forecasts is even more dramatic between organizations. The Southern

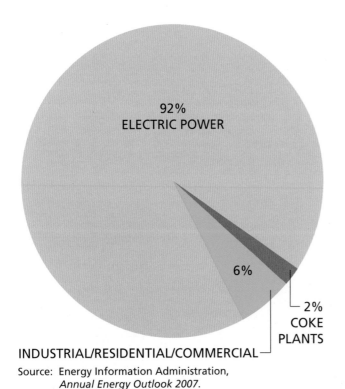

Source: Energy Information Administration,
Annual Energy Outlook 2007.

FIGURE 2-64. *U.S. Coal Consumption by Sector in 2005 (1.128 billion short tons)*

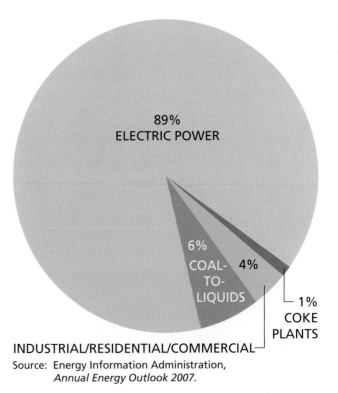

Source: Energy Information Administration,
Annual Energy Outlook 2007.

FIGURE 2-65. *U.S. Coal Consumption by Sector in 2030 (1.772 billion short tons)*

Facing the Hard Truths about Energy

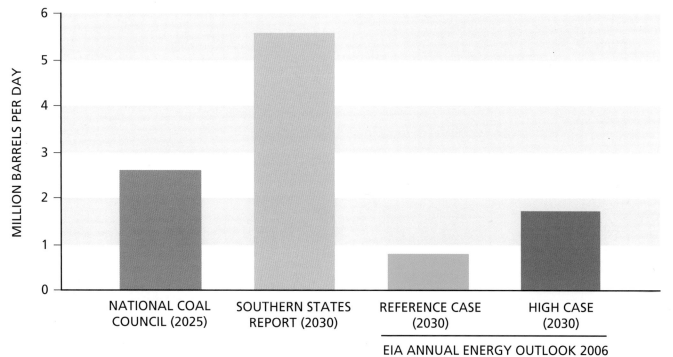

FIGURE 2-66. *Projected U.S. Coal-to-Liquids Production*

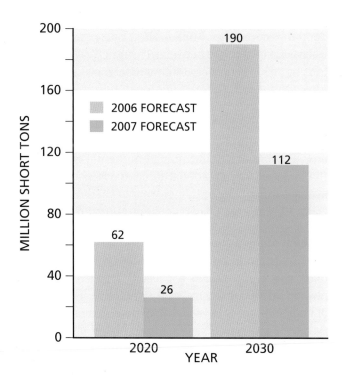

FIGURE 2-67. *One-Year Change in EIA Reference Case
Forecast of U.S. Coal-to-Liquids Coal Consumption*

States Energy Board and the National Coal Council also produced forecasts for converting coal to liquids and to gas in order to increase U.S. energy security and displace oil imports (Figure 2-68).[12] The Southern States Self-Sufficiency case projects U.S. CTL production reaching at least 20 percent of U.S. oil demand in 2030. This projection is an order of magnitude greater than the most recent EIA forecast.

Globally, China's relatively low-cost coal may allow economical production of CTL. In the IEA WEO 2006 Reference Case, CTL production will be less than 1 MB/D by 2030, primarily in China. Elsewhere, higher coal costs, capital costs, and significant CO_2 emission concerns are likely to constrain CTL production between now and 2030. The EIA IEO 2007 Reference Case projects global CTL production of 2.4 MB/D in 2030, while production reaches 3.9 MB/D in the High Price Case, or about 4 percent of global oil demand. For a full discussion of CTL technology, see the Coal-to-Liquids Topic Paper included on the CD distributed with the study.

---

12 Southern States Energy Board, "The American Energy Security Study," 2006; and The National Coal Council, "Coal: America's Energy Future," 2006.

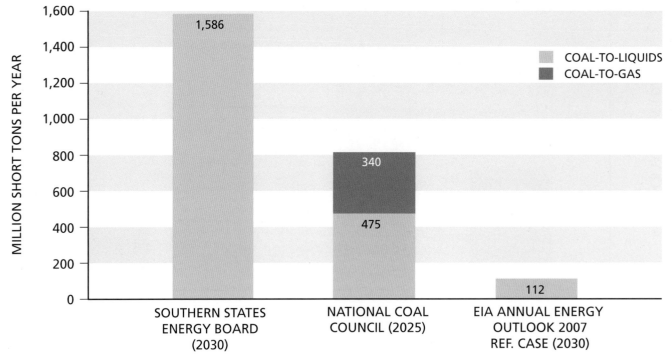

Source: NPC Survey of Outlooks.

FIGURE 2-68. *Projected U.S. Coal-to-Liquids and Coal-to-Gas Coal Consumption*

Infrastructure

The extent to which coal contributes to U.S. energy requirements will depend heavily on the capacity of coal transportation infrastructure. Railroads, barges, and trucks are all critical modes of transport for coal. Each mode faces challenges, some of which are unique to it and others that are common to all modes. For each mode, having adequate capacity to meet growing demand is perhaps the most pressing need. Roads and waterways depend on publicly owned and maintained infrastructure. Waterway infrastructure is generally in need of significant maintenance and improvement. Railroads, on the other hand, rely overwhelmingly on privately owned, maintained, and operated infrastructure. They will need a balanced regulatory and legislative environment to ensure sufficient private capital is invested to provide the additional capacity required by energy forecasts.

Global Coal Production and Disposition

Global coal production is projected to increase substantially, primarily to meet demand for electricity and, to a smaller extent, for CTL and CTG conversion. Most Reference Cases project a 50 to 60 percent increase in coal production between 2005 and 2030. Global production is currently 6.5 billion short tons per year and is forecast to increase to between 9.5 and 11.0 billion short tons by 2030. Figure 2-69 shows Reference Case supply forecasts for EIA, IEA, the European Commission, and the U.S. Climate Change Science Program (CCSP).[13] The Reference Cases are generally based on business-as-usual assumptions for economic and population growth, without significant environmental constraints. IEA forecasts that global coal demand will increase by an average annual rate of 1.7 percent per year from 2004 to 2030. EIA projects 2.0 percent annual growth.

Much of the world's coal is consumed in the country where it is produced. In 2004, 68 percent of global primary coal consumption was used to generate electric power and heat. Industry used 18 percent. This pattern of consumption is expected to remain quite stable over the study timeframe, although the higher efficiency of new generating plants will mitigate consumption growth. In 2030, coal for power and heat generation is projected at 73 percent of total primary coal consumption, while

---

13 European Commission, "World Energy Technology Outlook – WETO H2," 2006; and Climate Change Science Program, "CCSP Synthesis and Assessment Product 2.1, Part A: Scenarios of Greenhouse Gas Emissions and Atmospheric Concentrations," 2006.

Facing the Hard Truths about Energy

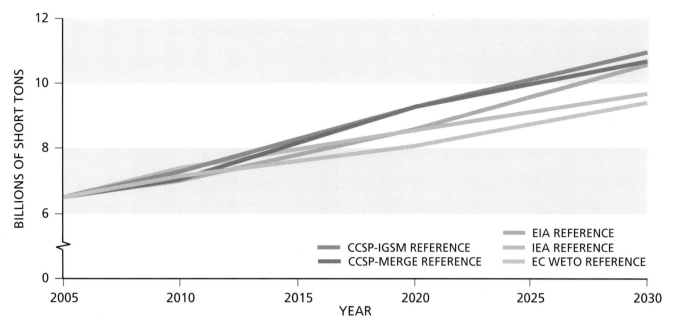

Note: All Forecasts Normalized to 6.5 Billion Short Tons In 2005.

Sources: Climate Change Science Program (CCSP); Energy Information Administration (EIA), *International Energy Outlook 2006*; International Energy Agency (IEA), *World Energy Outlook 2006;* and European Commission, *World Energy Technology Outlook 2050* (EC WETO), 2006.

FIGURE 2-69. *Global Coal Production Reference Cases*

industry remains at 18 percent. Electricity generation remains the primary driver of coal consumption. IEA projects the share of coal in global power generation as increasing from 40 percent in 2004 to 44 percent in 2030.

Most growth in coal production will occur in rapidly expanding economies. Coal consumption in developing Asia is projected to rise from 2.9 billion short tons in 2004 to 4.5 billion short tons in 2015 and 6.1 billion short tons in 2030, a growth rate over the period of 2.7 percent per year. China and India heavily dominate coal consumption in the region (Figure 2-70) accounting for nearly 80 percent of annual incremental demand through 2030. They also account for 71 percent of the projected 6 billion kilowatt-hour increase in coal-based electricity generation.

Coal consumption in OECD Europe is projected to grow only slightly in Reference Cases, increasing from 761 million short tons to 778 million short tons per year from 2005 to 2030. In this case, gains in power generation are offset by losses in industry. The coal share of power generation is projected to decrease from 29 percent to 27 percent to the benefit of natural gas. Coal inputs to power generation are projected to fall in the period to 2020 and then increase between 2020

and 2030 as nuclear power plants are retired and the assumed competitiveness of coal improves relative to natural gas. OECD-Europe coal production is projected to decline from 467 million short tons in 2005 to 324 million short tons in 2030. Given that consumption is projected to rise, this suggests an increase in net imports from 293 million short tons to 454 million short tons over the period.

Coal consumption in Russia and other countries of the former Soviet Union is projected to rise by an annual average of 1.1 percent between 2004 and 2015, then decline to the 2004 level by 2030. Industrial use of coal is projected to increase throughout the period while coal consumption in power generation is projected to fall. Coal-fired power generation capacity is forecast to decline throughout the period as natural gas replaces aging coal-fired plants. Coal's share of power generation is projected to fall significantly from 21 percent in 2015 to 15 percent in 2030. Latin America, the Middle East, and Africa are expected to be relatively minor consumers of coal.

Demand increases for coal vary geographically, and the remaining resource estimates vary widely for the five largest resource owners. While India has sufficient

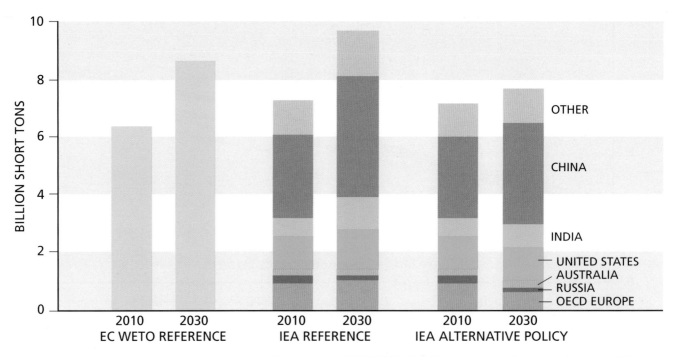

Sources: European Commission, *World Energy Technology Outlook 2050* (EC WETO), 2006; and International Energy Agency (IEA), *World Energy Outlook 2006.*

FIGURE 2-70. *Projected Regional Coal Consumption (2010 vs. 2030)*

coal reserves for more than 200 years of consumption at 2005 levels, China has coal reserves for only 52 years (Figure 2-71) at 2005 levels. China's planned coal production capacity in 2010 is 2.1 billion short tons. Restructuring of township coal mines is expected reduce production capacity to 1.65 billion short tons in 2020. When compared to many consumption forecasts, the reduction suggests that China may rely increasingly on coal imports or may need to develop new domestic reserves. With Chinese industrial demand growing significantly, especially for steel making, China will require not only coal in quantity, but the right type of coal. Restructuring plans should be viewed in this light.

China and India will be the fastest growing markets for coal exporters. Regions well situated to serve those markets are likely to experience the greatest growth. Russia has a large coal resource base and could supply foreign markets such as China. Australia is projected to increase exports from 257 million short tons in 2005 to 435 million short tons in 2025. Indonesia is expected to increase exports from 138 million short tons to 203 million short tons. This suggests that Australia and Indonesia will represent 70 percent of the increase in coal exports between 2005 and 2025, rising from 46 percent of global coal exports in 2005 to 53 percent in 2025.

Infrastructure is unlikely to present a long-run constraint on Australian coal exports, although Indonesia may prove to be more problematic. Although Indonesian coal resources are substantial, a significant proportion is located some distance from the coast and dedicated port terminals. Currently, a substantial portion of Indonesia's coal exports is transported by barge and later transshipped. Investment needed to provide the infrastructure for interior coal deposits is also likely to be significant.

Carbon Constraints

Carbon-constrained cases generally show flat-to-declining global coal production as energy demand is met by fuels with lower carbon content, including renewable sources (Figure 2-72). Total coal production continues to increase in the IEA Alternative Policy Case, but is approximately 20 percent less than coal production in the IEA Reference Case. Most of the reduction in coal demand results from fuel switching and energy savings in the power sector. The European Commission's *World Energy Technology Outlook 2050* (WETO) carbon-constrained case represents ambitious policies for long-term stabilization of atmospheric carbon

Facing the Hard Truths about Energy

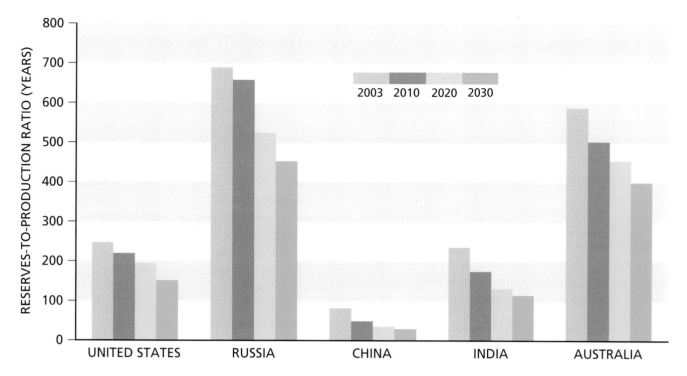

Sources: World Energy Council 2006; and Energy Information Administration, *International Energy Outlook 2006.*

FIGURE 2-71. *Reserves-to-Production Ratios in Major Coal-Producing Countries*

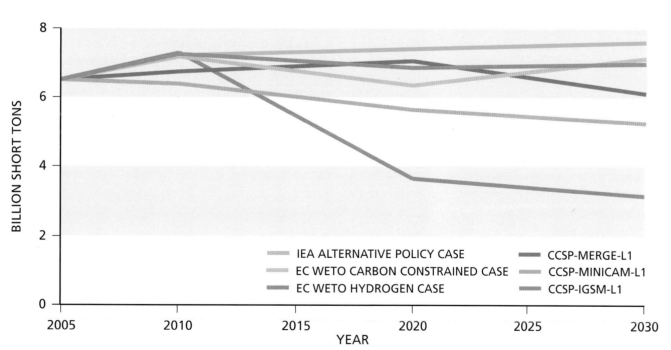

Note: All forecasts normalized to 6.5 billion short tons in 2005.
Sources: International Energy Agency (IEA), *World Energy Outlook 2006;* European Commission, *World Energy Technology Outlook 2050,* (EC WETO) 2006; and Climate Change Science Program (CCSP).

FIGURE 2-72. *Projected Carbon-Constrained Coal Production*

dioxide concentrations at 500 parts per million by volume (ppmv) by 2050.

Technology development is critical in shaping a future carbon-constrained energy system. WETO envisages incremental improvements in large-scale power generation and renewable technologies. The WETO-H2 scenario incorporates new technology to decrease total energy consumption and increase the use of hydrogen, which may be produced from lower carbon energy sources. The CCSP cases designated L-1 are based on stabilizing atmospheric carbon dioxide at 450 ppmv by 2100. Three integrated assessment models from MIT (IGSM), Stanford (Merge), and Joint Global Climate Change Research Institute (MiniCam) forecast climate change based on input assumptions, with each addressing the carbon issue for different energy inputs.

In a carbon-constrained world, CCS is one of the technology and policy prerequisites for maintaining coal's significant role in the energy system. For a full discussion of carbon management and carbon capture and sequestration, see the Carbon Capture and Sequestration Topic Paper included on the CD distributed with this report.

Coal Supply Challenges

Many challenges faced by the coal industry (Table 2-8) are common to other carbon-based fuels. The requirement for affordable energy must be balanced with environmental and other policy issues, while maintaining infrastructure to transport resources from supply to demand regions. Permitting new facilities takes longer, costs more, and is subject to more scrutiny than in the past. Construction, labor, equipment, and supply costs have escalated significantly in recent years and are more volatile than in the past, contributing to higher, less predictable production costs. Carbon management is likely to become a factor in future coal use as carbon policies develop in the United States and globally. Land owners and various interest groups are vocal in their objections to new surface mines, often delaying the permitting process and increasing development costs. Local, state, and federal regulations that place land use restrictions on private lands, such as populated areas, also limit mining access. Table 2-8 summarizes the coal supply challenges that will apply in different combinations and places over the study time frame.

Biomass

Key Observations—Biomass

- *Energy from Biomass can be converted to electricity, heat, and biofuels; forecasts show considerable growth potential while meeting the world's need for food.*

- *The cellulosic biomass resource is substantial, but technology does not currently exist to convert it to large volumes of liquid fuels at competitive economics.*

		Access	Investment	Infra-structure	People and Equipment	Environment
Large Producers	*Current Annual Production (Billion Short Tons)*					
China	~ 3		X	X		X
United States	~ 1	X	X	X	X	X
OECD Europe	~ 1					X
Production Growth	*2005-2030 Expected Growth (Billion Short Tons)*					
China	+ 1		X	X		X
India	~ 0.5		X	X		X

Note: An X in any column means that the matter is problematic or open to question.

Source: NPC Survey of Outlooks.

TABLE 2-8. *Coal Production Challenges*

- *In a carbon-constrained environment, biomass-fired power generation will be an attractive use of biomass.*

- *Biomass resources will continue to be converted to biofuels as a supplemental contributor to the U.S. transportation fuel mix, with public policy as a factor in overall market penetration.*

Biomass was the primary source of energy before the industrial age developed through intense use of coal, petroleum, and natural gas. Like coal and natural gas, biomass is a local energy source that could provide significant additional supply, although it constitutes only a small fraction of current primary energy supply. Like many unconventional and alternative energy sources, biomass presents new demands on other resources such as land and water. Since biomass is renewable, it is expected to have a lower carbon footprint than other widely available energy sources.

Biomass can be burned, gasified, fermented, or otherwise processed to provide energy as electricity, heat, and biofuels. However, the infrastructure developed for coal, petroleum, natural gas, and other energy sources may not have the capability to support biomass as the main source of primary energy. Where possible, biomass has been incorporated economically into the value chains that link energy sources to products and markets. For example, biomass has been co-fired with coal in power plants; ethanol produced from corn or sugarcane has been blended with gasoline; biodiesel has been produced from palm and soy. In each case, incorporating biomass in the corresponding value energy chains required only minor modifications to existing infrastructure.

The biomass energy value chain has many characteristics similar to those of oil, coal, and natural gas. However, since the underlying source is solar energy, biomass is characterized by low energy density and production over large areas. Land use, transportation logistics, harvesting, storage, and processing of biomass feedstocks and products are key hurdles to widespread production. The sources of energy used to convert biomass to products and the energy balance of the conversion processes are also significant considerations for biomass use. For example, coal is an important source of heat for some biorefineries in the United States. Significantly reducing the carbon footprint and improving the energy balance of these refineries would require developing and using processes that incorporate more biomass energy.

Biomass Forecasts

Most business-as-usual forecasts show continued growth of the energy supplied from biomass.[14] Great care must be taken when analyzing these forecasts, however, because they sometimes distinguish between commercial biomass and existing biomass use and incorporate energy conversion efficiencies of biomass into final fuels such as ethanol, and thus do not refer to real primary energy. The EIA Reference Case, for example, shows biomass growing at small rates. By comparison, the IEA Reference Case projects biomass use in 2030 at more than four times higher than 2005. Business-as-usual cases typically forecast biomass penetration as biofuels for transportation. These forecasts project up to 5 MB/D of biofuels in the year 2030, representing almost 5 percent of total liquids supplied. This projected volume is still a small fraction of the total energy mix.

Forecasts that are not business as usual project dramatic increases in biomass as an energy source based on policy objectives. Stabilizing atmospheric carbon dioxide, increasing the efficiency of energy consumption, or reducing carbon impact are typical policy objectives assumed in these forecasts. For example, a scenario that accelerates stabilization of carbon dioxide concentrations includes policies that impose carbon-neutral primary energy production in the coming decades. The policies result in rapidly increasing biomass use; rapid growth of new nuclear-based electricity generation; and widespread use of CCS for all fossil fuel based power plants. This case reduces total global liquids demand to 98 MB/D by 2030, of which biofuels supply more than 23 MB/D, or almost 25 percent.[15]

As with all resources, biomass needs to be produced, converted, and delivered in a useful form for consumers. Current processing technologies for corn and sugarcane seek to balance biomass use for food, feed, and fuel production. This delicate balance is subject to intense study. Many technology developments target the balanced and adequately supplied food, feed, and fuel markets. The use of co-products of ethanol processing,

---

14 Business-as-usual forecasts do not incorporate policies, taxes, or incentives that are not currently in force or would preclude direct economic competition between sources of energy within the established framework.

15 U.S. CCSP Level 1 Stabilization Scenario, IGSM Model. This scenario imposes a very high penalty on carbon-related emissions in order to achieve such an accelerated transition away from non-carbon neutral fuels. The model also constrains the growth in nuclear energy. The economic impacts of such carbon constraints can affect economic growth.

such as distiller's dry grains used in livestock feed, contribute to the balance by allowing the same corn crop to serve as a source of both fuel and feed.

Studies that estimate the annual potential for biomass production are balanced by forecasted future global demand for food and feed. Any surplus, in the absence of cross-competition, could be available to supply energy. Forecasts usually consider such factors as available arable land, water resources, and changes in land use. Assuming widespread use of recent advances in biotechnology and modern land management techniques, the potential energy available from biomass is estimated to be approximately 952 quadrillion Btu, or on the order of annual human energy consumption. The efficiency of converting potential biomass energy into forms suitable for widespread consumption is a matter of considerable interest.

Biotechnology is expected to play a significant role in expanding global biomass production, with crop yields in the next few decades increasing at a faster rate than historically. For example, marker-assisted plant breeding can increase trait development by a ten-fold rate over conventional breeding. The ability to engineer specific new traits into crops may bring about remarkable changes in crop production and crop adaptability to different growing conditions. New technologies could potentially increase U.S. corn production to 25 billion bushels by 2030. Using conventional conversion methods, a crop of this size could potentially yield 54 billion gallons of ethanol by 2030, or 3.5 MB/D. This forecast contrasts with both the carbon-constrained case, which shows volumes above 20 MB/D and with the more conservative EIA IEO 2007 Reference Case, which forecasts about 1.5 MB/D.

Ethanol

Ethanol is an alcohol that can be used directly as an alternative fuel or blended with gasoline. It is made by fermenting sugars from many agricultural products and food wastes, including cellulose. The technology for producing ethanol from corn (90 percent of U.S. ethanol) and sugarcane (Brazil) is well established. Current technologies such as direct combustion and the production of ethanol or biodiesel have made wood, dung, cereals, sugar crops, and oilseeds the current leaders in bioenergy crops. Global production of ethanol has more than doubled over the last five years, to about 9 billion gallons in 2005 or 0.6 MB/D.

As mentioned above, conventional conversion methods in a business-as-usual case may produce up to 3.5 MB/D of ethanol in the United States by 2030. Large additional increases would require technology development to convert lignin and cellulose more efficiently into useful fuel. Technologies that use non-foodstuff biomass could potentially augment energy crop use for fuel production by increasing (1) overall process efficiency and (2) the biomass resource available for conversion.

Infrastructure

Several steps are necessary to increase the use of biomass as an energy source: bioenergy crops, preferably perennial, must be developed for excess agricultural land and marginally arable land; systems are required to harvest, collect, and store energy crops; efficient conversion and delivery systems must be developed. Widespread adoption of agricultural best practices could enable development of better food crops and better use of arable land now in production. Much of the infrastructure needed to increase biomass use does not exist today, limiting the growth rate of biomass, much as with any new energy source. Development of the sugarcane-based ethanol industry in Brazil is an example of how public policy can guide development of a biomass energy source.

Biomass Resource Potential

The growing use of certain biomass feedstocks as an energy source raises concerns about the availability of biomass for foodstuffs. The multiple uses of land compete and increase the value (and cost) of land. However, forecasts show that available land could produce enough biomass to provide food, feed, and fuel. The United Nations Food and Agriculture Organization (FAO) confirms this expectation in its recent estimate of population, food needs, and agricultural development from 2015 to 2030. According to the FAO, agricultural production of food and feed will continue to expand to meet global needs through 2030. Second-generation or cellulosic ethanol would reduce the potential for competition between food crops and energy crops by using plant waste and a specific energy crop such as switchgrass. However, second-generation biomass conversion technologies are currently in the research and early demonstration phases. The timing of their transition to commercial operation at scale remains uncertain.

Various studies over the past 20 years have assessed the potential of agriculture to produce both energy and food for the world. While conclusions from these studies differ, the annual resource potential could reach approximately 238 to 476 quadrillion Btu of biomass

TABLE 2-9. *Biomass Categories and Energy Potentials*

Biomass Category	Main Assumptions and Remarks	Potential 2050 (EJ/yr) [1]	Potential as Cellulosic Ethanol (Quads)/BOE [5]	Potential as Pyrolysis Bio-Oil (Quads)/BOE [6]	Potential as Methanol (Quads)/BOE [7]	Potential as Methane via Anaerobic Digestion (Quads) [8]
Energy farming on current agricultural land	Potential land surplus: 0-4 Gha (more average: 1-2 Gha). On average higher yields are likely because of better soil quality: 8-12 dry t/ha/yr is assumed if intensive agricultural practices are used. [2]	0-700 (100-300)	0-305 Quads 0-52 billion BOE	0-464 Quads 0-80 billion BOE	0-398 Quads 0-68 billion BOE	0-199 Quads 0-34 billion BOE
Biomass production on marginal lands	On a global scale a maximum land surface of 1.7 Gha could be involved. Low productivity of 2-5 dry t/ha/yr. [2]	0-150 (60-150)	0-65 Quads 0-11 billion BOE	0-99 Quads 0-17 billion BOE	0-85 Quads 0-15 billion BOE	0-43 Quads 0-7 billion BOE
Bio-materials	Range of land required to meet the additional demand for bio-materials: 0.2-0.8 Gha (average productivity: 5 dry t/ha/yr.	0-150 (40-150) [3]	0-65 Quads 0-11 billion BOE	0-99 Quads 0-17 billion BOE	0-85 Quads 0-15 billion BOE	0-43 Quads 0-7 billion BOE
Residues from agriculture	Estimates from various studies. Potential depends on yield/product ratios and the total agricultural land area and type of production system.	15-70	6.5-30 Quads 1.1-5.1 billion BOE	9.9-46 Quads 1.7-7.9 billion BOE	8.5-40 Quads 1.5-7 billion BOE	4.3-20 Quads 0.7-3.3 billion BOE
Forest residues	The (sustainable) energy potential of the world's forests is unclear. Part is natural forest (reserves). Range is based on literature data.	0-150 (30-150)	0-65 Quads 0-11 billion BOE	0-99 Quads 0-17 billion BOE	0-85 Quads 0-15 billion BOE	0-43 Quads 0-7 billion BOE
Dung and Organic waste	Use of dried dung. Low estimate based on global current use. High estimate: technical potential. Utilization (collection) in longer term is uncertain.	5-105 [4]	2.2-46 Quads 0.37-7.8 billion BOE	3.3-69 Quads 0.57- 11.9 BOE	2.8-59 Quads 0.5-10.3 billion BOE	1.4-30 Quads .23- 6.1 billion BOE
Total	Most pessimistic scenario: no land available for energy farming; only utilization of residues. Most optimistic scenarios: intensive agriculture concentrated on the better quality soils.	40-1100 (250-500)	17.4-489 Quads 3 – 84 billion BOE	26.5-729 Quads 4.6-125 billion BOE	22.7-625 Quads 108 billion BOE	11.3-312 Quads 54 billion BOE

Notes

1 Bio-Energy supply, where two ranges are given, numbers between brackets give the range of average potential in a world aiming for large-scale utilization of biomass. A lower limit of zero implies that potential availability could be zero, e.g. if we fail to modernize agriculture so that more land is needed to feed the world.

2 Heating value: 19 GJ/t dry matter.

3 This value could even be negative: the potential biomass demand for producing bio-materials (such as bio-plastics or construction materials). These markets can represent a large demand for biomass that will reduce the availability of biomass for energy. However, the more bio-materials are used, the more organic waste (eventually) will become available for energy. Such use of biomass results in a "double" GHG benefit as well through avoided emissions in manufacturing materials with fossil fuels and by producing energy from the waste. Thus, calculating the potential biomass availability for energy is not straightforward adding the figures of the different rows. More details are given in [Hoogwijk et al., 2003].

4 The energy supply of bio-materials ending up as waste can vary between 20 and 55 EJ (or 1100-2900 Mt dry matter) per year. This range excludes cascading and does not take into account the time delay between production of the material and "release" as (organic) waste.

5 Future cellulosic ethanol yield – 46% on an energy basis (C. Hamelinck/ Dissertation, Outlook for Advanced Biofuels/Utrecht: Universiteit Utrecht, Faculteit Scheikunde, Proefschrift Universiteit Utrecht. Met literatuuropgave en samenvatting in het Nederlands. ISBN: 90-393-3691-1)

6 Future pyrolysis oil yield 70% on an energy basis (A.PC. Faaij / Energy Policy 34 (2006) 322–342).

7 Future methanol yield 60% via syngas on an energy basis (C. Hamelinck/ Dissertation, Outlook for Advanced Biofuels/Utrecht: Universiteit Utrecht, Faculteit Scheikunde, Proefschrift Universiteit Utrecht. Met literatuuropgave en samenvatting in het Nederlands. ISBN: 90-393-3691-1).

8 Future anaerobic digestion yield of 30% on an energy basis (T. Bridgwater J Sci Food Agric 86:1755–1768 (2006).

Source: Faaij APC, et al: *Energy for Sustainable Development*, Volume X, number 1 (March 2006).

energy, produced while still feeding a growing global population (Table 2-9). The higher estimate is equivalent to about 68 percent of projected global energy needs in 2030. However, various factors will influence the potential penetration of biomass as an energy source, the most important being the availability of conversion technology and infrastructure, and competing delivered energy costs. Business-as-usual forecasts project biomass as supplying approximately 10 percent of global energy needs by 2030. Forecasts that incorporate strong carbon-management policies see biomass energy growing considerably, to 15 percent of total global energy demand by 2030 and 30 percent by 2100.[16] Specifically, with targeted policies and restraints on carbon dioxide emission, the U.S. CCSP Level 1 Stabilization Scenario, IGSM Model, forecasts that bio-fuels will reach nearly 25 percent of liquid fuels on a volumetric basis in 2030 (Figure 2-73).

In summary, production of biofuels and energy from the large potential biomass resource is projected to grow over the study time frame. Policies to stabilize carbon dioxide concentrations are forecast to strongly

---

16 Energy demand in these highly carbon constrained scenarios is only marginally greater in 2100 than it is today. The carbon constraint greatly impacts economic activity.

stimulate growth in biomass use, though possibly with significant economic impact. There will be tradeoffs between different lower carbon alternatives depending on the type of carbon constraint. Ethanol from biomass is commercially produced today and is part of the energy supply. In order to reach its potential market penetration, energy from biomass requires considerable investment and supportive public policies. These requirements apply particularly to associated infrastructure and the development and demonstration of new fuel conversion technologies for biomass not intended for food or feed. For a full discussion of Biomass as a potential energy source, see the Biomass Topic Paper on the CD included with this report.

Non-Bio Alternative Energy Sources

Key Observations—Non-Bio Alternatives

- *Forecasts for the possible role of nuclear energy vary from limited growth to cases where nuclear power is employed for power generation as a replacement for fossil fuels with a higher carbon footprint.*

- *The diversity of views about nuclear energy's future reflects conflicting positions and perceptions about*

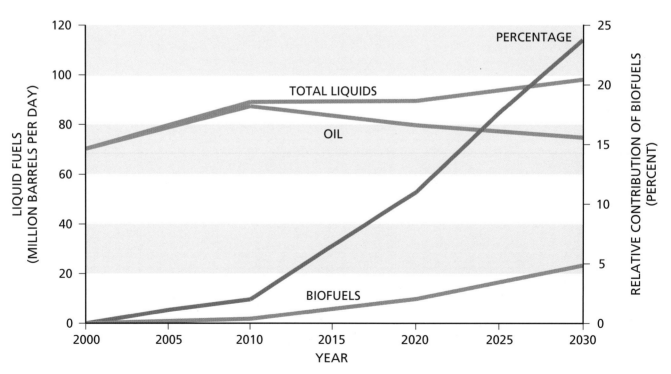

Source: U.S. Climate Change Science Program, Level 1 Stabilization Scenario, IGSM Model.

FIGURE 2-73. *Accelerated Global Biofuels Production under Considerable Carbon Dioxide Emission Constraints*

Facing the Hard Truths about Energy

safety, waste, nuclear proliferation, and the nuclear fuel cycle.

- *Some alternative sources of energy, much like unconventional fossil fuels, have secondary resource impacts (water, land, fuel, etc.) that are not completely understood and may be significant as they reach new scales of supply.*

This section summarizes discussions of alternative energy sources in the Renewables and the Hydrogen Topic Papers on the CD distributed with this report.

Hydropower and Ocean

Historically, hydroelectricity has dominated non-biomass alternative energy sources. Dams have been developed globally to provide vast supplies of electricity at very low marginal production costs. Industrialized nations have already developed most of their hydroelectric resources. Additional, limited opportunities to increase hydroelectric production may exist in industrializing and economically developing nations, subject to growing questions about their environmental and social impact. Ocean and small-scale hydroelectric technologies currently being developed and deployed may also provide additional distributed and localized power with reduced environmental footprint.

Wind

Energy from wind has grown significantly in recent decades and is forecast to grow several times faster than overall energy demand, thus increasing its share of the supply mix. Given infrastructure requirements and a current share of less than 2 percent of energy supply, it will be some time before wind supplies a significant portion of global energy requirements. One of the main challenges faced by wind and other intermittent sources of energy is the need to maintain ready reserve power capacity. Incentives and tax credits have made wind power an attractive option in many markets. Additional technology development could eliminate the need for incentives.

Solar

Concentrated solar power (CSP) technology is being deployed globally. CSP costs are not yet competitive with large-scale electricity production from fossil fuels, but may be attractive for smaller and remote applications. Research in new materials for photovoltaic electricity generation (PV) continues to reduce its costs. PV technology has niche applications, but does not make significant global contributions to energy supply.

Geothermal

Conventional geothermal is competitive as a base-load power source in areas with readily accessible, naturally occurring, and plentiful underground steam. As with large-scale hydroelectric dams, conventional geothermal energy presents limited opportunities for new supplies. However, enhanced geothermal systems (EGS) that harvest heat by introducing water into an underground heat source to produce steam may have future potential growth. EGS technology significantly leverages existing oil and natural gas related technologies.

Nuclear

Despite its considerable growth in previous decades, nuclear power represents only 5 to 6 percent of the total global energy supply mix and less than 20 percent of global electricity generation. Regions and countries, however, can vary significantly from the global average. Countries such as France that have made progress in developing nuclear power tend to show contributions that are much larger than average.

Views about nuclear energy's future role are diverse. Most forecasts that stipulate business as usual show only limited changes in the contribution of nuclear energy to the energy supply mix. These forecasts refer to difficulties in siting, financing, and operating nuclear facilities, as well as in disposing of nuclear waste given environmental and non-proliferation concerns in industrialized nations.

Nuclear power is forecast to grow in industrializing nations, particularly China, which have the greatest need for new sources of abundant energy. The forecasts reviewed in this study usually do not include constraints in the uranium fuel value chain, but do incorporate concerns about the fuel cycle and proliferation. Moreover, recent developments of futures contracts for uranium allow for risk mitigation. These forecasts show an increasing role for nuclear power in the latter part of the century, parallel with growth in coal-fired power plants.

As with biomass, nuclear energy becomes an important energy source in forecasts that include policy objectives to stabilize atmospheric carbon dioxide, promote efficient energy use, or reduce its carbon impact. The resulting forecasted growth is a function of the policies implemented and the technologies available. For example, if carbon capture and sequestration is delayed or never widely deployed for coal-fired power plants, nuclear power may grow considerably, perhaps to 25 percent of total global energy demand by 2100. On the other hand, if carbon capture and sequestration is successful and widespread, the projected growth of nuclear power remains significant but more moderate.

The greatest projected growth of nuclear power generation by 2030 results in an increase of more than 200 percent from current levels (Figure 2-74).

By comparison, forecasts that show a significant decrease in the share of nuclear energy show a marked increase in fossil fuel use. Or, they assume revolutionary gains in efficient energy use, resulting in only marginal demand growth.

Hydrogen

Hydrogen is being considered as a future energy carrier/fuel, given that its combustion emits only water. However, hydrogen's low molecular weight and energy density, as well as its production, handling, and storage, are very important hurdles to its widespread use. Hydrogen is an intermediate product, manufactured from a primary energy source and then used to move

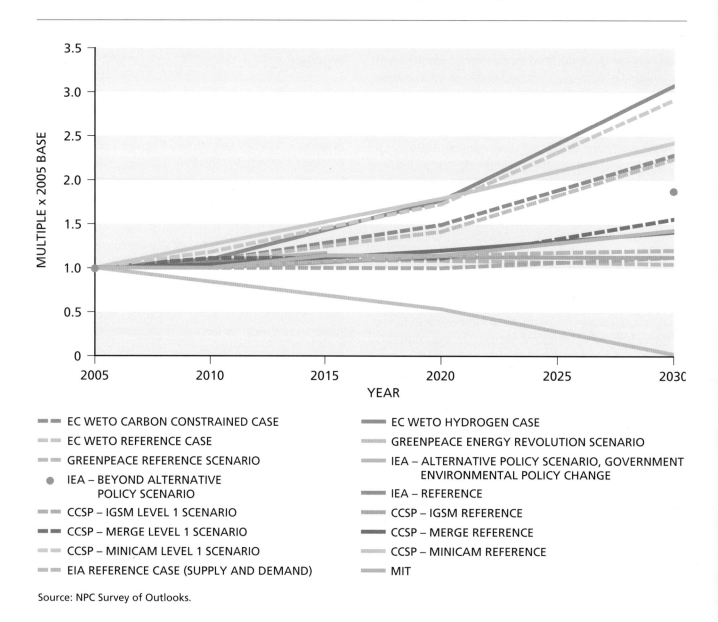

Source: NPC Survey of Outlooks.

FIGURE 2-74. *Projected Nuclear Power Generation Relative to 2005*

Facing the Hard Truths about Energy

energy from the source to a demand center. Currently, natural gas reforming is the main source of hydrogen. Integrated gasification combined cycle (IGCC) power plants could make coal an important source of hydrogen. Or, nuclear power could generate electricity to produce hydrogen via electrolysis or an alternative process.

Clearly, many primary energy sources can be used to produce hydrogen. If hydrogen became the transportation fuel of choice, it could provide convergence between all sources of energy and remove the end-fuel issue from carbon policy discussions. Policy discussions might then focus on the primary sources of hydrogen, which, given its centralized nature, could more easily fit with carbon capture and sequestration.

Forecasts for hydrogen use (Figure 2-75) are usually limited to the United States. Business-as-usual forecasts, such as the EIA Reference Case, do not show significant growth in hydrogen use for transportation. By comparison, forecasts that incorporate rapid technology development and targeted carbon constraints show considerable growth in the U.S. market. However, even in this growth case, hydrogen does not displace petroleum-based transportation fuels during the study time frame.

Energy Conversion and Delivery Infrastructure

Key Observations—Energy Infrastructure

- *Energy forecasts generally do not explicitly account for specific energy infrastructure requirements, such as capital requirements, return expectations, construction schedules, resources, and permitting processes.*

- *Uncertainty relating to energy demand outlooks may restrict or delay infrastructure investment.*

- *Data collection and analysis of energy transportation infrastructure is inadequate for evaluating infrastructure capacity, throughput, and future needs.*

- *A significant realignment in the global refining system is underway, following forecast demand growth in China and India.*

- *Infrastructure requirements of many alternative energy sources at scale are not well understood and may be significant.*

- *Complex permitting processes lengthen infrastructure construction times and reflect social, environmental, and land-use constraints on infrastructure development.*

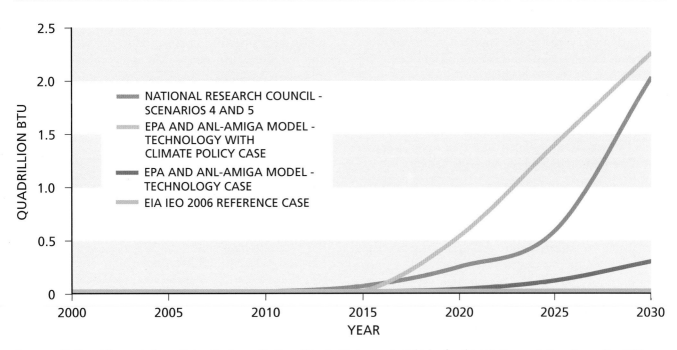

Sources: National Research Council, *Implications of a Transition to Hydrogen in Vehicles for the U.S. Energy System Scenarios*, 2004; Argonne National Laboratory, *AMIGA U.S. Technology Case Projections*, 2005; and Energy Information Administration, *International Energy Outlook 2006*.

FIGURE 2-75. *Projected U.S. Hydrogen Use for Transportation*

- *Implementing widespread carbon capture and sequestration will require significant new infrastructure.*

This section summarizes discussions in the Infrastructure and the Refining & Manufacturing Topic Papers on the CD distributed with this report.

The energy forecasts reviewed in this study do not show significant infrastructure development constraints other than those associated with siting and permitting nuclear power generation. Based on historical experience, forecasts generally assume that if sufficient economic incentive exists, new infrastructure will be developed or existing infrastructure expanded.

As with independent supply forecasts, a limited set of forecasts are available to assess new infrastructure requirements over a given period and supply-demand balance. These forecasts usually include capital and resource requirements, but focus on global or national scales that do not allow analysis of regional infrastructure development and requirements. In addition, considerably more infrastructure data are available for the United States than for the rest of the world, which increases the uncertainty of projections.

Growing international trade in natural gas and petroleum liquids will require the development of new infrastructure. For natural gas, the LNG supply chain will need considerable capital investment, from upstream development and natural gas liquefaction to LNG tankers and regasification facilities. Not all natural gas will be transported via LNG, so significant investments will also be required in long-haul natural gas pipelines. Similarly, the growing international trade in petroleum liquids will require considerable investment in oil pipelines and ocean tankers.

The evolving concentration of energy demand and energy production in different regions around the world will create new trade flows and associated infrastructure requirements. Limited infrastructure and energy trade routes that run through a few international choke points raise increasingly serious security risks (Figure 2-76).

Time and scale are significant considerations for energy infrastructure. The large, global infrastructure projects associated with forecast demand growth have long lead times. Building spare infrastructure capacity to deliver energy may not meet conventional economic thresholds. Therefore, potential project delays and lack of spare capacity increase the risk of temporary supply constraints.

Transportation infrastructure is a highly complex, robust network that delivers energy and other commodities from resource locations to manufacturing plants and ultimately to consumption centers. The transportation system is an immense network of pipelines, railways, waterways, and roads that has been in continuous development for the past two centuries. Safe, reliable infrastructure has been, and will continue to be, a prerequisite for economic growth. Figure 2-77 suggests the complexity of the energy supply system.

In 2002, for example, more than 19 billion tons of freight was delivered across the transportation system. Energy commodities—coal, natural gas, crude oil, ethanol, and petroleum products—comprise nearly one-third (by weight) of the freight shipped in the United States. Freight shipments are expected to grow 72 percent to nearly 33 billion tons by 2030, while shipments of energy commodities are expected to total 11.4 billion tons. Pipelines, tankers/barges, and railways are the main transport modes for energy commodities. Roads are the primary delivery routes for transportation fuels from blending facilities to consumer filling stations.

A reliable, economic, and flexible energy transportation infrastructure is essential to national security and economic prosperity. Demands on current and anticipated infrastructure are heavy and growing, both to supply conventional forms of energy and enable diversification to new sources.

Refining and Manufacturing

Petroleum refining capacity in the United States has changed significantly over the past 35 years. The rapid increase in capacity in the 1970s resulted from the combination of many factors, including incentives for small refiners (Figure 2-78). Coupled with reduced demand for products after the oil price shock in 1979, the incentives led to over-investment in small, inefficient refineries and poor margins for these investments. The last three decades have seen a rationalization of this inefficient capacity, while refinery outputs have increased at the same time. The number of refineries in the United States fell from more than 300 to 150 while the average capacity per refinery steadily increased, through efficiency gains and plant expansions. U.S. refinery output has

Facing the Hard Truths about Energy

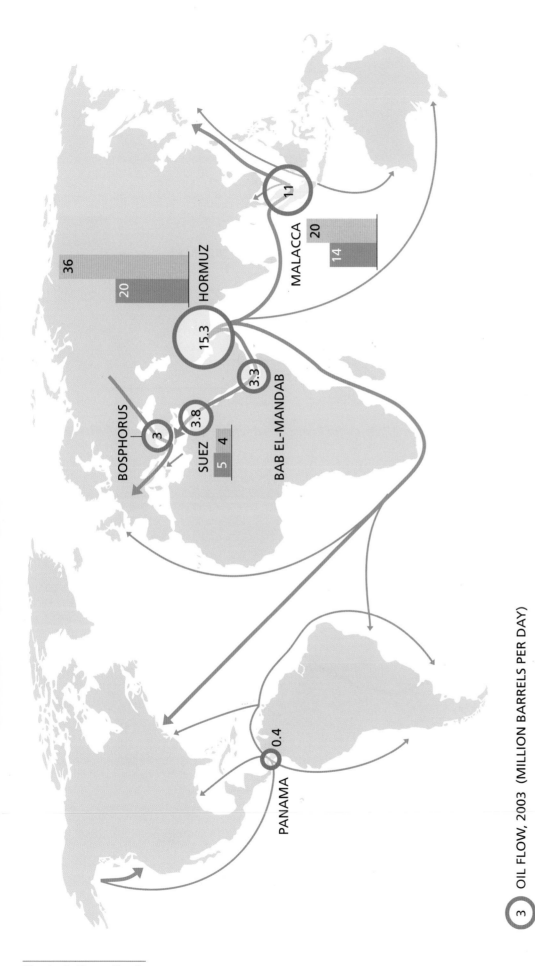

OIL FLOW, 2003 (MILLION BARRELS PER DAY)

SHARE OF WORLD OIL DEMAND (PERCENT)

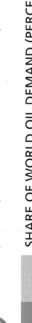

2003   2030

Source: International Energy Agency, *World Energy Outlook 2004*.

FIGURE 2-76. *Oil Flows and Geographic Choke Points, 2003*

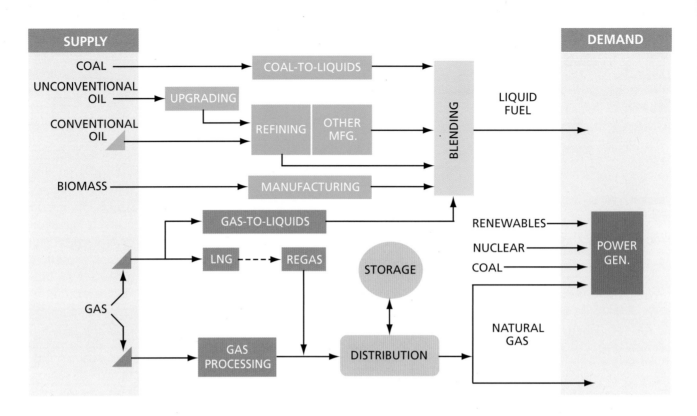

FIGURE 2-77. *Simplified Infrastructure Diagram for Energy Production, Conversion, and Delivery*

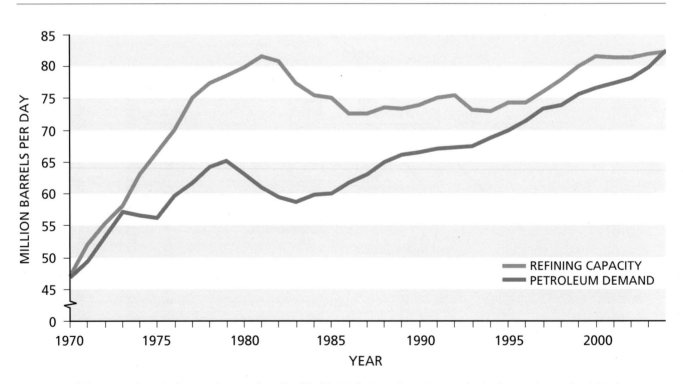

Sources: Refining Capacity: eia.doe.gov/international/iealf/table36.xls; Petroleum Demand: eia.doe.gov/emeu/ipsr/t46.xls.

FIGURE 2-78. *Global Historical Refining Capacity*

Facing the Hard Truths about Energy

increased continuously since 1985, while capacity increased by 11.7 percent between 1996 and 2005.[17] However, domestic refining capacity has not been able to keep up with product demand, resulting in increased U.S. imports of finished product and blendstock.

The study focused on four key questions to assess and understand global refining capacity projections over the next 25 years:

- What new refining capacity will be built over the next 25 years to process the projected crude oil demands?

- Where will the new capacity be located?

- What new technologies need to be developed to increase the capacity to process unconventional oil?

- What policies or regulatory barriers exist today that may inhibit development of new refining capacity?

Analysis of Refining Forecasts

Ten forecasts comprising 18 scenarios contained 27 direct or inferred projections for refining capacity.

17   Federal Trade Commission Report, *Investigation of Gasoline Price Manipulation and Post-Katrina Price Increases,* Spring 2006.

The primary integrated studies from the IEA and EIA were the context for assessing the refining capacity data from the other studies. Based on the IEA and EIA Reference Cases, global refining capacity must grow by 32 MB/D over the next 25 years to meet projected oil demand. The studies and cases reviewed in this study provide various projections based on different assumptions. However, *all* cases with a projection for 2015 show primary oil demand exceeding projected 2015 refining capacity, even assuming that all announced capacity expansion projects in the latest *Oil & Gas Journal Worldwide Construction Survey* are executed. The gap is consistent with the delicate balance between forecasted infrastructure demand and the uncertainty that governs it. Resolving the uncertainty around this projected imbalance can create incentives for additional projects to increase capacity.

Figure 2-79 is one projection of the balance between regional refining capacity and demand in 2030. Based on the IEA and EIA data, growing oil demand in the United States will continue to outpace rising refinery output, requiring continued imports of blending components and finished products. Europe, the Middle East, and Africa will

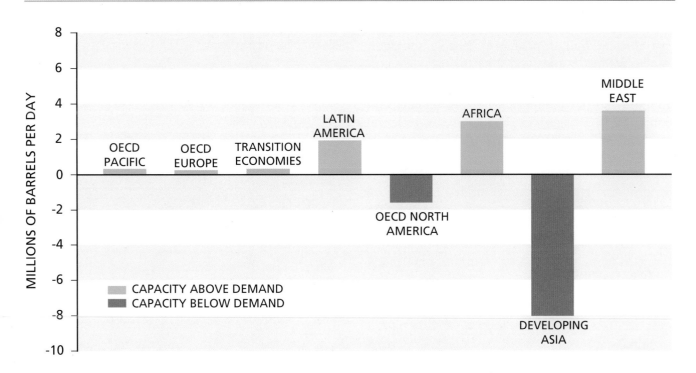

Source: Calculated from data in *Oil & Gas Journal 2005* and EIA *World Energy Outlook 2006.*

FIGURE 2-79. *Projected Balance between Regional Refining Capacity and Demand in 2030*

increase refining capacity above their oil demand, allowing export of finished products. Asia is projected to move from a balance between oil demand and refining capacity to an imbalance similar to the U.S. situation, with product imports needed to bridge the supply gap.

Increased unconventional oil production, primarily from Canada, is unlikely to require new technology development for the refining industry. Existing residual oil conversion technologies, including coking and solvent de-asphalting, should be sufficient to process the heavy oil into finished products. The unconventional oil-to-products value chain is tightly integrated because unconventional oil is generally less fungible than lighter conventional oil. Refineries that make the investments required to process heavy crude oil will become increasingly complex, as they add capacity to convert residual heavy oil, supply additional hydrogen, and provide hydrotreating.

The increasing integration of biofuels into the refined products distribution system can complicate distribution logistics, increase transportation costs, and reduce supply reliability. The requirements for transporting biofuels have led to large shipments by rail and truck from bio-refineries to product distribution terminals. This represents a shift in the fuels transportation system from large, cost-efficient, bulk shipments by reliable and dedicated pipelines, barges, and ships to small, less cost efficient shipments by non-dedicated railroads. The shift may reduce supply reliability while increasing

transportation costs. Efforts to incorporate biofuels into existing pipelines or construct new, dedicated pipelines for biofuels at significant cost are directed at overcoming such hurdles.

ACCESS TO RESOURCES

Governments around the world have restricted access to oil and natural gas resources for various reasons, including to preserve wildlife habitat or fragile ecosystems or to further domestic economic and energy security. Recent studies in the United States have identified over 20 billion barrels onshore and nearly 19 billion barrels offshore of technically recoverable oil resources that are under access restrictions which prevent their development. This section summarizes restrictions in the United States and globally.

United States Onshore

A recent comprehensive review of U.S. oil and natural gas resources showed that almost 97 percent, or 20.5 billion barrels, of undiscovered technically recoverable oil resources beneath onshore federal lands are inaccessible or have restrictions beyond standard lease terms[18] (Table 2-10).

Over 60 percent of U.S. technically recoverable oil resources and 66 percent of U.S. technically recoverable

18 Scientific Inventory of Onshore Federal Land's Oil and Gas Resources and the Extent and Nature of Restrictions or Impediments to Their Development (EPCA Inventory), 2006.

Study Area Onshore (including Alaska)	Area		Undiscovered Technically Recoverable Resources			
	Acres (x1,000)		Oil (Million Barrels)		Natural Gas (Billion Cubic Feet)	
Inaccessible or With Restrictions	75,452	76%	20,473	97%	161,647	87%
Standard Lease Terms	23,751	24%	743	3%	25,210	13%
Total	99,203	100%	21,216	100%	186,857	100%

Sources: U.S. Departments of the Interior, Agriculture, and Energy, 2006.

TABLE 2-10. *U.S. Onshore Oil and Gas Resources with Access Restrictions — Federal Lands*

Facing the Hard Truths about Energy

natural gas resources lie beneath state, tribal, and private lands. Over the past several decades, urban growth, competing land uses, and changing public values have placed ever-increasing constraints on existing and new oil and gas development.

Arctic National Wildlife Refuge

The Alaska National Interest Lands Conservation Act of 1980 established the Arctic National Wildlife Refuge (ANWR). In Section 1002 of the Act, Congress deferred a decision regarding management of the 1.5 million acre coastal plain, or 1002 Area, in recognition of its significant potential for oil and natural gas resources as well as its importance as wildlife habitat. Congress continues to debate whether to open this portion of ANWR to oil and gas leasing and exploration and to eventual development if economic oil and gas resources are discovered. Table 2-11 shows potential energy and economic impacts using USGS

estimates for mean and high undiscovered crude oil resources in the 1002 Area.[19]

Marginal Wells

In 2005, marginal oil wells provided over 17 percent of oil and 9 percent of natural gas produced onshore in the United States. The nation has over 400,000 marginal oil wells, each producing 10 barrels or less of oil

19 *Potential Federal Royalty and Income Tax Revenues Resulting from the Leasing and Development of the Coastal Plain of the Arctic National Wildlife Refuge*, Advanced Resources International for U.S. DOE, 2006. Also see EIA, *Analysis of Oil and Gas Production in the Arctic National Refuge*, March 2004, SR/OIAF/2004-04. USGS surveys suggest between 5.7 and 16.0 billion barrels of technically recoverable crude oil are in the coastal plain of ANWR, with a mean estimate of 10.4 billion barrels that includes oil resources in Native lands and state waters out to a 3-mile boundary within the coastal plain. The mean estimate for the federal portion of the ANWR coastal plain is 7.7 billion barrels of crude oil. In comparison, the estimated volume of technically recoverable unproven oil in the rest of the United States was 136 billion barrels as of January 1, 2006.

	2020	2025	2030	Cumulative by 2030 (Million Barrels)
Production Rate (1,000 Barrels/Day)*				
ANWR 1002 Mean	539	723	576	3,034
ANWR 1002 High	741	1,175	1,092	4,812
				Cumulative by 2030 (Million 2006 Dollars)
Federal Royalties (Million 2006 Dollars)				
ANWR 1002 Mean	$1,487	$1,993	$1,587	$22,922
ANWR 1002 High	$2,044	$3,240	$3,012	$36,353
Federal Income Taxes (Million 2006 Dollars)				
ANWR 1002 Mean	$1,372	$1,583	$1,346†	$19,014
ANWR 1002 High	$1,987	$2,886	$2,840	$33,801

* These production estimates are lower that some previous estimates, such as those reported by the Energy Information Administration, because they only include development of resources on federal lands in the coastal plain and not potential resources on Native lands or state offshore coastal waters.
† Tax revenues in 2030 are lower than those in 2020, despite higher levels of production, because larger, more profitable fields were assumed to be developed before smaller, less profitable fields.
Source: Advanced Resources International, 2006.

TABLE 2-11. *Estimated Production, Federal Royalties, and Federal Tax Revenues Associated with the Leasing and Development of the Arctic National Wildlife Refuge (ANWR) 1002 Area*

	Undiscovered Technically Recoverable Resources	
	Oil* (Billion Barrels)	Natural Gas (Trillion Cubic Feet)
United States – Federal OCS	**17.84**	**76.47**
Gulf of Mexico	3.65	22.46
Atlantic	3.82	36.99
Pacific	10.37	18.02
United States – Other	**1.38**	**6.78**
Great Lakes	0.43	5.23
State Waters	0.95	1.55
Canada	**10.86**	**51.10**
Northern Canada	0.10	4.00
Nova Scotia	1.06	5.30
British Columbia	9.80	41.80
Total in Moratoria Areas	**30.08**	**134.25**

*Oil includes natural gas liquids. Does not include resources in areas already under lease.

Note: In January 2007, the presidential moratoria were lifted for the entire North Aleutian Basin and a small portion of the Eastern Gulf. Revised resource estimates were released by the Department of the Interior in May 2007 and this table reflects those revised estimates.

Sources: Department of the Interior, Minerals Management Service and U.S. Geological Survey; and Interstate Oil and Gas Compact Commission.

TABLE 2-12. *U.S. and Canadian Offshore Oil and Natural Gas Resources in Moratoria Areas*

Moratoria Area	Incremental Production by 2025		Cumulative Production through 2025		Cumulative Investment to 2025	Value of Avoided Oil Imports to 2025	Cum. Federal Royalties to 2025	Cum. Federal Inc. Taxes to 2025	Max. Direct Jobs	Max. Total Jobs
	Crude Oil (MB/D)	Natural Gas (Bcf/year)	Crude Oil (Million Bbl)	Natural Gas (Bcf)	(Million $)	(Million $)	(Million $)	(Million $)		
Alaska – N. Aleutian Basin	0.02	46	89	601	$2,681	$4,671	$1,642	$1,132	2,221	8,577
Atlantic Offshore	0.17	392	400	2,717	$19,238	$21,095	$7,423	$5,115	25,447	57,860
Eastern Gulf of Mexico	0.20	370	488	2,564	$21,099	$25,736	$7,977	$5,490	40,820	76,039
Central Gulf of Mexico	0.15	286	650	3,786	$18,432	$34,273	$11,149	$7,684	19,020	79,440
Pacific Offshore	0.47	300	1,132	2,078	$36,714	$59,698	$12,937	$8,865	54,561	212,306
All Moratoria Areas	**1.01**	**1,394**	**2,758**	**11,746**	**$98,163**	**$145,473**	**$41,128**	**$28,285**	**130,634**	**328,984**

Note: Assuming MMS *mean* resource estimates and the January 2006 Congressional Budget Office price forecast (all estimates in 2006 dollars).

Source: Advanced Resources International, 2006.

TABLE 2-13. *Estimated Energy Supply and Economic Benefits from OCS Moratoria Areas*

Facing the Hard Truths about Energy

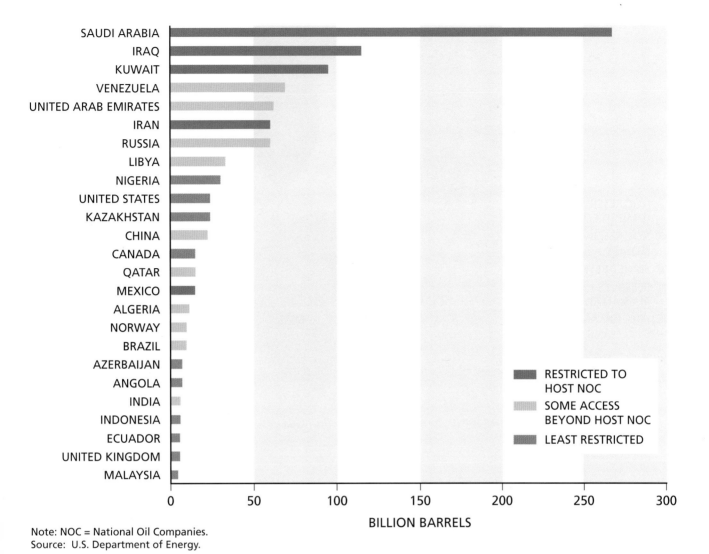

Chart data (left to right bars):

SAUDI ARABIA
IRAQ
KUWAIT
VENEZUELA
UNITED ARAB EMIRATES
IRAN
RUSSIA
LIBYA
NIGERIA
UNITED STATES
KAZAKHSTAN
CHINA
CANADA
QATAR
MEXICO
ALGERIA
NORWAY
BRAZIL
AZERBAIJAN
ANGOLA
INDIA
INDONESIA
ECUADOR
UNITED KINGDOM
MALAYSIA

RESTRICTED TO HOST NOC
SOME ACCESS BEYOND HOST NOC
LEAST RESTRICTED

0   50   100   150   200   250   300

BILLION BARRELS

Note: NOC = National Oil Companies.
Source: U.S. Department of Energy.

FIGURE 2-80. *Access to World Proved Oil Resources*

per day for an average 2.2 barrels per day. Without production from marginal wells, it has been estimated that U.S. oil imports would increase by nearly 7 percent.[20] Increasing operational and regulatory costs and diminishing access to markets via pipelines can contribute to the premature abandonment of marginal wells. When wells and fields are abandoned prematurely, the associated oil and gas resources may never be recovered due to economics, lease termination, and related issues.

North America Offshore

Approximately 30 billion barrels of undiscovered technically recoverable oil resources and 134 trillion

cubic feet of undiscovered technically recoverable natural gas resources in offshore waters of the U.S. and Canada are in moratoria areas precluded by law or public policy from leasing and development (Table 2-12). Of these resources, about 18 billion barrels of oil and 76 trillion cubic feet of natural gas are currently off limits to leasing and development in the United States. There is significant uncertainty in resource estimates for those areas of the Outer Continental Shelf (OCS) subject to long-standing moratoria or presidential withdrawal. In the north, mid-, and south Atlantic, most of the west coast, and portions of the eastern Gulf of Mexico, the last acquisition of geophysical data and drilling of exploration wells occurred from 25 to 40 years ago. There were a few prospective discoveries at that time and numerous indications for the potential occurrence of oil and gas.

20 Interstate Oil and Gas Compact Commission, *Marginal Wells: Fuel for Economic Growth*, 2006.

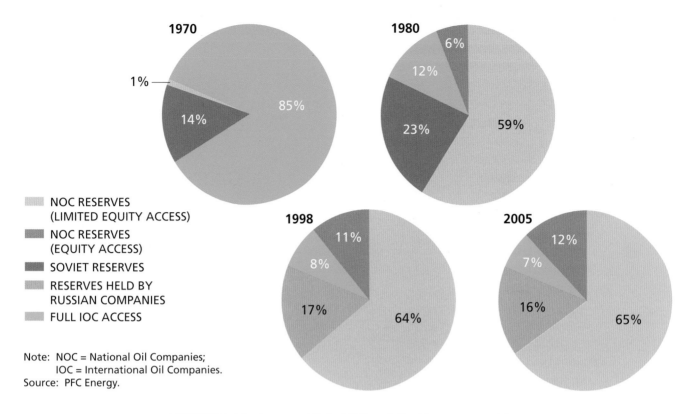

NOC RESERVES
(LIMITED EQUITY ACCESS)

NOC RESERVES
(EQUITY ACCESS)

SOVIET RESERVES

RESERVES HELD BY
RUSSIAN COMPANIES

FULL IOC ACCESS

Note: NOC = National Oil Companies;
       IOC = International Oil Companies.
Source: PFC Energy.

FIGURE 2-81. *Access to Global Oil and Gas Reserves over Time*

Estimates developed in 2006 show that the potential energy and economic benefits of increased access to oil and gas resources in OCS moratoria areas could be substantial (Table 2-13):[21]

- By 2025, U.S. crude oil production could increase by more than 1.0 MB/D.

- Nearly 2.8 billion barrels of crude oil could be produced between now and 2025—production that would not be realized if the existing moratoria were continued.

- Industry would spend $98 billion dollars in the U.S. by 2025 to develop these resources.

- Between now and 2025, the U.S. trade imbalance would be reduced by $145 billion if this domestically

produced crude oil were to offset imports on a one-to-one basis.

- The U.S. would collect an additional $41 billion in royalties by 2025 from OCS production.

- An additional $28 billion in federal income taxes would be collected from OCS production between now and 2025.

- The economic activity generated by this development would result in the addition of as many as 130,000 direct domestic, high-paying jobs.

Global Access

Figure 2-80 shows access restrictions for resource holding countries in addition to the United States. Figure 2-81 shows how access to global oil and gas reserves has become increasingly restricted over time. The trend line and the proportion of resources under restricted access raise uncertainties about secure energy supply and potentially diminishing opportunities for equitable access.

---

21 *Estimate of the Potential Economic Benefits From the Leasing and Development of Oil and Gas Resources in OCS Moratoria Areas*, Advanced Resources International for U.S. Department of Energy, June 6, 2006. Based on mean MMS estimates of undiscovered oil and gas resources in the areas in question.

Facing the Hard Truths about Energy

Abstract

Technology contributes significantly to both reducing energy demand growth and expanding and diversifying supply. Technological advances to extend conventional and expand unconventional fossil fuels are examined, along with technology breakthroughs that may reduce the cost, mitigate environmental drawbacks, and increase the volume potential of alternative energy sources. However, a majority of the U.S. energy-sector workforce—including skilled scientists, engineers, and technicians—is eligible to retire within the next decade and these workers must be replaced and new workers trained.

This chapter examines how technology can significantly improve energy-use efficiency in transportation and other sectors, while also expanding the energy industry's ability to find and produce resources. Expert teams assess commercial and environmental opportunities for conventional and unconventional hydrocarbons, biofuels, nuclear, and other energy sources, noting the time frames needed to bring promising new technologies to market. They also consider ways government and industry can cooperate to renew the vital energy workforce.

The outline of the Technology chapter is as follows:

- Key Findings
- Technology Development and Deployment
- Personnel Issues
- Carbon Capture and Sequestration
- Conventional Wells (including EOR and the Arctic)
- Exploration Technology
- Deepwater Technology
- Unconventional Natural Gas Reservoirs— Tight Gas, Coal Seams, and Shales
- Unconventional Hydrocarbons: Heavy Oil, Extra-Heavy Oil, and Bitumen
- Unconventional Hydrocarbons: Oil Shale
- Unconventional Hydrocarbons: Gas Hydrates
- Coal to Liquids
- Biomass Energy Supply
- Nuclear Outlook and Its Impact on Oil and Gas
- Transportation Efficiency.

The oil and natural gas industry has a long history of technological advancement, and today operates using materials, sensors, chemistry, and engineering that are marvels well beyond the limits envisioned by industry pioneers or, indeed, the general public (Figure 3-1). Many technical advances have been generated directly by research and development (R&D) in industry labs, through field trials, and by applied ingenuity.

Globally, the industry spends more than $6 billion annually on oil- and gas-related R&D. This spending is on the upswing, which will result in technological advances we can only imagine today. The percentage

© SCHLUMBERGER, LTD.

FIGURE 3-1. *Jackup Rig with Fracturing Stimulation Vessel in the Gulf of Mexico*

ogies required to exploit those resources. Similarly, technologies that require new facilities, such as coal-to-liquids conversion plants or nuclear power plants, depend on establishing permitting and regulation procedures.

Several specific technologies highlighted in this chapter have potential for industry-government co-operation. These include advanced materials research in nanotechnology and in materials that can sustain high temperatures and high pressures, robotics, and metocean research.[1]

Enhanced oil recovery and carbon capture and sequestration (CCS) are activities for which significant advances are expected in the coming decades. Today, technology is developing to reduce the cost of separating carbon dioxide (CO_2) and to sequester large amounts of the gas in deep underground formations. Beyond today's biofuels, research breakthroughs are expected in second-generation crops and cellulosic ethanol production.

Advancements are being achieved by the industry that reduce environmental impacts, particularly in fragile and ecologically sensitive locations. "Greener" chemicals are being deployed throughout operations. Further cost reductions and technology to reduce environmental effects will be applied in heavy-oil reservoirs and later in oil shales in the western United States and elsewhere. Water and other resource demands increase significantly with many of these new developments, however, and in some regions these demands may become the largest factor limiting growth.

of that $6 billion that is focused on U.S.-specific needs is relatively small. R&D dollars, like capital expenditures, follow the most attractive opportunities, and these are increasingly found overseas. However, the U.S. industry has had some dramatic successes that point the way forward, confirming that there is a continuing role for the U.S. government in this area.

Deepwater technology, which has allowed us to tap into resources in the Gulf of Mexico at water depths exceeding 1,000 feet, is far greater than was imagined even a few years ago, and has significantly increased U.S. reserves and production. Coalbed methane, long considered a hazard to miners, is now a significant resource thanks to technology specifically applied after the U.S. government encouraged its development. In both of these cases, technology was not developed by U.S. government funding, but by industry pursuing opportunities and access to resources, which has made and continues to make a significant difference.

Government policy can affect how technologies are developed and implemented. For example, opening new areas for exploration stimulates R&D in technol-

Clearly, a significant piece of the overall energy puzzle will be technology that increases the efficiency of energy use. This is an area rich in opportunity for both technology advancements and policy measures. It is, however, an area complicated by consumer preferences and diverse situations for technology's adoption. One can see this in the evolution of the U.S. auto fleet over the past decade, where technical improvements in drive-train efficiency have been mainly applied to increase performance rather than fuel economy. As with technology developments to increase supply,

---

1 Nanotechnology includes devices and materials whose size is in the range of 1 to 100 nanometers (billionths of a meter). Metocean is the "weather" of the offshore environment both above and below the surface of the water. The word is a contraction of "meteorology" (weather in the air) and "oceanology" (conditions below the surface of the water) and is used by all offshore industries.

Facing the Hard Truths about Energy

clear regulatory signals by governments and economic opportunities by the private sector combine to accelerate technology advances. The U.S. refrigerator efficiency standard, which raised efficiency requirements and reduced energy consumption, is a good example of a clear success that could be duplicated. Lighting, building-energy efficiency, and electricity-grid improvements are all areas where ingenuity combined with smart policy would yield big efficiency gains.

While current R&D by the oil and natural gas industry, along with entrepreneurial start-ups funded by increased venture and equity capital, is on the upswing, U.S. government funding for oil and natural gas research is trending down. Department of Energy monies have been a significant funding source for U.S. universities and national laboratories. This funding is particularly important, as it enables students to pursue advanced degrees that are relevant and vital to our country's energy future. One of the most significant issues facing the U.S. energy industry is a critical shortage of engineers and scientists. This stems from the cyclical nature of the industry and by public perceptions, as well as reductions in the number of U.S. petroleum and geoscience degree departments, and industry demographics. More than 50 percent of the industry's current technical workforce is eligible for retirement within the next decade, creating an experience and skill shortage at a time when demand will be increasing. Solving this challenge will require cooperation among federal and state governments, academia, and industry if the United States is to continue its historical leadership in oil and natural gas technology development.

Topics are arranged in six broad groupings in this chapter. The first group contains two topics that are part of all the others—technology development and personnel issues—and one that is likely to be important for many of the others—carbon capture and sequestration. The second group describes exploration and production (E&P) activities that are current today: conventional resources (including enhanced oil recovery and arctic activities), exploration, and deepwater technologies. The third group comprises unconventional natural gas production in shale gas, coalbed methane, and tight gas sands (reservoirs with extremely low permeability). The fourth group includes unconventional hydrocarbon sources in heavy oil, oil shale, and methane hydrate. The fifth group describes alternative sources for liquid fluids from coal and biomass. The final group has two

reports covering the effect that nuclear technology might have on the oil and natural gas sector, and the impact that technology improvements might have on transportation efficiencies.

Each section includes a description of the technology topic, information about the state-of-the-art within the topic, and, in many cases, the most important developments expected by 2010, 2020, and 2030. Details and technical discussions can be found in the individual Technology Topic Reports that are available on the CD that accompanies this report.

KEY FINDINGS

- The current and projected demographics of trained personnel in the broad U.S. energy industry indicate a shortage that is expected to worsen due to retirements in the next decade and beyond. The shortage affects both the E&P part of the business (upstream) and the refining part (downstream), construction, and other sectors, including the transportation industry. It ranges from skilled craftspeople through PhDs. Fewer academic departments are training students in petrotechnical areas now than in the 1980s. However, the problem is wider, with shortages of students in science, engineering, and mathematics. A similar situation exists for craft labor.

- Carbon capture and sequestration underground will facilitate the continued use of fossil fuels in an increasingly carbon-constrained world. CCS is technically achievable today, and has been demonstrated at a project level and applied in enhanced oil recovery. However, CO_2 has not been injected at the scales (both volumes and time periods) that will be necessary in the future.

- The prospect for advancements in technology is very good, but the Technology Task Group found no single, simple solution with the potential to provide energy security for the United States over the long term. The solution will involve as many of the available resources and potential technologies as can be developed and deployed.

- Technology can significantly improve transportation efficiency, particularly for light duty vehicles. Consumer preferences affect the deployment of technology in that sector, whereas a sound business case affects deployment in the other transportation sectors.

- Technology has had a significant impact on the industry's ability to find and produce resources. In exploration, 3D seismic technology created a boom in activity starting in the 1980s, driving down acquisition costs while improving the exploration success rate. In another area, after government policies were enacted in the 1980s, technologies were developed to understand and exploit coalbed methane, a resource that has been known since the beginning of the coal mining industry (Figure 3-2).

- Access to acreage with potential for economic oil and natural gas resources is itself a primary driver that encourages technology development. The onset of area-wide leasing for the U.S. Gulf of Mexico in the early 1980s led to significant acceleration of interest in deepwater regions.

- Commercializing technology in the oil and gas market is costly and time-consuming; an average of 16 years passes from concept to widespread commercial adoption.

- Recovery from existing and future resources is expected to improve because of continuing increases in the volume of the reservoir that is in proximity to a wellbore, thanks to both close well spacing and improved technologies such as multilateral horizontal wells. Environmental impact will continue to be reduced as technology allows operations with a smaller "footprint" and "greener" chemicals.

- Improved exploration and exploitation technology slowed the decline in discovery volumes. Although the future of exploration technologies is bright and the exploration success rate may continue to improve, it is still likely that the volumes of hydrocarbons discovered with time will continue to decrease.

- Unconventional natural gas resources in tight gas sands, coalbed methane, and gas shales have become commercial because of technological advances, and these new resources are likely to continue to be important.

- Technologies are available for production of heavy oil, extra-heavy oil, and bitumen, but these heavier crudes are in less demand than conventional oil because of the difficulty in processing to create refined products, and because fewer refineries have the capability to process them (Figure 3-3).

- Oil shales may become a commercial resource by 2020, although large-scale production is unlikely

© SCHLUMBERGER, LTD.

FIGURE 3-2. *Land Rig in the Rocky Mountains*

© SCHLUMBERGER, LTD.

FIGURE 3-3. *Heavy Oil Sample*

Facing the Hard Truths about Energy

until 2030. The technique used historically is surface processing in a high-temperature retort. An alternative process still in development, in situ conversion at lower temperature, has captured the industry's attention. In situ conversion technology is just emerging, so it is not yet clear which specific technologies can advance the state of the art over the coming decades.

- An economically viable method for production of natural gas from naturally occurring hydrate resources has not been developed. Hydrate sites are known to be in arctic areas, and in some marine locations in other parts of the world, but no efforts have been made to locate commercial marine deposits of hydrates in U.S. waters.

- Estimates for coal-to-liquids production are small relative to the overall petroleum market through 2030, for cost and environmental reasons.

- Biofuels face technological and logistics challenges before becoming a more significant part of the U.S. transportation fuel mix. Still required are efficient and scalable conversion techniques for cellulosic materials such as switchgrass, corn stover, and woody biomass; efficient transportation networks from field to plant; and ways to overcome water-supply shortages.

- Nuclear power plants provide base-load electrical power, whereas electricity generated using oil or natural gas is typically load-following. Therefore, if developed in the United States, growth of nuclear power will displace a much greater amount of coal-powered generation growth and a smaller amount of oil and natural gas generation.

- With many mature, marginal fields, the United States has specific R&D needs that have a lesser focus for the largest industry R&D organizations than the more prolific international prospects.

TECHNOLOGY DEVELOPMENT AND DEPLOYMENT

Since the beginning of the modern age of oil and natural gas, technology has played a fundamental role in supporting the efficient production of hydrocarbons. Oil and natural gas technologies are often destined for hostile, hard-to-reach environments such as deep offshore waters or in the high temperatures and pressures encountered at the bottoms of wells. Full-scale tests must be completed before a technology can be proved and the market will accept it. As a result, commercializing technology in oil and natural gas markets is costly and time-intensive; some studies indicate an average of 16 years from concept to commercialization. The Technology Development Topic Report examines both lessons from history and current trends in oil and natural gas technology development and deployment to make predictions for the coming years.

The sources of technology destined for the oil and natural gas markets have changed over time. Starting in the early 1980s, major oil and natural gas companies began to decrease their R&D spending, driven in large part by a decision to "buy versus build" new technology. Historically, independent oil and natural gas companies have spent little on R&D. Service companies have stepped in to partially fill the gap by increasing their R&D spending. There is little doubt that in the coming years, new technologies will be invented and applied to the global quest to maximize production from oil and natural gas reservoirs. As oil prices have risen over the past few years, so have R&D budgets, with the exception of U.S. government spending. The global industry will spend more than $6 billion on R&D, much of it in areas outside the United States.

The major oil and natural gas companies follow the best investment opportunities, including R&D, which are increasingly found overseas. This pursuit leaves U.S. onshore production largely in the hands of independent oil and natural gas companies. In a global marketplace, the service companies continue to respond to the needs of their worldwide customer base.

Being one of the most mature oil and natural gas producing countries, the United States has specific technology requirements compared with much of the rest of the world (Figure 3-4). More than 400,000 U.S. oil wells produce less than 10 barrels a day (of these, the average national production is 2.2 barrels per day). About 289,000 marginal natural gas wells produce less than 60 million cubic feet a day in the United States (an average of 16.7 million cubic feet per day per well). That is 17 percent of the oil and 9 percent of natural gas produced onshore in the United States.[2]

---

2 Interstate Oil and Gas Compact Commission, "Marginal Wells: Fuel for Economic Growth" (2006).

FIGURE 3-4. *Pumping Units that Produce Oil from Low-Pressure Reservoirs*

Research is key to the survival of these marginal wells. Unfortunately, the small, independent producers who operate these wells rarely have the ability to conduct research, even though R&D might keep them producing for many more years. As a result, unless the technology requirements of the U.S. oil and natural gas business align with the needs of the rest of the world, there is a danger that U.S. interests may not be addressed adequately.

Figure 3-5 shows U.S. government R&D funding in recent years, split between oil and natural gas.[3] Research undertaken by national laboratories and universities usually leads to fundamental understanding and basic technologies. These technologies are typically applied by other entities such as oil and natural gas, service, or start-up companies.

However, the U.S. government proposal for fiscal year 2007 to terminate the oil and natural gas program within the Department of Energy leaves only $50 million in royalty receipts that were set aside in the Energy Policy Act of 2005. The bulk of the funds ($35 million) is set aside for ultra-deepwater and

3   Lawson, William F, "Who Will Fund America's Energy Future?" Interstate Oil and Gas Compact Commission report (2006).

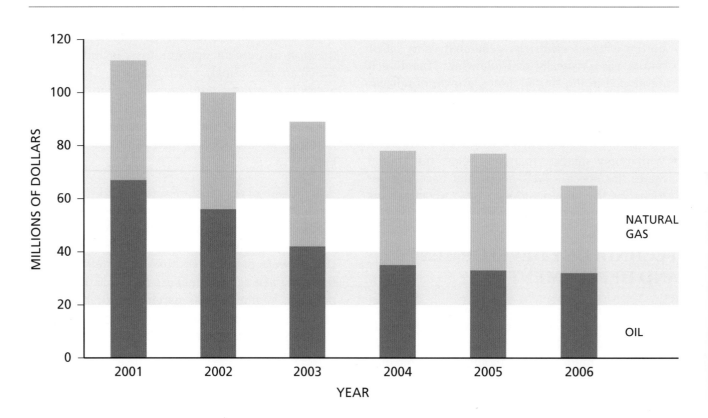

FIGURE 3-5. *Oil and Natural Gas R&D Funds Provided by the U.S. Government*

unconventional-hydrocarbon research programs as part of the Research Partnership for a Secure Energy America (RPSEA). The remainder ($15 million) is set aside for an internal National Energy Technology Laboratory program and administrative funds.

Many successful research programs have featured accountability as a key attribute. Examples show that it is possible to leverage funding, such as the Ansari X prize for privately funded manned space flight, the Orteig prize to Lindbergh for his solo flight across the Atlantic, and the Board of Longitude prize for the 18th century invention of the marine chronograph that enabled navigators to determine longitude at sea.

PERSONNEL ISSUES

The exploration and production industry is currently in a boom cycle after an extended bust that lasted about 20 years. The current and projected demographics of trained personnel in the broad U.S. energy industry are disturbing, leading to a shortage that is expected to worsen and last for decades. This problem is pandemic, affecting upstream and downstream, construction, and other sectors including the transportation industry (Figure 3-6). Personnel shortages range from skilled craftspeople through PhDs. Within the E&P

© SCHLUMBERGER, LTD.

FIGURE 3-6. *Skilled worker on rig site*

industry, the impending retirement and handoff to the next generation of employees has been referred to as the "big crew change;" the U.S. Department of Labor refers to it as the "demographic cliff."[4]

The majority of industry professionals are less than ten years from retirement eligibility. There are fewer academic departments in petrotechnical areas now than before the bust, and significantly fewer petrotechnical students are being trained to replace upcoming retirees. The industry's cyclical nature and its negative public image have kept the number of interested students low. Enrollment in petroleum engineering and geoscience departments of U.S. universities is down about 75 percent from its 1982 peak. However, the problem is wider, with a shortage of students in science, engineering, and mathematics. A similar situation exists for craft labor, with aggregate demand exceeding supply by an increasing margin over the next few years. Competition from other industries will intensify the shortage of personnel, which is exacerbated globally by an explosion in the rate of hiring by the industry in the past two years.

A study by Schlumberger Business Solutions in 2005 indicated a surplus of petrotechnical graduates in parts of the world, including Indonesia, Venezuela, and China, that is available to supply the areas with a deficit of graduates, such as the United States. However, a 2006 follow-up survey showed that the rapid increase in hiring has swamped even the ability of those countries to fill global needs. Even if the high rate of hiring lasts only a few years, language, culture, and immigration quotas pose barriers to a rapid flow of graduates from one part of the world to another.

Many E&P industry jobs can be (and are) filled by graduates of other engineering and scientific disciplines. However, the public's negative image of the industry makes recruiting those graduates difficult as well. The alternative of mid-career hiring is a negative-sum game when viewing the industry as a whole: although it helps one company, it does so to the detriment of another, and it is an expensive option.

Many of the Technology Task Group Topic Reports noted this problem as a barrier to implementing technological advances. For example, enabling development of coal-to-liquids technologies requires

4 U.S. Department of Labor, "Identifying and Addressing Workforce Challenges in America's Energy Industry," President's High Growth Job Training Initiative. U.S. DOL Employment Training Administration (March 2007).

additional coal miners, transportation crews, and plant personnel, both skilled and professional. Similar problems are noted for any substantial increase in biofuels production, shale oil development, carbon sequestration, and other areas.

CARBON CAPTURE AND SEQUESTRATION

It is likely that the world is moving into an era in which carbon emissions will be constrained. For a general discussion on carbon, see Chapter 5, "Carbon Management." Oil and natural gas contribute more than half the current, energy-related CO_2 emissions. In a carbon-constrained world, the use of oil, natural gas, and coal will be affected by policy measures to reduce carbon emissions. Carbon management will involve combining several measures to reduce CO_2 emissions, including improvements in the efficiency of energy use and the use of alternatives to fossil fuels such as biofuels, solar, wind, and nuclear power. However, to meet the energy demands of the nation, the United States will continue using fossil fuels, including coal, extensively over the next 50 years or more. To do so, and to extend the resource base to include unconventional hydrocarbons such as heavy oil, tar sands, and shale oil, it will be necessary, if carbon constraints are imposed, to capture and sequester a large fraction of the CO_2 produced by burning these fossil fuels.

Carbon capture and sequestration entails trapping CO_2 at the site where it is generated and storing it for periods sufficiently long (several thousand years) to mitigate the effect CO_2 can have on the Earth's climate. In this report, we only consider geological sequestration and do not discuss possible alternatives, such as deep-sea sequestration, which is fraught with environmental concerns and issues of public acceptance. Geological sequestration would target spent oil and natural gas reservoirs and deep saline formations; the potential capacity is discussed in the CCS Topic Report.

The technologies required for effective CCS are, by and large, viable. Projects continue at Sleipner field, the Weyburn enhanced oil recovery (EOR) project in Canada,[5] and the In Salah saline formation project in Algeria.[6] The hurdles to implementation are largely ones of integration at scale. Current possible scenarios of climate change predict that by 2030, the level of CO_2 to be mitigated could be 30 billion tons per year or more.[7, 8] Sequestering 5 billion tons of CO_2 each year would entail pumping volumes close to 100 million barrels per day of supercritical CO_2 into secure geological formations. This amounts to around a quarter of the volume of water currently pumped worldwide for secondary oil recovery. At the local level, sequestering CO_2 from a 1-gigawatt coal-fired power station would require pumping into the ground some 150,000 barrels per day of supercritical CO_2.[9] A power station of that size would generate electricity for about 700,000 typical American homes.

While the technologies for CCS are essentially available, in that capture and storage can be implemented now, extensive scope remains for improvement. In particular, the capture stage of CCS is key, and currently dominates the overall cost. Novel, lower-cost approaches to capture would have a significant effect on the implementation of CCS and would, in turn, greatly influence the usability of fossil fuels under carbon constraint. The CCS Topic Report discusses other areas where continued research is important:

- Fundamentals of storage, such as long-term physiochemical changes in the storage reservoir

- Characterization and risk assessment (faults, cap rocks, wells)

- Reservoir management for long-term storage

- Integration of fit-for-purpose measurement, monitoring, and verification

- Ability to inject CO_2 into formations

- Retention and leakage, such as leakage through wells.

It is also crucial at this stage to undertake an assessment of the total U.S. capacity for CO_2 sequestration.

---

5 Wilson M, Monea M. (Eds.), IEA GHG Weyburn CO_2 Monitoring & Storage Project Summary Report 2000-2004 (2004).

6 Riddiford, F, Wright, I, Espie, T, and Torqui, A, "Monitoring geological storage: In Salah Gas CO_2 Storage Project," GHGT-7, Vancouver (2004).

7 Pacala and Socolow, "Stabilization Wedges: Solving the Climate Problem for the next 50 Years with Current Technology," *Science* 305 (13 Aug. 2004): 968.

8 Third Assessment Report – Climate Change 2001, Intergovernmental Panel on Climate Change.

9 Socolow, R, "Can We Bury Global Warming?" *Scientific American* (2005).

While it is reasonable to expect that the combined capacity of existing hydrocarbon reservoirs and deep saline formations is large, a detailed understanding of the regional distribution of capacity throughout the United States is critically important.

It is important to note that there is no experience available with full-process integration, e.g., a coupled, large-scale coal-fired power plant with CCS. Several projects worldwide, most notably FutureGen in the United States and Zero-Gen in Australia, are in the process of designing and constructing an integrated large-scale power and CCS operation. Operating such facilities successfully is central to understanding the true economics and practical requirements for large-scale CCS.

Experience Basis	Significance	Limitations
CO_2 enhanced oil recovery (EOR)	> 30 years experience; injection >> 1 million tons CO_2/year	Very limited monitoring programs; questions of applicability of experience to saline formations
Acid gas injection	> 15 years experience injecting CO_2 and H_2S into over 44 geologic formations	Generally small volumes; very little publicly available technical information
Hazardous waste disposal/ underground injection control	...	Most hazardous waste is not buoyant or reactive
Natural gas storage	~100 years experience injecting natural gas into rocks	Limited monitoring; different chemistry; built for temporary storage
Natural analogs	Several large (> 50 trillion cubic feet) carbo-gaseous accumulations globally; proof of concept	Most at steady state, transient knowledge unavailable; limited geography and geology
Conventional oil and gas E&P	Nearly 150 years of technology and experience in predicting and managing buoyant fluids in crust	Hydrocarbon recovery has goals and needs which differ from those of carbon sequestration
Capture/gas separations technology	> 70 years separating CO_2 and other acid gases from gas streams, including at power plants	Costs still higher than preferred under widespread deployment; still no integration of large power plants with CCS
Large CO_2 storage projects	3 large-scale projects; > 6 pending before 2010	Still limited monitoring program; limited geologic representation
CO_2 pipelines and transportation	> 30 years experience at large scale; existing regulations likely to apply	None

TABLE 3-1. *Basis for Experience Relevant to Commercial Carbon Capture and Sequestration*

One activity in which CO_2 is pumped into reservoirs currently is enhanced oil recovery. This provides a proving ground for various techniques that are relevant to CCS, and can be implemented while other carbon-management solutions are under development. (A section of the Topic Report discusses the role of CO_2-EOR in the development of CCS technologies.) At present, CO_2-EOR is not directed towards effective storage of CO_2 but the techniques can be modified to improve carbon sequestration.

There is a growing scientific consensus that anthropogenic CO_2 is driving detrimental climate change.[10] Moreover, the Intergovernmental Panel on Climate Change (IPCC) Special Report on CCS indicates that

including it in a mitigation portfolio could help stabilize CO_2 concentrations in the atmosphere (at double the pre-industrial level) with a cost reduction of 30 percent or more, compared to other approaches.[11] More recently, the UK's Stern Review estimated that the cost of meaningful mitigation—maintaining atmospheric levels of CO_2 at no more than double the pre-industrial levels—would amount to about 1 percent of global GDP.[12] Doing nothing, on the other hand, would likely incur a cost greater than

---

10 Oreskes, N, "The Scientific Consensus on Climate Change," *Science* 306 (3 Dec. 2004): 1686.

11 "IPCC Special Report on Carbon Dioxide Capture and Storage," Intergovernmental Panel on Climate Change, Interlachen (2005), available at http://www.ipcc.ch/.

12 "The Stern Review of the Economics of Climate Change," available at http://www.hm-treasury.gov.uk/independent_reviews/stern_review_economics_climate_change/stern_review_report.cfm.

Technology	Significance	Brief Discussion
CO_2-EOR	Natural arena for exploring CCS	Provides a direct commercial incentive to pumping CO_2 into a reservoir
Evaluation of CCS in association with coal-fired plant	Development of integration of required technologies	Projects in United States, Australia, and China to develop CCS with coal plants
Improved capture technologies	Key determinant of cost of CCS	Significant efforts in United States, Europe, and Japan to drive down cost of capture
Injection of CO_2 into subsurface formations	Demonstration of injection and test of storage	CO_2 currently injected at the million tons/year level
Development of models for subsurface migration of CO_2	Understanding of migration behavior underpins characterization and MMV	Combination of modeling and experiment (e.g., Sleipner) to establish CO_2 migration
Reservoir characterization for storage	Reservoir characterization techniques migrate to CO_2 storage estimates	Available techniques tested at several sites
Measurement, monitoring and verification (MMV)	Available MMV technologies applied to CO_2 injection and storage	Available techniques tested at several sites
Development of CO_2 resistant cements	Primary leakage path is likely to be existing wells	Improvements in resistance of cements to corrosion are currently being pursued

TABLE 3-2. Summary of Carbon Capture and Sequestration Technologies in Priority Order

Facing the Hard Truths about Energy

Technology	Significance	Time Frame
Extensive CO_2-EOR with substantial CO_2 sequestration	Enhanced security of supply through better recovery	2010
Measurement, monitoring and verification (MMV) techniques	Necessary prerequisite for implementation	2010
Site characterization and risk assessment	Determination of site suitability for sequestration	2010
CO_2 leak remediation technology	Necessary for implementation of CO_2 storage	2010
Demonstration of coal-fired power with CCS	Establish precedent for the technology	2010
Assessment of U.S. CO_2 sequestration capacity	Primary requirement for siting power stations	<2020
Novel, inexpensive capture technology	Key cost determinant of CCS	<2020
Next-generation CO_2-EOR with maximum CO_2 storage	Increases usable CO_2 storage capacity in structurally confined geologic settings by three- to ten-fold	2020
Ubiquitous coal-fired power with CCS	Extensive power generation without CO_2 emissions	2020
Rig-site or sub-surface hydrocarbon processing to generate low-carbon fuels or feedstocks and recycle CO_2 within the reservoir or field for EOR followed by CCS	Keeps most of the carbon in or near the reservoir, simplifying CCS logistics and costs, enabling low carbon fuels/heat/power from oil and gas	2030

TABLE 3-3. Summary of Carbon Capture and Sequestration Technologies in Time/Priority Order, with Time Frame to Commercial Use

5 percent of world GDP, with a worst-case estimate of 20 percent, to ameliorate the damage caused by a deteriorating climate. These studies indicate that the financial risk to the nation of delaying action is now so high that a concerted emphasis on CCS is already strongly warranted.

Summary: Technical Issues

Tables 3-1, 3-2, and 3-3 describe the basis for experience relevant to commercial CCS, current technologies in priority order, and future technologies in time/priority order, with time scales to commercial use.

Technology today is well-understood and effective and can probably deliver what is needed. However, there are some outstanding technical issues:

- Novel, lower-cost capture technologies

- Integration and fit-for-purpose deployment of monitoring and verification

- Well-leakage characterization and mitigation

- Protocols for site characterization

- Technical basis for operational protocols and risk characterization.

Summary: Nontechnical Issues

Given the scope of commercial CCS, there are many issues that are not technical, per se, but relate to technical readiness and ways to maximize early investment:

- There is a high likelihood of a critical gap in human capital. Currently, workers who can execute CCS are the same as those employed in oil and natural gas exploration and production. In a carbon-constrained economy, there will not be enough skilled workers to go around. This is particularly true for geoscientists, but also true for chemical and mechanical engineers.

- Development of a comprehensive set of energy policies and strategies is critical to provide certainty to make investment decisions.

- The legislative and regulatory framework within which CCS is conducted will have a major impact on how rapidly the technology is implemented and ultimately will determine whether CCS can effectively mitigate carbon emissions and provide access to future hydrocarbon supplies. A section of the CCS Topic Report is devoted to regulatory issues and details the various aspects of regulation that will be critical to the success of CCS.

- It is not clear that the science and technology programs in place today will provide answers required by regulators and decision makers. Greater dialogue between individuals working with technology and those developing a regulatory framework would help to reduce unnecessary regulation and guide R&D goals toward the most immediate needs.

- Infrastructure to transport CO_2, such as pipelines, is essential for commercial deployment. However, there is concern that pipelines for early project opportunities will not be able to carry additional future projects. Incentives and government action for this infrastructure can help to build networks sufficient to support large-scale, commercial CCS deployment in the United States.

CONVENTIONAL WELLS (INCLUDING EOR AND IN THE ARCTIC)

Large volumes of technically recoverable, domestic oil resources—estimated at 400 billion barrels—

remain undeveloped and are yet to be discovered, from undeveloped remaining oil in place of over a trillion (1,124 billion) barrels (Figure 3-7). This resource includes undiscovered oil, stranded light oil amenable to CO_2-EOR technologies, unconventional oil (deep heavy oil and oil sands), and new petroleum concepts, such as residual oil in reservoir transition zones. As the leader in EOR technology, the U.S. oil industry faces the challenge of further applying this technology towards economically producing the more costly remaining domestic oil resources.

While pursuing this remaining domestic oil-resource base poses considerable economic risk and technical challenge to producers, developing the technical capability and infrastructure necessary to exploit this resource reduces our dependence on foreign energy sources and helps our domestic energy industry maintain worldwide technical leadership.

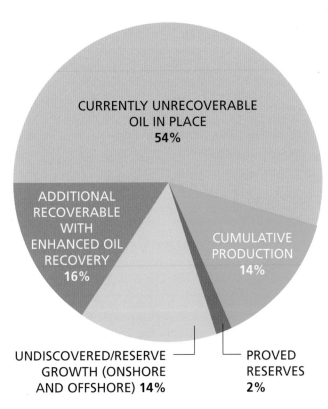

Source: Kuuskraa, V.A., "Undeveloped Domestic Oil Resources: The Foundation for Increasing Oil Production and a Viable Domestic Oil Industry," prepared for the U.S. Department of Energy, Office of Fossil Energy–Office of Oil and Natural Gas, Advanced Resources International (2006).

FIGURE 3-7. *Original, Developed, and Undeveloped Domestic Oil Resources*

Facing the Hard Truths about Energy

The Conventional Wells Topic Report examines the current state of technology relating to conventional oil and natural gas wells, including enhanced oil recovery (EOR) and arctic resources, and makes projections on how technology could influence these businesses in the future (Figure 3-8).

The size and nature of the original, developed and undeveloped domestic oil resources are included in Table 3-4. Note that the domestic oil resources described in this report do not include oil shale. As points of comparison with this table, current proven crude-oil reserves are 22 billion barrels and annual domestic crude-oil production is about 2 billion barrels.

Of the 582 billion barrels of oil in place in discovered fields, 208 billion barrels already have been produced or proved, leaving behind 374 billion barrels. A significant portion of these 374 billion barrels is immobile or residual oil left behind (stranded) after application of conventional (primary and secondary) oil-recovery technology.[13] With appropriate EOR technologies, 110 billion barrels of this stranded resource from already discovered fields may become technically recoverable, although the conditions for economic recoverability will change over the study period to 2030.

Undiscovered domestic oil is estimated to be 360 billion barrels in place, with 119 billion barrels (43 billion barrels from onshore, 76 billon barrels from offshore) being recoverable with primary or secondary recovery. Application of advanced EOR could add another 60 billion barrels of technically recoverable resource from this category.

Future reserve growth in discovered oil fields could amount to 210 billion barrels of oil in place, with 71 billion barrels (60 billion barrels from onshore and 11 billion barrels from offshore) being recoverable with primary and secondary recovery. Application of advanced EOR could raise this technically recoverable volume by up to 40 billion barrels.

With advances in thermal EOR technology, domestic oil sands holding 80 billion barrels of resource in place could provide up to 10 billion barrels of future technically recoverable domestic oil resource.

© SCHLUMBERGER, LTD.

FIGURE 3-8. *Seismic Vessel in Iced-In Conditions*

The estimates of remaining, recoverable, domestic oil resources from undiscovered and reserve growth are from the national resource assessments by the United States Geological Survey (USGS) and the U.S. Minerals Management Service (MMS). The estimates of recoverable oil resources using EOR technology on stranded oil and oil sands are based on work by Advanced Resources International for DOE/Fossil Energy's Office of Oil and Natural Gas.

Since the preparation and publication of the Kuuskraa paper that provided a basis for this report, considerable additional work has been completed by the author's firm that further confirms the estimates of undeveloped U.S. oil resources. A total of 10 domestic oil basins and areas have now been assessed (up from the original 6). These 10 assessments indicate that the technically recoverable oil resource from application of "state-of-the-art" CO_2-EOR is 89 billion barrels. The earlier estimate of 80 billion barrels for applying EOR to the stranded light oil resource has been updated to 90 billion barrels (rounded off), as shown in Table 3-4.

---

13 Although the definitions vary, simply speaking, primary recovery comes from a reservoir's natural energy, while secondary recovery involves flooding with water or gas.

Crude Oil Resources*	Original Oil In Place	Developed to Date		Remaining Oil In Place	Future Recovery[†]		
		Conventional Technology	EOR Technology		Conventional Technology	EOR[‡] Technology	Total
Discovered	582	(194)	(14)	374	0	110	110
Light Oil	482	(187)	(2)	293	0	90	90
Heavy Oil	100	(7)	(12)	81	0	20	20
Undiscovered	360	0	0	360	119	60	179
Reserve Growth	210	0	0	210	71	40	111
Transition Zone	100	0	0	100	0	20	20
Tar Sands	80	0	0	80	0	10	10
Total	1,332	(194)	(14)	1,124	190	240	430

* Does not include oil shale.
† Technically recoverable resources rounded to the nearest 10 billion barrels.
‡ Based on ten basin-oriented assessments and residual oil zone resource potential highlighted in reports released by the Department of Energy Office of Fossil Energy in February 2006. V.A. Kuuskraa provided the updated EOR technology numbers for this table.

Sources: This table updates numbers from a table of U.S. oil resources recovery potential in a report from Advanced Resources International by V.A. Kuuskraa, "Undeveloped Domestic Oil Resources: The Foundation for Increasing Oil Production and a Viable Domestic Oil Industry," prepared for the U.S. Department of Energy's Office of Fossil Fuel in February 2006, and available at http://www.fossil.energy. gov/programs/oilgas/publications/eor_co2/Undeveloped_Oil_Document.pdf. The updated numbers are available from ARI at http://www. fossil.energy.gov/programs/oilgas/publications/eor_co2/G_-_Updated_U_S__Oil_Resources_Table_2-1.pdf. Note that the EIA estimates of remaining reserves are lower than those used here, see information in the NPC data warehouse and http://tonto.eia.doe.gov/dnav/pet/ pet_crd_pres_dcu_NUS_a.htm.

TABLE 3-4. *Original, Developed, and Undeveloped Domestic Resources (Billions of Barrels)*

New work on the transition/residual oil zone resource documents the presence of 42 billion barrels of this category of oil in place in just three domestic oil basins (Permian, Big Horn, and Williston). Detailed reservoir simulation assessment shows that about 20 billion barrels of this oil in place could become technically recoverable by applying CO_2-EOR. This work provides support to the transition/residual oil zone resource estimate of 100 billion barrels in Table 3-4 and indicates that an important portion of this resource may become recoverable.

Finally, the author and his firm took an in-depth look at the additional oil recovery from applying "next-generation" CO_2-EOR technology. This work shows that combining: (1) advanced, high reservoir contact well designs; (2) mobility and miscibility enhancement; (3) large volumes of CO_2 injection; and (4) real-time performance feedback and process control technology could bring about "game changer" levels of improvement in oil recovery efficiency. This work provides support that a national average oil recovery efficiency target of 60 percent could become realistic, assuming a successful program of advanced technology development, affordable supplies of CO_2 and other EOR injectants, and appropriate risk-mitigation policies, such as federal and state tax incentives to help overcome the risk of applying these new technologies. The NPC studied EOR in 1976 and 1984, and raised great expectations for domestic EOR activity (projecting 3 million and 2 million barrels per day, respectively). These expectations have not been met. Peak domestic EOR

Technology	Time Frame	Discussion
Big increase in controlled reservoir contact	2015	Technologies allowing a continuing increase in the number of strategically placed horizontal wells will allow much greater commercial access to reserves.
Horizontal/multilateral/fishbone wells	2020	Multiple, placed drainholes from a main wellbore will further extend commercial access to reserves.
Arthroscopic-well construction	2025	The ability to place drain holes to within feet of every hydrocarbon molecule in the formation allows the ultimate in recovery.
SWEEP (see, access, move)	2020	The combined technologies (including the four immediately below) allowing us to see, access, and move the hydrocarbons in the optimum way will bring a big increase to recoverable reserves.
Smart well (injection and production)	2015	The ability to control what fluids go where (at the wellbore).
Reservoir characterization and simulation	2015	Extending current technology to include simultaneous inversion of all measurements with a forward model.
Reservoir vision and management in real time	2020	Combining reservoir-scale measurements (pressure, seismic, electromagnetic, and gravity) in a joint inversion, with uncertainty and without data loss.
Mission control for everything	2020	Representation and control of the full system (subsurface and surface) allowing true optimization.
CO_2 flood mobility control	2020	Measurement and control of the CO_2 flood front is critical for successful implementation.
Steam-assisted gravity drainage (SAGD)/steam and alkaline-surfactant-polymer (ASP) technology	2030	Technologies to perfect and optimize SAGD operations (including the use of ASP) will be key to widespread economic exploitation of heavy oil.
Arctic subsea-to-beach technology	2020	Ice scouring of the seafloor surface presents a huge challenge to conventional approaches to subsea and subsea-to-beach operations.
Faster and more affordable, higher-definition, 3D seismic	2015	Quicker, better, cheaper could extend this already impressive specialized technology into universal use.

TABLE 3-5. *Summary of Highly Significant Technologies for Conventional Wells*

production occurred in 1992 at 761,000 barrels per day. Current activity is 680,000 barrels per day. In the interim, many technologies have been tried, but most failed. Two successes are CO_2-miscible floods and steam (cyclic, steam-assisted gravity drainage, and steam flood).

A broad portfolio of oil-recovery policies and technologies, plus targeted risk-mitigation incentives, would help industry convert these higher-cost, undeveloped domestic oil resources into economically feasible reserves and production. Table 3-5 lists the future technologies that study participants believed will provide the greatest impact on conventional wells, including EOR and arctic.

EXPLORATION TECHNOLOGY

Exploration technology has evolved significantly since 1859, when the first commercial oil well in the United States was drilled adjacent to an oil seep in Pennsylvania. Perhaps the most significant technological advance was the development of two-dimensional (2D) reflection seismology in the 1920s. The emergence of 2D seismic lines with improved processing led to the discovery of many of the world's largest oil and natural gas fields in the following decades. In the 1990s, three-dimensional (3D) seismic technologies became the industry standard, with improved resolution and characterization of the subsurface geology. Today, new ways of looking at seismic data focus on specific attributes and derivative properties that enhance identification of hydrocarbon prospects (e.g., direct hydrocarbon indicators) as well as computer tools that aid in quantitative interpretation of rock and fluid properties.

Improvements in exploration technology have had a significant impact on discovering resources, reducing finding costs, and improving exploration success rates both in the United States and globally.[14] Thanks to technological improvements, costs for 3D seismic acquisition and processing fell by almost a factor of 5 from 1990 to 2001 (Figure 3-9).[15, 16] Despite the substantial improvements in exploration technology and reduction in deployment costs since the 1970s, oil and gas explorers have not maintained the high discovery volumes of that earlier period. This decrease came despite the increased amount of 3D seismic surveys being shot over the period. Several authors

FIGURE 3-9. *Graphic of Towed Seismic Streamers*

concluded that improved exploration and exploitation technology has prevented a more drastic decline in discovery volumes.[17]

Some authors have suggested that improved methods of exploring for unconventional resources might reverse the trend; however, it should be noted that many unconventional resources have already been discovered and await new exploitation technologies.

The future of exploration technologies is bright, but it is still likely that the volumes of hydrocarbons discovered with time will continue to decrease, as shown historically in Figure 3-10, although the exploration success rate may continue to improve.[18] The Exploration Technology Topic Report identified five core exploration-technology areas in which future developments have the potential to significantly improve exploration results over the next 25 years:

- Seismic technology—High- and ultrahigh-density acquisition technologies have great potential for

14 Boutte, D, "The Role of Technology in Shaping the Future of the E&P Industry," *The Leading Edge* 23, no. 2 (2004): 156-158.

15 Voola, J, "Technological Change and Industry Structure: A Case Study of the Petroleum Industry," *Economics of Innovation and New Technology* 15, no. 3 (2006): 271–288.

16 Voola, JJR, Osaghae, O, and Khan, JA, "Risk Reducing Technology and Quantity Competition: The Seismic Story," paper SPE 88583 presented at the SPE Asia Pacific Oil and Gas Conference and Exhibition, Perth, Australia (October 18–20, 2004).

17 Cuddington, JT and Moss, DL, "Technological Change, Depletion and the U.S. Petroleum Industry: A New Approach to Measurement and Estimation," Georgetown University Working Paper #96-10R (1998).

18 Bahorich, M, "End of Oil? No, It's a New Day Dawning," *Oil & Gas Journal* (August 21, 2006): 30–34.

advances. Rapid data processing could significantly improve seismic resolution of complex sub-salt, deep, or subtle geologic features.

- Controlled source electromagnetism (CSEM)—CSEM identifies subsurface hydrocarbon accumulations through a contrast in resistivity between hydrocarbon-saturated and water-saturated reservoirs. Two key potential improvements are:

  – Development of fast 3D modeling and inversion to reduce the number of erroneously identified "anomalies" (false positives)[19]

  – Extension of the technology to shallow-water and onshore settings.

- Interpretation technology—Interpreters struggle with the sheer volume and complexity of data and the need for increasingly quantitative interpretations. Two advances that could have significant results are:

  – Better integration of geophysical and geologic data to develop quantitative interpretations

  – Development of seismic search engines to interrogate increasing data volumes.[20]

- Earth-systems modeling—Modeling natural systems of basin formation, fill, and fluid migration is becoming increasingly common. Advances in modeling more-integrated earth systems along with capturing uncertainties in potential scenarios and parameters could significantly help explorationists to identify new plays (areas for exploration) and "sweet spots" (localized exploration targets).

- Subsurface measurements—Measurement of subsurface properties (fluid type, porosity, permeability, temperature, etc.) is crucial to exploration success. Advances in sensor types, durability, sensitivity, and deployment could improve exploration programs significantly by identifying both penetrated and bypassed "pay," that is, economically producible hydrocarbons that may or may not have been intercepted by a wellbore.

19 Inversion is a mathematical process by which data are used to generate a model that is consistent with the data. See www.glossary.oilfield.slb.com/Display.cfm?Term=inversion.

20 Barnes, A, "Seismic Attributes in Your Facies," *CSEG Recorder* (September 2001): 41-47.

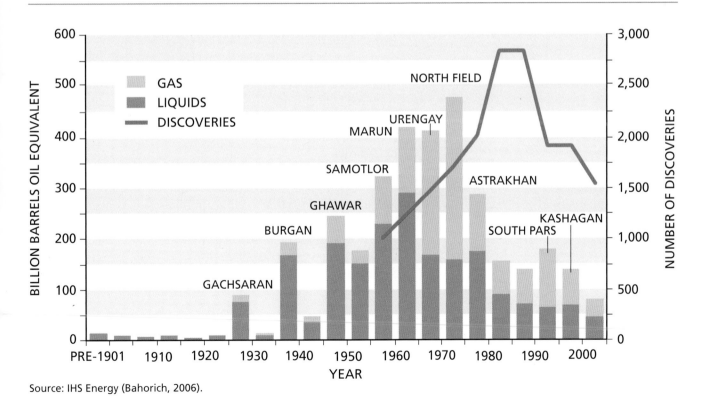

Source: IHS Energy (Bahorich, 2006).

FIGURE 3-10. *Evolution of Oil Discovery Volumes with Time (Total Discovered Resources to End-2004, excluding United States and Canada)*

This Exploration Technology Subgroup highlighted unconventional resources as a special category in the early stages of understanding (both exploration and exploitation) to which many of the core exploration technologies could potentially be applied. Two key advances could improve the effectiveness of exploration for unconventional resources:

- Improved measurement capabilities and predictive modeling of the geologic factors controlling hydrocarbon distribution and deliverability.

- Significant improvements in exploration or exploitation technologies that could help define exploration targets ("sweet spots") and the technologies needed to identify them.

The Exploration Technology Topic Report also identified auxiliary technologies in which future developments or applications have the potential to significantly improve exploration results by 2030:

- Drilling technology—Projected technical advances could improve the ability to tap new environments and encourage more exploration drilling of higher risk, new play types via reduced drilling costs.

- Nanotechnology—The most likely opportunities for applications are in increased sensor sensitivity, improved drilling materials, and faster and more powerful computing.

- Computational technology—Improvements in speed, memory, and cost will impact data acquisition, processing, and interpretation industry-wide.

Research into technologies that could mitigate potential environmental impacts will continue to

Technology	Significance	Brief Discussion
High-density seismic data and rapid data processing	High	Higher-density seismic-data acquisition with greater signal-to-noise ratios result in greater resolution, which allows for more robust interpretations of reservoir character and hydrocarbon potential to be made. However, for higher-density data to have commercial impact, substantial improvements in processing methods must be made.
Subsalt imaging (seismic)	High	Salt is a highly distorting acoustic lens that creates "blind spots" beneath it. Considerable efforts have been made to produce high-quality subsalt images resulting in drilling success in the Gulf of Mexico. Enhanced subsalt imaging will undoubtedly result in new discoveries and improved economics.
Fast controlled source electromagnetism (CSEM) 3D modeling and inversion	High	CSEM can discriminate between scenarios that are indistinguishable via seismic amplitudes; e.g., commercial oil versus residual (non-commercial) natural gas. However, false positives are common; e.g., hydrates, salts, and volcanics can yield a response similar to a commercial petroleum response. Fast 3D modeling and inversion capability can help discriminate against such false positives.
Integration of CSEM with structural information from seismic surveys	High	An important approach to increase the resolution of information obtained via CSEM methods.

TABLE 3-6. *Summary of Highly Significant Nearer-Term (by 2010) Exploration Technologies*

Facing the Hard Truths about Energy

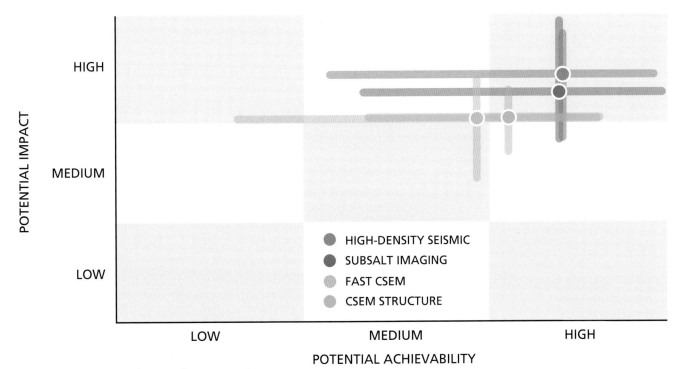

Note: CSEM = controlled source electromagnetism.

FIGURE 3-11. *Potential Impact versus Achievability for Nearer-Term Exploration Technology Advances*

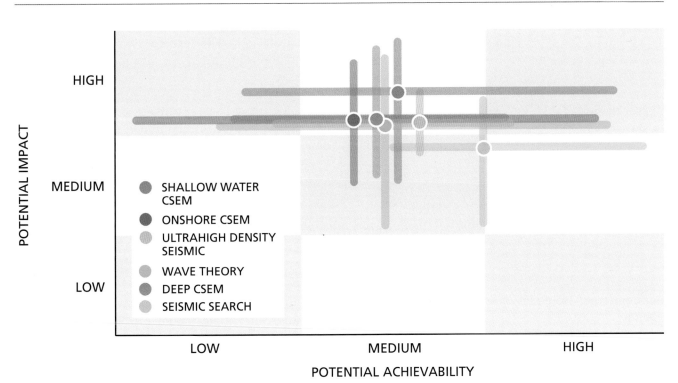

Note: CSEM = controlled source electromagnetism.

FIGURE 3-12. *Potential Impact versus Achievability for Longer-Term Exploration Technology Advances*

Technology	Significance	Brief Discussion
Shallow water controlled source electromagnetism (CSEM)	High	The shallow-water environment is much noisier than the deepwater environment for CSEM techniques. Substantial advances are needed to enable robust signal acquisition and analysis in such an environment. But, if successful, it can open up the application domain for CSEM beyond deepwater basins.
Onshore CSEM	High	The onshore environment is much noisier than the deepwater environment for electromagnetic techniques. Substantial advances are needed to enable robust signal acquisition and analysis in such an environment. But, if successful, it can open up the application domain for CSEM beyond deepwater basins.
Ultra high-density data and processing	High to medium	Data density and processing continue to improve at incremental steps. However, if extremely high-density data could be acquired and processed rapidly at low costs, game-changing breakthroughs could occur. These include new hydrocarbon discoveries as well as exploitation efficiencies.
Wave theory research (seismic)	Potential high impact but with attendant high risk	Basic research into wave theory is a continuing effort in both industry and academia. Synergistic collaborations between the two have led to gradual improvements in processing and could result in large leaps forward. For example, it should enable more accurate quantitative modeling of key seismic data.
Deep CSEM	High to medium	Even in deep water, current application is limited to relatively shallow reservoirs (6,500 to 10,000 feet below sea floor). Advances in penetration depth could open up applications in several new basins.
Development of an automated "seismic search engine" to find new opportunities	Medium to high	This type of technology would take advantage of advances in computational power, pattern-recognition technology, geophysical data, and geological concepts in a highly automated fashion.

TABLE 3-7. *Summary of Highly Significant Longer-Term Exploration Technologies*

be important. Examples of active areas of research include:

- Mud recovery without a riser from seabed to surface, which reduces discharge
- Ultra-extended-reach drilling, which can help avoid sensitive surface environments
- Research into seismic sources that are alternatives to the conventional seismic airgun arrays.

Complementary research efforts on marine biology and other topics could provide better data to improve informed-risk assessment, public debate, and informed decision-making by regulatory agencies.

Significant nearer-term technologies are outlined in Table 3-6 and Figure 3-11, with longer-term technologies described in Table 3-7 and Figure 3-12.

DEEPWATER TECHNOLOGY

Deepwater oil and natural gas resources are conventional reserves in an unconventional setting. They constitute a resource class of their own, largely because they face a common set of technological challenges as they are identified, developed, and produced (Figure 3-13).

The U.S. Gulf of Mexico represents a clear case where the more we know, the more attractive the opportunities for oil exploration and discovery become. Figure 3-14 illustrates that our appreciation for the scope of the potential total Gulf of Mexico resource has grown dramatically as deepwater production has come online.[21]

Deepwater exploration is a success for both technology and policy that is still in the making. The data continue to support significant scope for economic oil and natural gas resource development in both U.S.

© SCHLUMBERGER, LTD.

FIGURE 3-13. *Offshore Platforms*

and global deep oceans. Ahead lie four top-priority, deepwater-specific technological challenges:

1. Reservoir characterization: predicting and monitoring the production behavior of increasingly complex reservoirs with fewer—but more costly—direct well penetrations.

---

21 Report to Congress: Comprehensive Inventory of U.S. OCS Oil and Natural Gas Resources, Energy Policy Act of 2005 – Section 357. Available at www.mms.gov/revaldiv/PDFs/FinalInvRptToCongress050106.pdf .

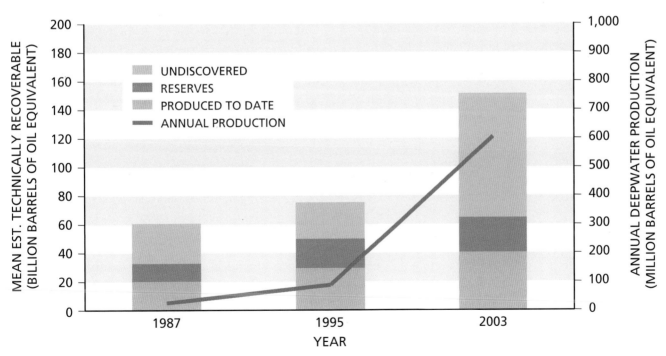

Source: Report to Congress: Comprehensive Inventory of U.S. OCS Oil and Natural Gas Resources, Energy Policy Act of 2005 – Section 357.

FIGURE 3-14. *U.S. Gulf of Mexico Oil and Natural Gas Resource Endowment*

2. Extended system architecture: subsea systems for flow assurance (the ability to produce and move fluids to surface), well control, power distribution and data communications that improve recovery and extend the reach of production hubs to remote resources.

3. High-pressure and high-temperature (HPHT) completion systems: materials and equipment to reliably produce the growing number of deepwater resources in corrosive environments with extraordinary pressures and temperatures.

4. Metocean (combined meteorological and oceanic) forecasting and systems analysis: integrated models to predict both atmospheric and below surface "weather" and engineering system response.

Within these four priority areas, HPHT completion systems and metocean forecasting and systems analysis represent opportunities for practical government and industry cooperation. Accelerating progress in HPHT service is likely to cost hundreds of millions of dollars over many years. Excellent potential exists to transfer or co-develop fundamental materials science and engineering technologies across industry boundaries—most notably aerospace and military (especially naval). Thus, although these are domains of intentional industry pursuit, there is compelling scope for collaborative research in academia and government labs. Theoretical developments for both the weather and engineering systems could be accelerated with a few millions of dollars. Development and operation of regional data-acquisition technologies and associated predictive capabilities will likely cost tens to hundreds of millions of dollars.

Additionally, it is important to understand that deepwater technology is tightly related to topics covered by other NPC Technology Topic Papers (Table 3-8). We have also identified two issues that we conclude are critical to the continued successful development of oil and natural gas resources in ever-harsher ocean environments (Table 3-9).

Marine sciences and engineering is a specialty field in which many disciplines (e.g., mechanical and civil engineering) can be taught to apply known techniques. However, the few small centers of excellence that have historically trained the leading marine thinkers, conceptualizers, and innovators are disappearing due to university competition for research in information-, nano-, and bio-technologies—MIT, Michigan, and Berkeley, for example. The U.S. Navy has also recognized this nationally important concern. Improving the current situation is likely to cost tens of millions of dollars for top-tier universities in ocean sciences and marine engineering.

A second key issue, policies about access to acreage for the purposes of oil and natural gas exploration and development, raises complex matters. However, access to acreage with potential for economic oil and natural gas resources is itself a major—perhaps primary—driver encouraging technology development. For example, the onset of area-wide leasing for the U.S. Gulf of Mexico in the early 1980s led to significant acceleration of interest in deepwater regions.

Technology	Significance	Brief Discussion
Subsalt imaging (Exploration technology topic)	Finding large new resources	Novel seismic processing methods that enable one to accurately image below complex salt layers
Gas liquefaction (Supply topic)	Bringing remote natural gas to market	Technology to convert natural gas into more easily transportable forms becomes more valuable with both distance from shore and water depth
Arctic (Conventional well technology topic)	Large untapped offshore regions	Economic development of oil and natural gas in the offshore arctic will likely build on traditional deepwater technologies

TABLE 3-8. *Summary of Technologies Related to Deepwater Technology, in Priority Order*

Facing the Hard Truths about Energy

Technology	Significance	Brief Discussion
Future marine technology leadership	Innovation capability	Reduced centers of excellence in specialized field of marine science and engineering will limit inflow of technical experts required to keep industry moving forward after the "big crew change"
Valuing technology to enable access	Innovation motivation	Access to acreage with potential for economic oil and natural gas resources is in and of itself a primary, if not the largest, driver that encourages technology development

TABLE 3-9. *Summary of Key Deepwater Issues, in Priority Order*

The coming decade will be pivotal for determining our ability to safely and economically develop the energy resource endowment in U.S. and global oceans. At the very time the drive to ultra-deep waters is increasing both the magnitude and complexity of the challenge, the technological capacity of the workforce faces untimely impairment by "the big crew change." The future of deepwater exploration and production depends on industry and governments successfully co-navigating this linked technology and policy transition.

UNCONVENTIONAL NATURAL GAS RESERVOIRS—TIGHT GAS, COAL SEAMS, AND SHALES

Unconventional natural gas resources—including tight sands, coalbed methane, and gas shales—constitute some of the largest components of remaining natural gas resources in the United States. Unconventional natural gas is the term commonly used to refer to low-permeability reservoirs that produce mainly natural gas with little or no associated hydrocarbon liquids. Many of the low-permeability reservoirs that have been developed in the past are sandstone, but significant quantities of gas are also produced from low-permeability carbonates, shales, and coal seams. One way to define unconventional natural gas is that "the reservoir cannot be produced at economic flow rates nor recover economic volumes of natural gas unless the well is stimulated by a large hydraulic fracture treatment, a horizontal wellbore, or by using multilateral wellbores."[22]

Research and development on the geologic controls and production technologies required to evaluate and produce these unconventional natural gas resources have provided many new technologies during the past several decades. New technologies have enabled operators in the United States to unlock the vast potential of these challenging resources, boosting production levels to about 30 percent of current U.S. natural gas production (Figure 3-15).

Around the world, unconventional natural gas resources are widespread but, with several exceptions,

© SCHLUMBERGER, LTD.

FIGURE 3-15. *Land Drilling Rig*

---

22 Holditch, SA, "Tight Gas Sands," SPE Paper 103356, Distinguished Author Series (2006).

---

they have not received close attention from natural gas operators. This is due, in part, because geologic and engineering information on unconventional resources is scarce, and natural gas policies and market conditions have been unfavorable for development in many countries. In addition, there is a chronic shortage of expertise in the specific technologies needed to successfully develop these resources. As a result, only limited development has taken place to date outside North America. Interest is growing, however, and during the last decade development of unconventional natural gas reservoirs has occurred in Canada, Australia, Mexico, Venezuela, Argentina, Indonesia, China, Russia, Egypt, and Saudi Arabia.

Many of those who have estimated the volumes of natural gas in place within unconventional gas reservoirs agree that it is a large resource (Table 3-10). Using the United States as an analogy, there is good reason to expect that unconventional gas reservoir production will increase significantly around the world in the coming decades.

Tight Gas Sands

From a global perspective, tight gas resources can be considered vast, but undefined. No systematic evaluation has been carried out on global emerging resources. The magnitude and distribution of worldwide resources of natural gas in tight sands, as well as gas shales and coalbed methane formations, have yet to be understood.

From almost no production in the early 1970s, today unconventional resources, particularly tight sands, provide almost 30 percent of domestic natural gas supply in the United States. The volumes of natural gas produced from U.S. unconventional resources are projected to increase in importance over the next 25 years, reaching production levels as high as 22 billion cubic feet per day (Figure 3-16).

Region	Coalbed Methane	Shale Gas	Gas in Tight Sands	Total
North America	3,017	3,840	1,371	8,228
Latin America	39	2,116	1,293	3,448
Western Europe	157	509	353	1,019
Central and Eastern Europe	118	39	78	235
Former Soviet Union	3,957	627	901	5,485
Middle East and North Africa	0	2,547	823	3,370
Sub-Saharan Africa	39	274	784	1,097
Centrally Planned Asia and China	1,215	3,526	353	5,094
Pacific	470	2,312	705	3,487
Other Asia Pacific	0	313	549	862
South Asia	39	0	196	235
World	9,051	16,103	7,406	32,560

Source: Kawata and Fujita, "Some Predictions of Possible Unconventional Hydrocarbons Availability Until 2100," Society of Petroleum Engineers, SPE Paper 68755, 2001.

TABLE 3-10. *Distribution of Worldwide Unconventional Natural Gas Resources (Trillion Cubic Feet)*

Facing the Hard Truths about Energy

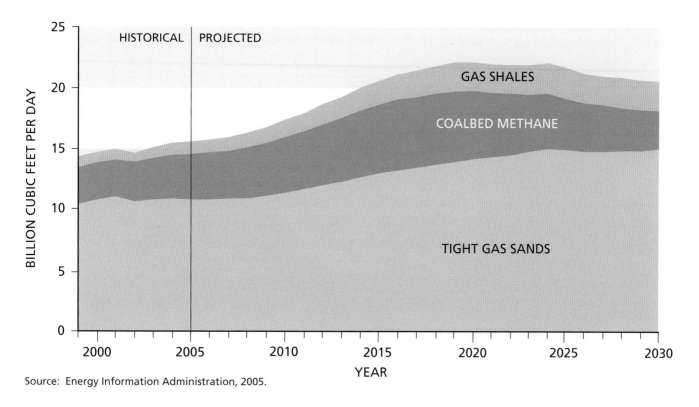

FIGURE 3-16. *U.S. Unconventional Natural Gas Production and Future Projection*

Coal Seams

Coalbed methane (CBM) perhaps best exemplifies how technology can influence the understanding and eventual development of a natural gas resource. While natural gas has been known to exist in coal seams since the beginning of the coal-mining industry, only since 1989 has significant production been realized (Figure 3-17).

CBM is a resource that was drilled through and observed for many years, yet never produced. New technology and focused CBM research ultimately unlocked the production potential. CBM now provides more than 4.4 billion cubic feet of natural gas production a day in the United States, and is under development worldwide, including the countries of Canada, Australia, India, and China.

In many respects, the factors controlling CBM production behavior are similar to those for conventional natural gas resources, yet they differ considerably in other important ways. One prominent difference is the understanding of the resource, especially the values of gas in place. Natural gas in coal seams adsorbs to the coal surface, allowing for significantly more to be stored than in conventional rocks amid shallow, low-pressure formations. To release the adsorbed gas for production, operators must substantially reduce the pressure in the reservoir. Adsorbed gas volumes are not important for conventional gas resources, but are critical for CBM reservoirs. Significant research was required in the 1990s to fully understand how to produce the adsorbed gas in coal seams, and to develop the technology required to explore for—and produce—CBM reservoirs.

A major difference between CBM reservoirs and sandstone gas reservoirs is that many of the coal seams are initially saturated with water. Thus, large volumes of water must be pumped out of the coal seams before realizing any significant gas production. This water production reduces the pressure so desorption will occur. The technology developed in the 1990s for understanding and dewatering coal seams allowed significant CBM development in several U.S. geologic basins.

Shale Gas

Shale rocks act as both the source of the natural gas and the reservoir that contains it. Natural gas is stored

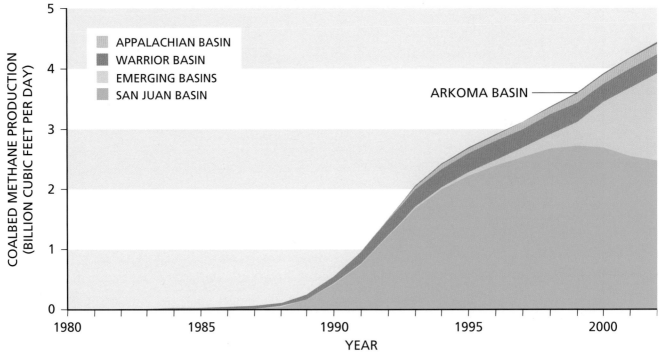

FIGURE 3-17. *Natural Gas Production from Coal Seams in the United States*

Source: IHS Energy.

in the shale in three forms: free gas in rock pores, free gas in natural fractures, and adsorbed gas on organic matter and mineral surfaces. These different storage mechanisms affect the speed and efficiency of gas production.

Shale gas production in the United States has shown that stimulation techniques, especially hydraulic fracturing, are almost always necessary for shale gas production. Other important technology advances include applying horizontal and directional drilling, and characterizing reservoirs. For wells in the Barnett Shale (near Fort Worth, Texas), using technology currently available, the per-well recovery factor averages 7 percent of the gas in place. This is far below a potentially achievable 20 percent recovery factor.

In areas with limited surface access and landowner restrictions, horizontal drilling has been applied. Horizontal wells provide greater wellbore contact within the reservoir rocks than do vertical wells. Microseismic fracture mapping has also been successfully used to improve the evaluation of hydraulic fracturing in the horizontal wells.

Tables of Advances

Tables 3-11, 3-12, and 3-13 describe current technology under development and that which needs to be developed and used in future years. These tables indicate only the high-impact technologies; others are described in the Unconventional Gas Topic Paper. The priority was determined by estimating the difference in impact between a business-as-usual case and an accelerated-technology case. High impact includes those technologies having greatest possibilities for producing more gas or reducing cost, while for moderate impact effectiveness is lesser or is more difficult to measure.

The amount of research and development needed to fully develop a given technology is described in these tables as follows:

- Incremental—research and development as usual
- Accelerated—research and development as usual, but with a major increase in funding (factors of 3 to 5)
- Breakthrough—substantial increase in funding (factors of 10 to 100) and more use of consortiums.

Facing the Hard Truths about Energy

Unconventional Gas Technology Under Development or Anticipated by 2010	Research and Development Required for Success	Discussion
Fracture modeling and analysis, full 3D models for new types of treatments	Accelerated	Incorporating new physics for fracture propagation, in naturally fractured reservoirs, fracture-proppant transport, and better models for horizontal and multilateral wells.
New fracturing fluids and proppants	Incremental	Strong, light-weight proppants are needed. Better fluids that do not damage the reservoir and fracture must be developed.
Hydraulic fracturing methods used in horizontal wells	Incremental	Fort Worth basin (Barnett Shale): increased production rate by 2 to 3 times rate of vertical well.
Stimulation methods used in naturally fractured formations	Incremental	Gas shales and coal seam reservoirs are normally naturally fractured. We need a better understanding and better technologies for such reservoirs to include better models to determine gas storage and gas production using multiple gas systems, such as CO_2, wet gas, and N_2.
Micro-seismic fracture mapping and post-fracture diagnostics	Accelerated	Fort Worth basin (Barnett Shale): improved understanding of hydraulic fracturing in horizontal wells so that designs can be improved.
Data collection and availability during drilling, completions, stimulations, and production	Incremental	Significant data are being generated by increased drilling and new tools and techniques. The ability to handle and use data is being challenged. The data need to be evaluated in detail to learn more about formation evaluation, fracture treatments and production.
Integrated reservoir characterization of geologic, seismic, petrophysical, and engineering data	Accelerated	More complex reservoirs, lower permeability, greater depth and more cost require a more in-depth understanding of reservoir petrophysics. Better models will be required to properly integrate all the data and optimize the drilling and completion methods.
Horizontal drilling and multilateral wellbore capability	Accelerated	Enables development of stacked, thin-bed coal seams and reduces environmental impact. Also need to develop multiple wells from a single pad. This technology is very important in shale-gas reservoirs, and sometimes important in tight-gas reservoirs.
Reservoir characterization through laboratory measurements	Accelerated	We need better core-analysis measurements for basic parameters such as permeability, porosity, and water saturation. In coal seams and shales, we need better methods for estimating sorbed gas volumes and gas-in-place values in the reservoir.
Reservoir imaging tools	Incremental	Understanding the reservoir characteristics is an ongoing challenge and priority for all unconventional reservoirs.
Overall environmental technology	Accelerated	We need to reduce the impact of operations on the environment by reducing waste, reducing noise, using smaller drilling pads and adequate handling of waste water.
Produced water handling, processing and disposal	Accelerated	Coal seams and shale gas continue to produce significant volumes of water. Efficient handling and environmentally safe and low impact disposal are needed.

TABLE 3-11. *Summary of Currently Developing Technologies for Unconventional Natural Gas from Now to 2010 (Those with High Significance Only)*

2020 Technology for Unconventional Gas Reservoirs	Research and Development Required for Success	Discussion
Real-time sweet-spot detection while drilling	Breakthrough	Will allow the steering of the drill bit to the most productive areas of the reservoir.
Coiled tubing drilling for wells less than 5,000 ft.	Accelerated	Will allow the advantages of continuous tubing drilling to be realized (fast drilling, small footprint, and rapid rig moves) for currently difficult drilling areas.
3D seismic applications for imaging layers and natural fractures in shale reservoirs	Accelerated	We could improve recovery efficiency from existing wells if we used well testing methods to better understand the reservoirs.
Produced-water processing	Accelerated	Produced water is processed and utilized such that it no longer is viewed as a waste stream but as a valuable product for agriculture, industrial use, and for all well drilling and completion needs.
Deep drilling	Incremental	We need to determine how deep we can develop coalbed methane, shale gas and other naturally fractured unconventional reservoirs.
Enhanced coalbed methane production via CO_2 injection/ sequestration	Accelerated	We need to determine the technological solutions and screening of suitable pairing of deposits and CO_2 sources.
Data handling and databases	Incremental	Databases are available and user-friendly allowing access to geologic and engineering data for most North American basins, and are being developed for geologic basins worldwide.

TABLE 3-12. *Summary of Technologies Anticipated for 2020 (Those with High Significance Only)*

2030 Technology for Unconventional Gas Reservoirs	Research and Development Required for Success	Discussion
Resource characterization and gas-in-place potential	Accelerated	All of the basins worldwide need to be assessed for unconventional gas potential. The results should be recorded in databases and made available to the producing community around the world.
Well drilling and completion	Accelerated	Well drilling technology must be advanced through improvement in downhole drilling systems, better metallurgy and real-time downhole sensors allowing drilling to sweet spots, use of underbalanced drilling where needed, advantages of continuous tubing drilling, and efficient utilization of multilaterals.

TABLE 3-13. *Summary of Technologies Anticipated for 2030 (Those with High Significance Only)*

UNCONVENTIONAL HYDROCARBONS: HEAVY OIL, EXTRA-HEAVY OIL, AND BITUMEN

Heavy oil, extra-heavy oil, and bitumen are unconventional oil resources that are characterized by high viscosity (resistance to flow) and high density compared to conventional oil. Most heavy oil and bitumen deposits originated as conventional oil that formed in deep formations, but migrated almost to the surface where they were degraded by bacteria and by weathering, and where the lightest hydrocarbons escaped (Figure 3-18). Heavy oil and bitumen are deficient in hydrogen and have high carbon, sulfur, and heavy metal content. Hence, they require additional processing (upgrading) to become a suitable feedstock for a normal refinery.

The IEA estimates that there are 6 trillion barrels of heavy oil worldwide, with 2 trillion barrels ultimately recoverable.[23] Western Canada is estimated to hold 2.5 trillion barrels, with current reserves of 175 billion barrels. Venezuela is estimated to hold 1.5 trillion barrels, with current reserves of 270 billion barrels. Russia may also have more than 1 trillion barrels of heavy oil. Heavy-oil resources in the United States amount to 100 to 180 billion barrels of oil, with large resources in Alaska (44 billion barrels), California (47 billion barrels), Utah (19 to 32 billion barrels), Alabama (6 billion barrels), and Texas (5 billion barrels). Heavy oil has been produced in California for 100 years, and currently amounts to 500,000 barrels per day of oil. Heavy oil resources in Alaska are being developed on a small scale with less than 23,000 barrels per day of oil in 2003.[24] Heavy oil and bitumen resources in Western Canada and the United States could provide long-term, stable, and secure sources of oil for the United States. Most of these resources are currently untapped.

Heavy oil is also located—and being produced—in Indonesia, China, Mexico, Brazil, Trinidad, Argentina, Ecuador, Colombia, Oman, Kuwait, Egypt, Saudi Arabia, Turkey, Australia, India, Nigeria, Angola, Eastern Europe, the North Sea, Iran, and Italy.

© SCHLUMBERGER, LTD.

FIGURE 3-18. *High-Viscosity Heavy Oil Acquired by Wireline Sampling*

Exploration technology has minor significance since large resources have already been discovered, but optimizing production technology is important. Because heavy oil, extra-heavy oil, and bitumen do not flow readily in most reservoirs, they require specialized production methods. Very shallow oil sands can be mined. Slightly deeper deposits can be produced by increasing reservoir contact with horizontal wells and multilaterals (multiply branched wellbores), producing the oil with large amounts of sand, or by injecting steam, which lowers the viscosity and reduces the residual oil saturation, thus improving recovery efficiency (Figure 3-19). In situ combustion has also been used to heat the reservoir, but several technical and economic challenges limit application of this technique. A few reservoirs are sufficiently hot that heavy oil can be produced using essentially conventional methods.

The production of heavy oil, extra-heavy oil, and bitumen is economic at current oil prices with existing production technologies. However, heavy oil and bitumen sell at a lower price than conventional oil because it is more difficult to process the heavier crude to create refined products, and because fewer refineries have the capability to process it. In addition, production is more costly than for conventional oil, so the profit margin is less. If an oil company has equal access to conventional oil and to heavy oil,

23 Christian Besson, *Resources to Reserves, Oil & Gas Technologies for the Future*, International Energy Agency (2005), p. 75.

24 *Undeveloped Domestic Oil Resources: The Foundation for Increasing Oil Production and a Viable Domestic Oil Industry*, Advanced Resources International, Feb. 2006, p. 12, 18.

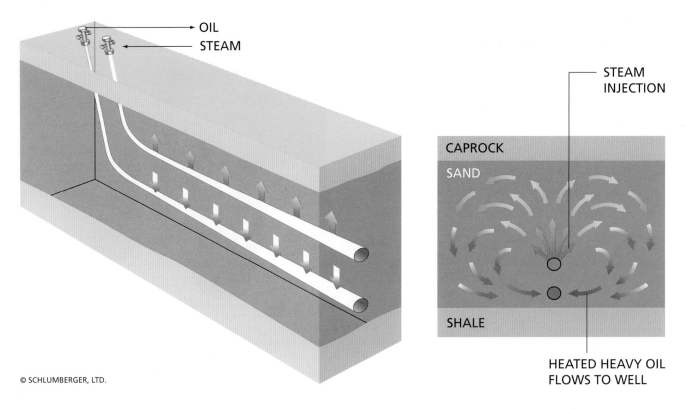

OIL
STEAM

STEAM INJECTION

CAPROCK

SAND

SHALE

HEATED HEAVY OIL FLOWS TO WELL

© SCHLUMBERGER, LTD.

FIGURE 3-19. *Steam-Assisted Gravity Drainage Process for Producing Heavy Oil*

economics would favor conventional oil. However, gaining access to conventional oil resources is becoming more difficult in many countries.

There are several barriers to the rapid growth of heavy oil, extra-heavy oil, and bitumen production. Open-pit mining has a large environmental

Method	Locations used	Factors
Open pit mining	Canada, for shallow oil sands	High recovery factor, but high environmental impact
Cold production using horizontal wells and multilateral wells	Venezuela and some use in North Sea	Low recovery factor, may use water drive (North Sea)
Cold heavy oil production with sand (CHOPS)	Western Canada, to exploit thin layers	Low recovery factor, needs good gas/oil ratio, unconsolidated sands
Cyclic steam stimulation (CSS)	United States, Canada, Indonesia, many others	Reduce viscosity of heavy oil, needs good caprock, fair to good recovery factor
Steam flood	United States, Canada, Indonesia, many others	Follow-up to CSS for inter-well oil, good to high recovery factor
Steam-assisted gravity drainage (SAGD)	Canada	Allows production from shallower sands with weaker caprock

TABLE 3-14. *Major Commercial Production Methods for Heavy Oils*

Facing the Hard Truths about Energy

Method	Time Frame	Description	Advantage
Vapex	2010	Use solvent rather than steam in SAGD-type wells	Lower energy consumption, low production rates
Hybrid	2010	Solvent plus steam in SAGD, CSS, and steam-flood wells	Lower energy consumption, increased production
In situ combustion with vertical and horizontal wells	2010	Uses heavy oil in reservoir and injected air	Eliminate need for natural gas for steam generation
Downhole heating with electricity	2010	Resistance, induction, or radio-frequency	Offshore, deep and arctic regions
Alternative fuels with gasification and carbon capture and sequestration	2020/ 2030	Uses coal, coke, or heavy ends for energy and hydrogen	CO_2 reduction in a CO_2 limited world
Nuclear power plant fit-for-purpose	2020/ 2030	Small scale for energy and hydrogen production	CO_2 reduction in a CO_2 limited world, safety, proliferation, fuel disposal, societal concerns
In situ upgrading	2020/ 2030	Application of in-situ thermal energy with or without catalysts to upgrade oil in place	Critical energy balance
Downhole steam generation	2020/ 2030	Possible options include generating heat downhole from either electricity or combustion of fuel.	Arctic, offshore, deep formations
Combination subsurface mining and well production techniques	2020/ 2030		Arctic and extremely restricted surface footprint environments

TABLE 3-15. *Major Heavy-Oil Production Methods, with Time Frame for Commercialization*

impact and can only exploit resources near the surface; further, it is a mature technology and only evolutionary improvements in efficiency are likely. By contrast, there are several commercial in situ production technologies, and several more are in research or the pilot phase. Many of the in situ production methods require an external energy source to heat the heavy oil to reduce its viscosity. Natural gas is currently the predominant fuel used to generate steam, but it is becoming more expensive due to tight supplies in North America. Alternative fuels such as coal, heavy oil, or byproducts of heavy-oil upgrading could be used, but simply burning them will release large quantities of CO_2. One option is gasification with carbon capture and sequestration. Nuclear power has also been proposed as a heat source, but faces societal opposition. Another fuel option is using the unconventional oil itself by injecting air into the reservoir for in situ combustion.

Other in situ methods are undergoing pilot testing. Vapex uses a solvent to reduce heavy-oil viscosity by itself or in combination with steam. These could reduce energy requirements and possibly open resources that are too deep, in arctic regions, or offshore where steam injection is difficult. Other options are generating steam downhole, or directly heating the formation by electricity—such as resistance, induction, or radio-frequency heating. Research indicates that some in situ upgrading may also be possible with heat, combustion, solvents, or catalysts.

Heavy oil, extra-heavy oil, and bitumen projects are large, capital-intensive undertakings. This capital spending includes the production infrastructure and additional upgrading, refining, and transportation facilities, plus pipelines for heavy oil and possibly for CO_2 sequestration. Another issue is obtaining a sufficient supply of diluent for moving heavy oil by pipeline. These projects also have long operating and payback periods, so unstable oil prices can deter long-term investments. Skilled people are also required to staff these projects.

Technologies that upgrade value, drive down costs, and reduce environmental effects will have the greatest influence on increasing the production of heavy oil, extra-heavy oil, and bitumen. There are a large number of technologies that can achieve these goals, but there is no single, simple solution owing to the tremendous variety of heavy oil, extra-heavy oil, and bitumen resources.

A list of commercial production methods is shown in Table 3-14, and a list of pre-commercial production methods is in Table 3-15.

UNCONVENTIONAL HYDROCARBONS: OIL SHALE

Oil shale comprises a host rock and kerogen. Kerogen is organic matter that has not gone through the "oil window" of elevated temperature and pressure necessary to generate conventional light crude oil. Kerogen has a high hydrogen/carbon ratio, giving it the potential to be superior to heavy oil or coal as a source of liquid fuel (Figure 3-20). Globally, it is estimated that there are roughly 3 trillion barrels of shale oil in place, which is comparable to the original world endowment of conventional oil. About half of this immense total is to be found near the common borders of Wyoming, Utah, and Colorado, where much of

FIGURE 3-20. *Shale Core, with Scanning Electron Micrograph indicating Kerogen Content*

the resource occurs at a saturation of more than 25 gallons of product per ton of ore (about 10 percent by weight) in beds that are 100 to 1,000 feet thick. Like heavy oil reservoirs, oil shale is found near the surface, ranging from outcrops down to about 3,300 feet.

In the past, the most common production technology has been surface mining in conjunction with processing in above-ground retorts. With process temperatures at about 930°F, these techniques convert kerogen to oil in about an hour. This approach has the virtue of simplicity, but requires expensive surface facilities and the disposal of vast quantities of spent rock. Both pose significant economic and environmental problems. Moreover, raw product quality is poor compared to conventional crude oil; however, upgrading using conventional hydroprocessing techniques yields high-quality finished products.

The mining and retort method is an old approach that could benefit from new technology. Improved methods for spent shale remediation would clearly make this approach more acceptable. Improved retorting methods are also a priority. Innovations that allow oil shale to be processed at lower temperature without an increase in reaction time would result in improved economics and improved product quality.

An alternative process still in development, in situ conversion, has captured the industry's attention. Wells are drilled, and the oil shale reservoir is slowly heated to about 660°F, at which point kerogen is converted to oil and gas over months. Using an in situ conversion process at pilot scale, Shell has extracted a good quality middle distillate refinery feedstock, requiring no further upgrading. In order to contain nascent fluids, and to prevent groundwater from seeping into the reaction zone, Shell generates a "freeze wall" around the production area. Chevron has proposed a simpler technique that takes advantage of the low hydraulic permeability of oil shale formations to isolate heated process volumes from surrounding aquifers.

Because in situ conversion technology is just emerging, it is not yet clear which specific techniques can advance the state of the art over the coming decades. However, the efficient use of heat is almost certain to be an important issue. The ability to map the temperature and the saturation of generated oil and natural gas throughout the reservoir would enable advanced control strategies. It will also be useful to monitor the freeze wall or low permeability barrier, to ensure that there is no fluid mixing between the reaction zone and surrounding formations.

As a domestic source of transportation fuel, oil shale could compete with heavy oil and coal-derived liquids. Oil shale, heavy oil, and coal are all abundant in North America. Canadian tar-sand production is already commercial. Coal can be treated with coal-derived solvents and gaseous hydrogen at high temperature to produce high-grade synthetic crude oil. An advantage of oil shale is that it has the potential to produce a superior liquid fuel product. However, the direct and indirect costs for fuel production from oil shale have yet to be fully evaluated.

The estimated time frames in which the commercial application of potential advances in oil shale technologies occur are listed below.

- 2010—None.

- 2020—Improved methods of shale remediation; innovative surface retort architecture and chemistry; and pilot scale in situ conversion methods.

- 2030—Large-scale oil shale production.

UNCONVENTIONAL HYDROCARBONS: GAS HYDRATES

Gas hydrates constitute a class of crystalline compounds in which individual gas molecules reside within cages of water molecules. Gas hydrates are solids and have physical properties similar to those of ordinary ice. They form when a hydrocarbon gas, such as methane or a natural gas mixture, comes in contact with liquid water at high pressure and low temperature.

Gas hydrates are found within and under permafrost in arctic regions. They are also found within a few hundred meters of the seafloor on continental slopes and in deep seas and lakes. The reservoir architecture, technology needs, and eventual economic importance of hydrates in arctic and marine environments may be very different. Therefore they are considered separately in this report.

Arctic Hydrates

Gas hydrates are found within and beneath permafrost on the North Slope of Alaska, in the Canadian arctic, and in northern Siberia. Some of these accumulations are in areas where there has been significant conventional hydrocarbon development, with associated modern seismic and well-data surveys. In those areas, resources have been quantitatively evaluated. The results suggest that arctic hydrates have the potential to become economically viable sources of natural gas.

The best-documented Alaskan accumulations are in the Prudhoe Bay-Kuparuk River area. These contain about 30 trillion cubic feet of natural gas, which is about twice the volume of conventional gas found in the Prudhoe Bay field.[25] The proximity to highly developed oilfield infrastructure makes the Prudhoe-Kuparuk accumulation particularly attractive. The absence of a natural gas pipeline to market means that currently the gas is stranded. However, even without a pipeline, this resource may possibly enable the development of the nearby Schrader Bluff and Ugnu heavy oil reservoirs, which together amount to about 25 billion barrels of original oil in place.

The main technology barrier is the lack of validated methods for economically viable natural-gas production from hydrates. An arctic site capable of supporting multi-year field experiments would provide an opportunity for significant progress beyond the present state of knowledge.

25 Collett, TS, "Energy Resource Potential of Natural Gas Hydrates," *AAPG Bulletin* 86 (2002): 1971–1992.

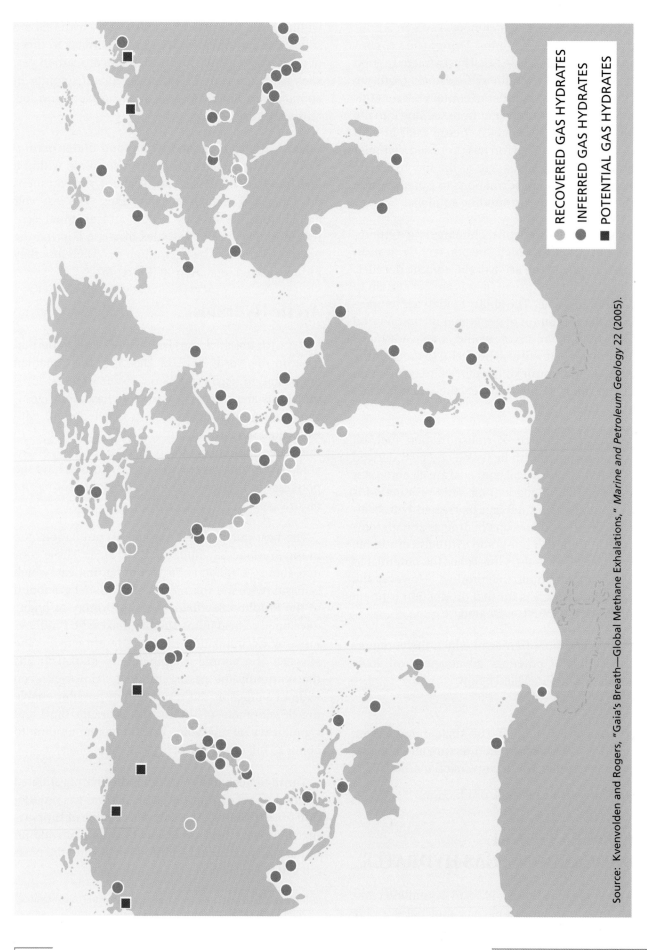

Source: Kvenvolden and Rogers, "Gaia's Breath—Global Methane Exhalations," *Marine and Petroleum Geology* 22 (2005).

FIGURE 3-21. *Sites where Natural Gas Hydrates have been Recovered or are Inferred*

Marine Hydrates

A widely quoted USGS estimate predicts that there is twice as much organic carbon in gas hydrates as in all recoverable and unrecoverable conventional fossil fuel resources, including natural gas, coal, and oil.[26] Much of this endowment has been thought to be located on continental slopes in close proximity to major energy-consuming nations (Figure 3-21).[27] Estimates of hydrate-bound gas abundance have been repeatedly scaled back over the years, although large uncertainties remain.[28, 29]

Worldwide, only a few dozen boreholes have been drilled to assess marine hydrate resources. Most of these boreholes were drilled offshore around Japan in 2004,[30] and offshore from India in 2006. Comprehensive reports of these campaigns are not yet in the public domain, so there is a scant record available on which to assess the efficacy of exploration paradigms. Thus, the main technology barrier is the lack of validated means of reliably finding significant marine gas hydrate resources. A multi-site geological and geophysical exploration program, followed up with a multi-site drilling campaign, would accelerate the assessment of marine gas hydrates as an energy resource.

The estimated time frames in which the commercial application of potential advances in gas hydrate technologies occur are listed below.

- 2010—None.

- 2020—Production methods for arctic reservoirs developed through field tests and reservoir simulation; and broad-based exploration and delineation of gas hydrate resources in U.S. waters.

- 2030—Production methods for marine gas hydrates.

26 Kvenvolden, KA, "Gas Hydrates—Geological Perspective and Global Change," *Reviews of Geophysics* 31 (1993): 173–187.

27 Kvenvolden, KA and Rogers, BW, "Gaia's Breath—Global Methane Exhalations," *Marine and Petroleum Geology* 22 (2005): 579–590.

28 Milkov, AV, "Global Estimates of Hydrate-Bound Gas in Marine Sediments: How Much Is Really Out There?" *Earth-Science Reviews* 66 (2004): 183–197.

29 Klauda, JB and Sandler, SI, "Global Distribution of Methane Hydrate in Ocean Sediment," *Energy & Fuels* 19 (2005): 459–470.

30 Fujii, T et al., "Modes of Occurrence and Accumulation Mechanism of Methane Hydrate – Result of METI Exploratory Test Wells Tokai-oki to Kumano-nada'," *Proceedings of the Fifth International Conference on Gas Hydrates*, Trondheim, Norway (2005).

COAL TO LIQUIDS

In addition to direct combustion to produce heat and power, coal can be used as a feedstock for producing liquid and gaseous fuels. The Coal-to-Liquids Topic Report presents the issues associated with—and the potential for—coal-to-liquids (CTL) and coal-to-gas (CTG) technologies. CTL and CTG offer an opportunity for the United States to reduce its petroleum imports by producing petroleum products, such as diesel fuel and gasoline, from domestic coal resources. The primary technology reviewed is CTL; most reports have focused on CTL due to the cost and transportation issues associated with CTG. The other important objective included in the Topic Report is viewing and understanding the inputs and assumptions from various publications and the range of production estimates from CTG and CTL technology. A large uncertainty exists for CTL due to various assumptions including petroleum price and technological abilities. The quality of coal and the technological ability of converting the coal varied among the studies. Key assumptions were left unexamined, such as product transportation, labor, equipment availability, and environmental risk.

Overall, the published CTL production estimates are small in the total global petroleum market perspective. Even in the most optimistic scenario from the Southern States Energy Board (SSEB), the volume from CTL amounts to only 20 percent of the U.S. petroleum market.[31] The National Coal Council (NCC) indicated a 10 percent market share,[32] whereas various EIA scenarios had 0 to 6 percent of the U.S. market share.[33] The NCC and SSEB both mentioned the added benefit of using the CO_2 for enhanced oil recovery (EOR), however the increased oil volumes directly associated with using CO_2 from CTL are left unmentioned in those reports. The Topic Report discusses each of these reports in depth.

Even though the production estimates are small relative to the overall petroleum market, the incremental

31 "American Energy Security: Building a Bridge to Energy Independence and to a Sustainable Energy Future," The Southern States Energy Board, Norcorss, Georgia (July 2006). Accessible at www.americanenergysecurity.org/studyrelease.html.

32 "Coal: America's Energy Future," The National Coal Council, Washington, DC (March 2006). Accessible at nationalcoal council.org/report/NCCReportVol1.pdf .

33 "Annual Energy Outlook 2006 with Projections to 2030," Energy Information Administration (February 2006). Accessible at www.eia.doe.gov/oiaf/archive/aeo06/index.html.

gains from this technology added to gains from other technology areas, such as oil shale, could have a significant effect on U.S. energy cost and import dependency. The use of coal provides the added benefit of relying on a resource that is more plentiful domestically than petroleum. However, this reliance must be carefully balanced with the economics of developing the resource, since CTL facilities can cost more than $1 billion for each 10,000 barrels per day of production. This has implications for the competitiveness of the U.S. economy within the global economy.

The primary routes for converting coal to liquid products are called *direct* and *indirect liquefaction*. Both technologies were used by Germany to produce fuels before and during World War II (direct liquefaction more extensively).

From the 1970s through the early 1990s, the U.S. Department of Energy conducted research and development related to direct liquefaction. Plans to construct large demonstration plants based on direct coal liquefaction were cancelled during the 1980s, in response to concerns about technical risks, increasing estimates of investment costs, and decreasing world oil prices. Additionally, fuels generated by direct liquefaction are rich in high-octane aromatics, but current clean-fuel specifications in the United States limit the benzene and aromatics content, and the toxicity of gasoline.

In the early 1980s, South Africa's Sasol Company expanded its 1950s production base by building two large indirect coal-liquefaction facilities. Currently, these two Sasol facilities produce a combined total of about 150,000 barrels per day of fuels and chemicals using coal as the primary feedstock.

Dakota Gasification Company's Beulah plant produces about 170 million cubic feet per day of substitute natural gas from lignite. In 2000, the plant began exporting CO_2 for use in EOR. Currently, about 95 million cubic feet per day of CO_2 produced at the plant are transported via a 205-mile-long pipeline to EnCana Corporation's Weyburn oil field in southern Saskatchewan. The CO_2 is used for enhanced oil recovery, resulting in 5,000 barrels per day of incremental oil production, or an additional 130 to 140 million barrels of oil over the life of the project. The Weyburn field is the subject of a long-term monitoring program to assess the final disposition of the CO_2 being injected in this project.

Engineering analyses indicate that co-production or *polygeneration* plants may offer superior economic and environmental performance, as compared to separate dedicated fuels-only plants. The co-products most often considered in previous projects and studies have been electric power and liquid fuels, usually diesel, produced through a process developed by Fischer and Tropsch.

No commercial scale CTL plant has been sited or permitted in the United States. Given that these plants will have aspects of both a refinery and a power generation facility, it is not clear how quickly this untested permitting process can be expedited, particularly if opponents intervene aggressively. These potential delays have associated financial risks to the first plants.

Unfortunately, at the time of this writing, many large construction projects, including GTL, are experiencing dramatic capital-cost increases from rising material costs, skilled-labor shortages, and contractor backlogs. It is unclear how long this current trend will continue. If these escalations are cyclical, their effect on future CTL growth may be marginal. Otherwise, they may have a pronounced effect on the construction of CTL, especially in the developed world.

The various reports used to predict the production outlook for coal-to-petroleum products differed in production range, and all seemed to be missing discussions on many significant fundamental variables required to develop a sound economic decision. The reports discussed variables such as labor, equipment, product transportation, environmental risk, and feedstock only briefly, if that. Though the reports had significant analyses showing the large untapped resources of coal, practicalities for actually making the coal available—such as labor issues and the price impact of greater demand—should be investigated further before launching a significant coal-to-liquids program.

BIOMASS ENERGY SUPPLY

Some forecasters have expectations that renewable resources will be able to play a significant role in satisfying future energy demand. Others have a more pessimistic view and forecast that they will not make up even 2 percent of the total energy mix by 2030.[34] At issue is whether agriculture and forestry sources

---

34 McNulty, S, "An Unsustainable Outlook," *Financial Times*, Oct 20 2006: 1.

Facing the Hard Truths about Energy

can supply food and fiber as well as significant energy needs for a growing population.

In 2001, global primary energy consumption was 396 quadrillion Btu per year (Quad).[35] Of this total, biomass supplied 43 Quad. This is significantly more than the 2 percent predicted to be used by 2030, but is probably overlooked because about 37 Quad of this was from traditional heating and cooking. Global biomass production on the Earth's land surface is equal to 4,320 Quad, of which half is lost by autotrophic respiration and decomposition, leaving 2,160 Quad.[36] This still would indicate that there is considerable potential for biomass to play a role of some type in global energy production beyond heating and cooking.

Numerous studies have been carried out to determine the global biomass production that could be used to meet some of the world's energy needs.[37] All of the studies have had to deal with the variety of paths that biomass takes in the modern world, and have had to deal with estimates of global population, changing diets, and changes in crop yields. A recent report by the Food and Agriculture Organization of the United Nations (FAO) has estimated population, food needs, and agricultural development for the time between 2015 and 2030.[38] The report covers many of the pertinent factors that will determine whether sufficient agricultural output will be available for providing food, fiber, and fuel in the future.

According to the FAO, agricultural production of food and feed will continue to grow at a pace to meet the needs of the world population through 2030. Population growth will continue to decrease during this time period and on into the next century. Over the last 40 years, food production has been controlled by demand rather than supply, leading to a decline of almost 50 percent in the value of commodity crops— in constant dollars—over this time period. This has had a dramatic effect on crop productivity globally: crop yields and production have reached the highest levels only in countries with farm support programs, while third-world production has lagged.

Over the last 20 years, many studies have been carried out looking at the potential of agriculture to produce both energy and food for the world, if such production were optimized. While these studies have had varying conclusions, most estimate between 237 and 474 Quad of biomass energy could be produced while still feeding a growing world population. The most optimistic studies have as a criterion that the global agricultural food production per hectare, under equivalent environmental conditions, reaches optimal levels. This condition would allow large areas of land to become available for energy-crop production. If only waste biomass and dung were used from our current agricultural production, an energy supply of ~95 Quad could be expected.

Biotechnology is predicted to increase crop production in the next few decades at a faster-than-historical rate. This increase is being brought about by marker-assisted breeding, which can increase trait development by a ten-fold rate over conventional breeding. Along with this increased breeding rate, the ability to engineer specific new traits into crops will bring about remarkable changes in crop production. This increase could be expected to double the average yield of crops such as corn by 2030.

Such an increase in the U.S. corn crop would allow U.S. corn production to reach 25 billion bushels, compared with 11 billion bushels produced in 2005. A corn crop of that size would make it possible to produce 54 billion gallons of ethanol by conventional means, 6 billion gallons of biodiesel from the corn oil, and 21 billion gallons of ethanol from the excess stover (e.g., stalks). On top of all of this, 154 million metric tons of distiller's dried grain would swamp the animal feed market that is currently being met by corn and soybean production.

Many of these predictions require that some pressure be brought upon agriculture to spur production globally. The energy market could provide this new opportunity for agriculture by speeding investment in production. The development of new energy crops has the potential to produce even more bioenergy per hectare with fewer inputs and more environmentally friendly production means. This will not happen without the development of local conversion methods and logistics for efficiently handling the low energy density of most biomass feedstocks.

In the past, first-generation biomass conversion to fuels has been based on crops like corn, sugarcane,

---

35 Biomass energy is often measured in exaJoules (EJ), where 1.055 EJ is about a Quad.

36 Smeets, EMW, Faaij, APC, Lewandowski, IM and Turkenburg, WC, "A Quickscan of Global Bio-energy Potentials to 2050," *Progress in Energy and Combustion Science* 33 (2007): 56–106.

37 See Biofuels Topic Report for the full list of reports examined.

38 Bruinsma, J (editor): *World Agriculture: Towards 2015/2030, An FAO Perspective*. Earthscan Publications Ltd., London (2003).

and soybeans, which are also food sources. Developing second-generation biomass conversion technologies in the future, such as cellulosic ethanol that uses trees and plant waste as a feedstock, would—if technically and economically successful—allow non-food vegetation to become fuels and improve the energy balance. Energy balance is the ratio of the energy output obtained from a given energy input.

As with any newly developed energy sources, certain technical, logistical, and market requirements must be met for biofuels to achieve any significant scale. Challenges include: expanding rail, waterway, and pipeline transportation; scaling-up ethanol production plants and distribution systems; developing successful cellulosic conversion technology; and dealing with water and land-use issues. Collecting and utilizing the largest amount of potential biomass for conversion into fuels will need new technology development. This includes converting the biomass into a storable, stable form near its production site. That material would be shipped to a facility that can convert it into its final fuel form. This technology should optimally be able to take a variety of feedstocks in wet or dry form. The logistics of collection will demand such a complementary conversion technology.

While agriculture and forestry look like environmentally sound future-energy sources, this will only be true if it is done sustainably. This requires a systems approach to ensure that the natural resources at our disposal are not depleted. Closed-loop systems with energy production linked to meat production from the process wastes and methane production from the animal wastes generated are attempts at such systems. Much research must be done to truly understand what the consequences will be of these different options.

NUCLEAR OUTLOOK AND ITS IMPACT ON OIL AND NATURAL GAS

Nuclear power is a significant contributor to the world's energy supply, representing about 6 percent of all energy utilized, and about 16 percent of the world's electricity. Nuclear power is projected to grow in the future, but this growth could be hampered by adverse public perceptions, policies, and economics.

In power generation, nuclear power is an asset that provides base-load electric power, meaning that nuclear power plants are operating at or near capacity all the time. This type of power generation does not typically compete with generation from traditional oil and natural gas power, which are typically load-following: that is, they are able to quickly increase or lower the amount of power supplied based on fluctuations in electricity demand. It is because of these different types of power systems that nuclear power displaces a much greater amount of coal-power generation growth and a smaller amount of oil and natural gas generation.

Over the past 40 years, nuclear power has emerged as a significant source of electricity. The majority of today's operating nuclear power plants were constructed during the 1970s and 1980s. However, because of high capital costs and a lack of public acceptance due to safety concerns, new nuclear power plant construction has significantly declined from its peak of 200 gigawatts during the decade of the 1980s.

Many forecasts show nuclear power increasing in amount of power generation, but declining as a percentage of total electricity generated. The majority of nuclear power plant construction is projected to be in non-OECD countries, with the majority of growth forecast in Asia. The period before 2030 forecasts that nuclear power will use existing technology fissile reactors, with more advanced technologies coming online after 2030.

The 2006 IEA World Energy Outlook has a "business as usual" reference case and an alternative policy forecast (Figure 3-22). The alternative policy case assumes that there is an effort to curtail global warming that includes measures to boost the role of nuclear power. The reference case forecasts for 2030 that nuclear power growth will trail alternative methods of power generation by about 3 to 1. The percentage of total electricity produced declines from 16 percent to 10 percent. In the IEA alternative policy forecast, nuclear power grows at a more rapid rate, but it is still outpaced by alternative power generation technologies, declining from 16 percent to 14 percent of total electricity generated.

The 2006 EIA International Energy Forecast is a "business as usual" scenario, with growth in non-OECD countries offset by decommissioning of nuclear power plants elsewhere.

With the current forecasts for nuclear power growth, it is believed that there is sufficient uranium as fuel and that the infrastructure could be constructed to

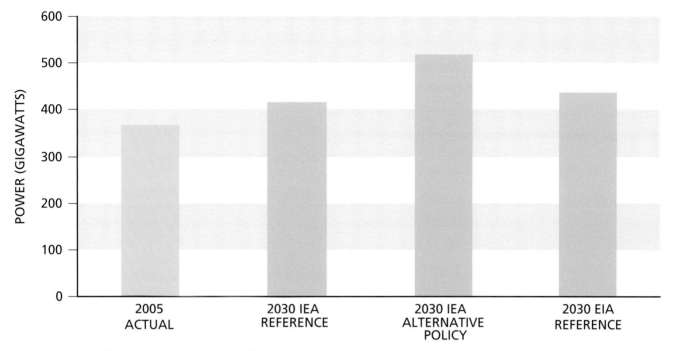

Sources: Energy Information Administration (EIA), *International Energy Outlook 2006;* and International Energy Agency (IEA), *World Energy Outlook 2006.*

FIGURE 3-22. *Projected Nuclear Power Growth, 2005 to 2030*

support the level of growth indicated in the forecasts. If growth is significantly higher than forecast, there is a possibility that the supply chain for critical nuclear components will need additional time to increase their manufacture.

Four issues can delay new nuclear construction. First is cost: the high capital costs for nuclear power plant construction, the financing required to construct these plants, and the resulting cost of energy often make new nuclear construction a difficult investment decision for a utility. There are government measures both domestically and abroad to encourage new construction of nuclear plants. One significant measure that would increase the competitiveness of nuclear power would be a pricing mechanism on CO_2; a CO_2 mechanism could result in a faster rate of adoption of nuclear energy than forecast.

The second issue facing nuclear energy is the storage and processing of spent fuel; waste management must be a strategic part of any nuclear development plan. The third issue is public perceptions around nuclear power safety. Fourth, there are global concerns about the proliferation of nuclear materials. If these four issues are not addressed, it is likely that

nuclear power will grow at a global rate that is slower than the forecasts.

TRANSPORTATION EFFICIENCY

Advanced technologies have the potential to reduce petroleum fuel demand for the five subsectors of transportation (light duty vehicles, heavy duty vehicles, air transport, marine shipping, and rail transport) between now and 2030. Over time, new technologies will enter the marketplace if one or more of the following occur:

- The technologies mature and costs decrease

- Fuel costs increase and remain high

- The technologies are valued by the consumer

- Policies encourage adoption of improved technologies.

Government and industry play important roles in filling and maintaining the technology pipeline for transportation efficiency, can encourage academic research in high-profile transportation-technology areas such as advanced batteries and bio-based fuels, and can encourage students to enter engineering, science, and mathematics professions to work on these challenging issues. In addition, increased funding of R&D increases the number of breakthrough concepts that can be pursued, making the odds more favorable for some to be successfully commercialized.

The various modes of freight shipment have different energy requirements on a ton-mile basis, as do the various modes of passenger travel (automobiles, buses, trains, and aircraft). Policies that encourage efficient use across transportation subsectors were not addressed in the Transportation Efficiency Topic Report, and the costs, benefits, and hurdles of mode-shifting should be studied further.

Finally, alternative fuels have a generic impact across all of the subsectors by displacing some petroleum-based fuel, but have little effect on reducing the energy demand (e.g., Btu per mile) for a subsector. Hydrogen—when used as an energy carrier in fuel cells—and electricity, in plug-in hybrids or battery-electric vehicles, result in higher efficiency than existing technologies. Infrastructure requirements and the energy required to produce the fuels should be considered for these alternatives (e.g., well-to-tank assessment).

U.S. fuel demand for the five transportation subsectors, shown in Table 3-16, is based on EIA projections and is defined as the Reference Case in the Topic Report. Subsectors are discussed here in their order of the percentage of transportation demand. In all of the transportation subsectors, fuel consumption was considered at the end-use point (e.g., tank-to-wheels for the light duty vehicle sector). Energy is required to produce the fuels associated with the various transportation modes. These well-to-tank energy requirements can be substantial for some alternatives to petroleum (i.e., hydrogen, biofuels, and electricity, depending on the source). The Topic Report contains detailed tables of potential advances and their impacts for each subsector.

General Conclusions

The study team concluded that technology can make a significant difference in improving transportation efficiency. The light duty vehicle sector offers the greatest opportunities, but also has a number of challenges. Technology hurdles, costs, and potential infrastructure investments are some of these. In addition, the ways that consumer preferences affect the deployment of various technologies are complex. For the other sectors, a sound business case affects the deployment of technology, including fuel cost savings and operational factors.

It is important that all of the technologies are analyzed from a wells-to-wheels efficiency and cost basis. This was not done in the Topic Report, because the focus was on transportation efficiency at the point of end use (excluding fuel availability, production, and distribution issues).

It should be noted that, although the technologies discussed below are analyzed from a U.S. perspective, they are generic and can be applied in all parts of the world, when the appropriate attributes and constraints are considered for the specific countries of interest.

Sector	Quadrillion Btu Per Year		Percent of Transportation	
	2005	2030	2005	2030
Light Duty Vehicles	16.28	22.98	61.6	60.5
Heavy Duty Vehicles	5.65	8.73	21.3	23.0
Air	2.81	4.15	10.6	10.9
Marine	1.06	1.12	4.0	3.0
Rail	0.67	0.97	2.5	2.6
Total	26.47	37.95		

TABLE 3-16. *EIA Reference Case—U.S. Transportation Fuel Demand*

Facing the Hard Truths about Energy

Light Duty Vehicles

The EIA reference case projects that, in 2030, technology improvements will result in ~13 percent improvement in new vehicle fuel consumption from 2005 levels. It is estimated that this includes technological improvements of ~30 percent at constant vehicle performance, and vehicle attribute changes that reduce this improvement by about half. Based on this study's analysis, technologies (drive train and body improvements, and hybridization) exist, or are expected to be developed, that have the potential to reduce fuel consumption of new light duty vehicles by 50 percent relative to 2005 vehicles. This assumes constant vehicle performance and entails higher vehicle cost. The extent to which these technologies translate into reduction in fuel consumption depends on factors not evaluated in this study, including customer preferences, vehicle and fuel costs, and vehicle attributes (acceleration, weight, size). Improvements beyond 50 percent will require breakthroughs in batteries or fuel cells, potentially resulting in significantly higher vehicle costs and significant infrastructure investments.

Technologies such as hybrids and fuel cells will take longer to deploy in the fleet than more conventional changes (such as improved fuel injection or turbocharging). Hydrogen for fuel cells would displace petroleum-based fuels. However, the source of the hydrogen, costs, technical hurdles, and infrastructure requirements are major unknowns and it is difficult to estimate the impact of fuel cells in 2030.

Heavy Duty Vehicles

Technologies exist to reduce new heavy-duty-truck fuel consumption by 15 to 20 percent in the United States by 2030, which is about equal to the EIA reference case. These technologies (e.g., engine efficiency, rolling resistance, and aerodynamic improvements) will involve higher cost and require an associated financial business case. Operational improvements such as reduced idling and improved logistics can provide a benefit of 5 to 10 percent across the fleet during this period. Advanced technology solutions, such as

hybridization and fuel cells, offer fuel consumption reductions of an additional 25 percent, and applications would likely be initiated in local-delivery, short-haul, medium-duty delivery trucks and buses. In the near term, U.S. heavy-duty emission standards will limit the potential to reduce fuel consumption.

Air

Fuel consumption improvements on the order of 25 percent are the basis for the EIA reference case. This is an aggressive projection and all of the known technologies appear to be included in the EIA estimates. New technologies will need to be discovered to achieve additional improvements in efficiency. These new technologies will require a reinvigoration of U.S. research, development, and demonstration initiatives, similar to programs currently being carried out in Europe.

Marine Shipping

The EIA reference case is based on a 5 percent improvement in marine shipping fuel consumption by 2030. This level of improvement is achievable with operational solutions and existing technologies. Improvements greater than 5 percent will require new hull designs and new propeller designs. Given the long life of ships (greater than 20 years), migration of these solutions into the fleet will not have a large impact until later in the study period. Operational changes, affecting the entire fleet, may be more significant than technological improvements.

Rail Transport

The EIA reference case assumes that fuel consumption will improve by 2.5 percent between 2005 and 2030. Incremental improvements in engine design, aerodynamics, and use of hybrids have the potential to reduce new locomotive fuel consumption by up to 30 percent over 2005 technology. Rollout of new technology into the fleet is slow due to low turnover and will be difficult to achieve during the years considered in this study. Emissions standards will tend to increase fuel consumption.

Chapter GEOPOLITICS 4

Abstract

The world energy map is changing. Projected energy demand will come increasingly from developing and emerging economies, as will supply. The global energy future is also distinguished by an increasing concentration of energy suppliers and demand centers, which are geographically farther apart; requiring increased investment, longer transport routes, and raising security and environmental concerns. The emergence of new market players, new alliances, and evolving rules further complicates the global energy picture.

This chapter recognizes that the global energy resource endowment is, indeed, enormous, but also examines "above-ground" risks such as access, resource nationalism, security concerns, political shifts, and environmental and security considerations. These can significantly affect the producibility, conversion, and deliverability of energy, and the timing of needed investments. The chapter also addresses implications of carbon constraints and seeks to recast calls for "energy independence" by endorsing opportunities for enhanced "energy security" in a truly global and inter-dependent energy market.

The outline of the Geopolitics chapter is as follows:

- How the world is changing

  - Dramatic growth in global demand

  - New patterns of trade

  - The pressures of globalization

  - Changing evaluation of risks

  - Governance and resource nationalism

  - The growing power of national oil companies

  - Climate change

  - Sustainable development and related policy challenges

  - Security and terrorism

  - Other risks and scenarios

- Implications for the United States

- Conclusions.

International energy trade is increasingly influenced by geopolitical considerations at the expense of the free play of open markets and commercial actions by a competitive oil and gas industry. As demand grows, oil and natural gas become strategic commodities susceptible to being used for geopolitical leverage. Alternative energy sources have the potential to become viable substitutes, but making them available at a scale that reduces global dependence on fossil fuels will take time. Meanwhile, global competition for oil and natural gas is intensifying as new players enter the market; suppliers are increasingly seeking to exploit their resources also for political ends; and consumers are exploring new ways to guarantee sources of supply.

The growing influence of geopolitical factors on global energy trade has profound implications for U.S.

interests, strategies, and policy making as well as for the ways that oil companies conduct their business. Many of the expected changes could pose heightened risks to U.S. energy security, in a world where relative U.S. influence is likely to decline as economic power shifts to other rising nations. In years to come, security threats to the world's main sources of oil and natural gas may persist and possibly worsen.

In geoeconomic terms, the biggest impact will come from increasing demand for oil and natural gas from developing countries, which may outpace the development of new sources of supply, thereby putting pressure on prices. In geopolitical terms, the consequences of such an imbalance will be magnified by the fact that demand is rising most strongly in China, India, and other large emerging economies.

Key questions abound: Will competition for scarce resources lead to political or even military clashes among major powers? Will bilateral arrangements among nations become common as governments attempt to "secure" energy supplies outside of traditional market mechanisms? How far will countries go in using their national oil companies to further foreign policy and internal political objectives? Will non-market forces divert needed investment in the energy sector?

These developments are taking place amid rising hostility to globalization in large parts of the world, including many industrialized countries that benefit from it. The political will to complete multilateral trade negotiations is ebbing, with major trading nations turning to bilateral or regional preferential agreements that fragment world trade, increase costs, and diminish market efficiency. It is even possible that the global trading system itself may fracture from geoeconomic and geopolitical stress.

On the security front, the spread of militancy is likely to continue in some of the major oil producing regions. Terrorism and weapons proliferation (including nuclear arms and other weapons of mass destruction) will probably continue to grow, as may the risk of war. The impact would be particularly acute if this happens in the Middle East, with its vast and critical oil and natural gas resources.

Government policy making is also likely to be increasingly influenced by non-governmental organizations and other groups promoting environmental interests, demanding new policies to combat climate change and other issues such as human and labor

rights violations, supported by shifts in public opinion. The result will be mounting pressure on international oil companies to conform to new regulations and/or voluntary controls, thus altering the economic and political order within which they operate.

HOW THE WORLD IS CHANGING

Dramatic Growth in Global Demand

Current forecasts are for continued increases in global energy demand and changes in the pattern of energy flows, with a decided shift eastward on the "world energy map" due to higher demand in Asia. To appreciate the scale and pace of demand expansion, consider that it took world oil demand 18 years (1977-1995) to grow from 60 to 70 million barrels per day, but only eight years (1995-2003) to increase from 70 to 80 million barrels per day. If present projections prove accurate, demand could exceed 90 million barrels per day by 2010 and 115 million barrels per day by 2030.

Continued world population growth will lead to rapid increases in demand for food, housing, and other products and services that invariably require energy to produce and deliver. In addition, over a billion of the world's inhabitants currently have little or no access to the most basic forms of energy, an unsustainable predicament with potentially ominous consequences to the welfare of that population.

Most forecasts predict that during the next 25 years, the world will continue to rely essentially on the same forms of energy as it has for the past century—oil, natural gas, coal, and nuclear power—along with a broad range of renewable sources that includes solar, hydroelectric, biomass, and wind energy. Although global energy demand is forecast to double between 2001 and 2030, little change is expected in the relative shares of the major fuel sources (Figure 4-1) with over 80 percent of demand in 2030 projected to be met by fossil fuels.

Energy use in North America, which currently accounts for about 30 percent of worldwide consumption, essentially followed larger global trends. By contrast, greater reliance on nuclear energy in Europe slightly altered the total mix, with lower demand for coal and natural gas. In developing countries, often the least able to afford or employ the best available technology, fossil-fuel use approaches 90 percent.

Facing the Hard Truths about Energy

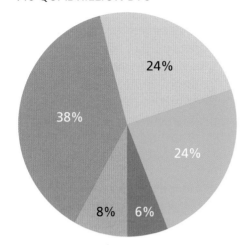

2005 – 446 QUADRILLION BTU

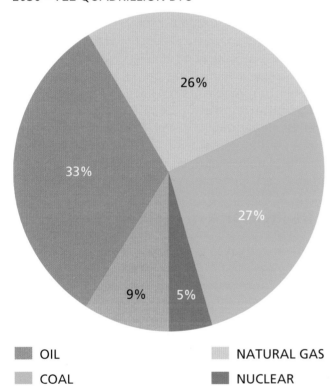

2030 – 722 QUADRILLION BTU

- ■ OIL
- ■ COAL
- ■ HYDROELECTRIC/RENEWABLES
- ▨ NATURAL GAS
- ■ NUCLEAR

Source: EIA, *International Energy Outlook 2006*.

FIGURE 4-1. *Global Energy Demand — Fuel Shares*

Given the long lead times necessary to develop and introduce new conventional fuel supplies and alternative energy forms, demand for fossil fuels (oil, natural gas, and coal) is expected to continue to dominate the global energy mix for at least the next two decades—absent radical changes in

economic or foreign policies, environmental crises, terrorist or war devastation, or a major technological breakthrough.

The trend is particularly dramatic in the developing world. Both the International Energy Agency (IEA) and the Energy Information Administration (EIA) of the U.S. Department of Energy predict that developing countries in Asia, including China and India, will continue their current economic expansion, driving the doubling of energy demand in the developing world by 2030 (Figure 4-2).

New Patterns of Trade

As demand rises in Asia, a new global energy picture is emerging that requires an increased focus on investment, transportation infrastructure, security, environmental, and geopolitical considerations, as well as a reevaluation of overall strategies by government and industry.

In the global oil and natural gas market, demand will continue to shift to emerging economies with growing populations. These nations will not only emerge as large energy consumers, but some will also control a large share of energy resources. At the same time, conventional oil and natural gas production in the developed world is declining.

The major regions of expanding production are the Middle East, West Africa, Russia, and the Caspian Sea, together with a few areas where unconventional production is rising (e.g., oil sands in Canada and extra-heavy crude in Venezuela). The three major consuming areas are North America, Europe, and Asia.

The growing need for transportation of energy between these areas raises important concerns over geographical "choke points," both for oil shipments and, increasingly, for natural gas—whether delivered by pipeline or in the form of liquefied natural gas (LNG). The most potentially congested, difficult, or dangerous transit passages, such as the Straits of Hormuz and Malacca and the Bosporus, pose both security and environmental challenges (Figure 4-3; see also Figure 2-76 in Chapter 2, "Energy Demand").

As patterns of demand and transportation change, new regional and international, commercial and strategic alliances may emerge, marking the beginning of a "new game" in the geopolitics of

2004 – 445 QUADRILLION BTU PER YEAR

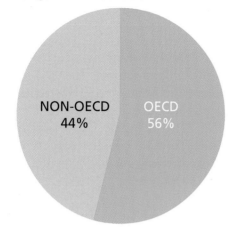

2030 – 678 QUADRILLION BTU PER YEAR

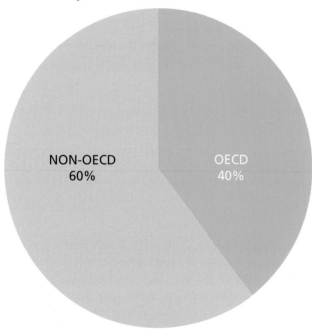

Source: IEA, *World Energy Outlook 2006.*

FIGURE 4-2. *World Energy Demand Growth from 2004 to 2030*

oil and natural gas, in which different countries and corporations will develop new strategies and techniques to secure access to resources. Although the implications for international energy companies and smaller "independent" companies seeking to explore and produce oil and natural gas overseas—especially U.S. companies—are not yet fully evident, such companies may find themselves at a competitive disadvantage in gaining access to resources and new business opportunities.

Evidence suggests that this new game may already be under way. In the future, non-OECD nations will include both the largest holders of conventional energy resources and their fastest-growing consumers. The national oil companies (NOCs) and energy ministries in these countries will play an increasingly important role in policy decisions about how to develop their resources and whether to rely on the global market or instead to negotiate bilateral supply arrangements with other countries. These bilateral deals may include provisions that extend well beyond conventional commercial terms and require foreign aid and other commitments from the governments of consuming countries.

Energy's growing strategic importance may thus encourage producers to leverage their advantageous positions when dealing with consumer nations, either to gain commercial benefits or to further their national geopolitical or foreign-policy objectives. With shifts in bargaining power, the open-market rules and norms that have characterized global energy trade and investment for the past several decades may well be under threat. Yet all energy producers and consumers would benefit from greater investment and freer trade that open-market practices promote in an increasingly integrated world.

The Pressures of Globalization

For more than 60 years, growing areas of the world have enjoyed the fruits of expanding free trade and economic integration. Globalization has been driven by the communications revolution, the increasing ease of international financial movements, rising living standards, the continued opening of markets for products and services, the worldwide reach of multinational corporations, and other modernizing forces. The resulting unprecedented economic growth has been boosted by a global oil market that has relied on ready access to resources and the efficient application of investment capital, technology, and management by an internationally competitive petroleum industry. Many of these long-standing conditions, however, now face new challenges to their sustainability in the years ahead.

As new entrants such as China and Russia play an increasingly important role in the international economic system, the fundamental, Western-inspired values that have underpinned the system—representative government, the rule of law,

Facing the Hard Truths about Energy

2000

2030

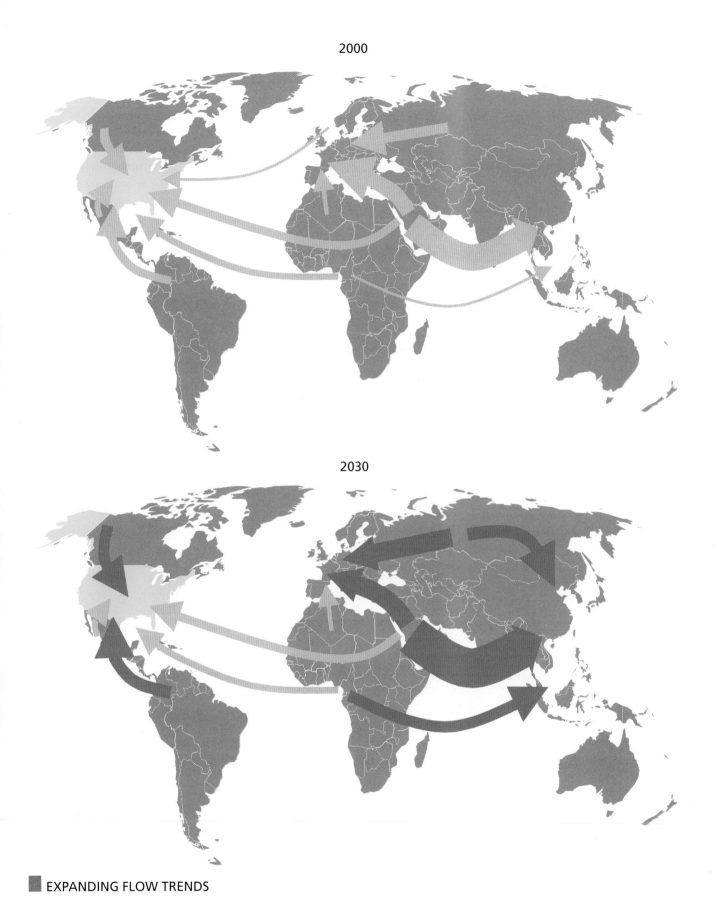

■ EXPANDING FLOW TRENDS

FIGURE 4-3. *Global Oil Flow Trends*

transparency, accountability, and open markets—can no longer be taken for granted. The balance of global economic power is shifting to emerging countries, not only to major, fast-expanding nations such as India and Brazil, but also to the main group of developing countries that populate the halls of international organizations such as the World Trade Organization (WTO), the international financial institutions, and United Nations agencies.

Increasingly, these developing countries are joining forces to increase their political clout. Not all are as committed to the principles of free trade, transparency, and the rule of law as the governments that founded the current world institutional framework after World War II. International institutions, and particularly the WTO, may have to adjust to the requirements and wishes of these new economic powers, as they assert increasing influence over the global agenda and the rules of the international trading system. Many international economists hope that as developing countries grow richer, they will increasingly appreciate the need for open markets and the rule of law in order to protect their own exports and growing prosperity.

If, however, moves toward more open markets stall, and even reverse, the world economy will become less efficient, costs will rise, and individual governments may apply their own rules to investments, taxation, and the way they select energy trading partners. There may be more preferential trading among regions and an increasing number of bilateral or regional deals struck for political rather than purely economic reasons. U.S. influence for resolving these problems would diminish if agreed multilateral rules are disregarded. Such developments are all the more likely as a worldwide backlash against globalization has been growing in recent years, not least in the Western countries themselves. Rising economic nationalism and protectionism at home would make it harder for the United States to continue to exert global leadership in favor of open markets.

Various countries and interest groups are resisting the forces of globalization and many of the international norms and institutions designed to facilitate the spread of liberal market systems. At one extreme, rising anti-Western and particularly anti-American sentiments and actions—as exhibited by militant movements, terrorism, and economic populism—pose fundamental threats to globalization. Whether resistance is directed against the pace of globaliza-

tion, its perceived inequities or alleged failures, or its social/cultural impacts, countries and ideological movements often challenge the international system and the forces of economic liberalization.

It is unclear whether this resistance will ultimately slow, reverse, or otherwise alter the progress of globalization, or change the prevailing norms of the international system. Many opponents blame globalization for ills for which it is not responsible, although that does not necessarily diminish the political impact of their grievances. A prolonged and spreading backlash against globalization and international norms could threaten their long-term viability, thus introducing greater uncertainty and risk when energy investors and governments consider investment and management decisions.

Changing Evaluation of Risks

When evaluating global investment opportunities, international oil companies (IOCs) have traditionally relied upon an inventory of investment-risk criteria. In exploration and production ventures, these considerations typically comprise:

- Geological risk—are the hydrocarbons present?

- Technological risk—can resources be accessed with existing/available technology?

- Commercial risk—at what price, and under what terms? Are these adequate to ensure a favorable return on investment relative to shareholder and portfolio risk?

- Political risk—what threats do political conditions pose to the project and investments? What if the political situation changes? Can these risks be managed?

- Environmental risk—can the resources be developed in environmentally acceptable ways?

- Human-resource risk—are there enough suitably trained and qualified people available to develop the resources?

Some of these traditional assessments concern the location and nature of underground resources, others relate to "above-ground" risks, such as political and labor-market developments. As conditions for resource extraction change, however, it may well be that the "above-ground" risks pose greater challenges to meeting future global oil and natural gas demand than concerns over the resources themselves.

Such "above-ground" issues include conditions of access to resources, security, the kinds of investment required, transportation infrastruture, availability of skilled labor, the quality of governance and political stability in the country holding the resources, terrorism, corruption, and various environmental considerations. Over the past decade, investment risk has increasingly been reevaluated in the light of these factors, and it seems inevitable that this trend will intensify in coming years.

Governance and Resource Nationalism

Since at least the first half of the 20th century, host governments have attempted to take direct control of their countries' oil resources. Now, high global oil prices have encouraged a new wave of resource nationalism. Most recently, a new generation of sovereign governments has begun to reassert greater control over natural resources, in an effort to extract maximum commercial advantages—often by violating existing contracts. Sometimes, these governments also select partners on the basis of national geopolitical or broader economic

priorities, rather than on open market competition. Increasingly, NOCs are operating outside their own countries or traditional areas and are competing internationally with the support of their governments.

A predominant share of the world's known oil and natural gas reserves is not available for direct investment by international oil companies. These reserves are primarily in member countries of the Organization of Petroleum Exporting Countries (OPEC) located around the Persian Gulf, where resources are most plentiful and can often be developed at low cost (Figures 4-4 and 4-5). Countries outside the Middle East that once welcomed foreign investment, such as Venezuela and Russia, have turned increasingly hostile. Thus, investment capital, as well as the best industry technology and manpower, cannot be applied in the most economically effective manner to increase supplies of oil and natural gas for the world market, even at a time of historically high energy prices.

In a world of growing energy demand, producing countries are more inclined to dictate political or other conditions that often distort market efficiency. As Russia explores new ways to increase control over

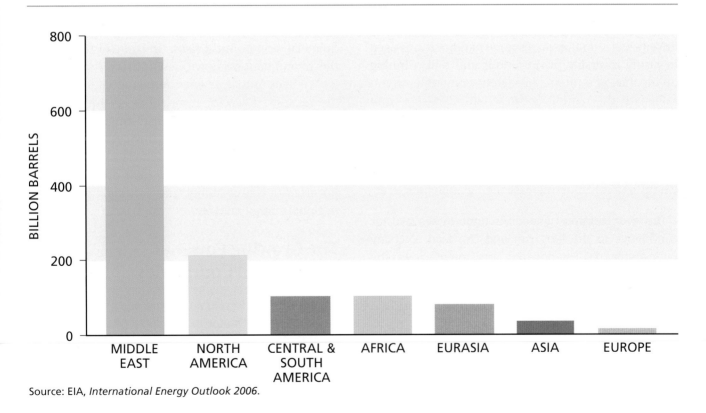

Source: EIA, *International Energy Outlook 2006*.

FIGURE 4-4. *World Crude Oil Reserves — Regional Shares*

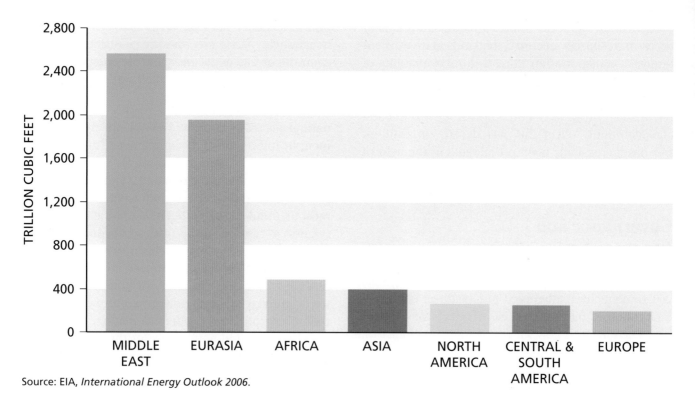

TRILLION CUBIC FEET

MIDDLE EAST — EURASIA — AFRICA — ASIA — NORTH AMERICA — CENTRAL & SOUTH AMERICA — EUROPE

Source: EIA, *International Energy Outlook 2006*.

FIGURE 4-5. *World Natural Gas Reserves — Regional Shares*

investors and consuming markets, similar developments are occurring in Latin America, most especially in Venezuela. In Russia, resource nationalism is used to justify reversing privatizations and redistributing oil income, and often considered a desirable way to safeguard the nation's greatest natural assets from rapid "exploitation" by profit-maximizing international companies that would endanger national plans to stretch out use of the resources over as many years as possible. Russia and other countries also view energy as a means to increase their global influence.

However, resource nationalism undermines investor confidence in the long run and can lead to many undesirable results: deferred investment slows the pace of resource development; oil rents are diverted to unconnected social, political, or military activities; infrastructure and resource development are neglected; and the expertise available from international industry is rejected in favor of state control or cooperation with other NOCs.

High prices for producing countries—together with popular pressure for jobs and other government programs—further encourage resource nationalism and erode the sanctity of contracts. Consequently,

investments in production capacity either slow or flow instead to areas of higher geological, technical, financial, and political risks. In some of these areas the phenomenon known as NIMBYism (from "Not In My Back Yard") or environmental concerns may further restrict access. Restrictions on timely investment in an industry with long lead-times prolong the normal cycles of the petroleum business. The result is to extend periods of supply shortfalls, as in the 1970s, and surpluses, as from 1984 to 1999, and to increase uncertainties, inflexibility, and consequent volatility in global energy markets.

The Growing Power of National Oil Companies

Over the last 30 years, national oil companies have become a major factor in the global oil market. Most owed their creation to a feeling in many resource-rich countries that their energy endowments would only be used for the national good if a national company were directly involved in the process. This was accomplished in various ways, ranging from seizing foreign-owned resources and facilities, to nationalizing with compensation, to creating new companies to

Facing the Hard Truths about Energy

participate in developing the resources. Many of the early NOCs (e.g., Aramco and Statoil) have grown into world-scale, efficient energy-market players operating globally in ways largely indistinguishable from IOCs. Because of non-commercial operating mandates or other local factors, other NOCs have remained inefficient or even marginal suppliers, and most operate only within their own borders.

With the increasing concentration of reserves in countries where NOCs have a dominant role by law, the future development strategies adopted by NOCs will play a key role in determining whether future oil supply meets expanding global demand. This will be even more important as reserves are depleted in other parts of the world or cannot be developed because of environmental, economic, or political constraints. NOCs from countries with growing oil imports, such as China and India, are increasingly participating in the global market, both to try to safeguard their own energy security and to foster other trade relationships.

With few exceptions, producing-country NOCs have proved to be reliable suppliers on the world market. Absent a fracturing of the global oil market, which would make political use of "the oil weapon" more feasible, NOCs may continue to develop in this way—if only to ensure access to the markets they want. The concern is, if bilateral energy deals become more common, governments may be tempted to achieve political or foreign policy objectives by utilizing their energy "leverage." A more immediate and important concern is whether sub-optimal development of resources controlled by NOCs could pose a major and long-term supply risk. Inefficiency could result from:

- Subsidized or below-market domestic product prices

- Diversion of revenues and deferral of investment for social purposes, or for other government uses

- Uncompetitive labor practices or government employment requirements

- Low levels of technology.

These disadvantages may be partly offset by low production costs, easy access to reserves, preferential regulatory treatment, and, in many cases, small dividends to shareholders. More generally, NOCs may have a competitive advantage when dealing with certain problems, largely because they are not accountable to shareholders in the same way as IOCs

and because they often enjoy tangible advantages accorded by their national governments. On the other hand, if energy prices decline significantly, producing countries may once again need to attract foreign investment in order to maintain or increase production levels.

Climate Change

Greenhouse gas emissions have hitherto come primarily from industrialized countries. In the future, emissions from emerging economies and the developing world are expected to increase dramatically, accounting for over 60 percent of new growth in global greenhouse gas emissions (Figure 4-6). Greenhouse gas emissions from the developing world will exceed those of the industrialized world before 2010.

Climate change and the policy responses it triggers will have significant effects on global oil and natural gas supply and demand. There is widespread agreement among climate scientists that the world is growing warmer, regardless of whether most of the temperature increase is due to human activities. As a result, national, state/provincial, and local governments, as well as companies are beginning to work toward a carbon-constrained future and are trying to anticipate its consequences. Growing consensus on the need for technological, policy, and commercial responses to rising temperatures, sooner rather than later, would ultimately have an effect on energy/fuel choices by both producers and consumers. Significant impacts fall into two general categories: the effects of climate change itself, and the effects of policy responses to it—notably the move to a carbon-constrained economy.

Climate Change

- Climate change will physically affect the supply of oil, natural gas, coal, and other fuels both positively and negatively; for example, as a result of longer ice-free periods in higher latitudes and lost ice roads.

- Climate change will increase or lower the demand for oil and natural gas as changing weather patterns modify seasonal demand for heating and cooling, and as changes in crop growth and water resources alter population patterns.

- If the earth becomes significantly warmer, pressures arising from population migrations, altered food supplies, and new growing seasons could create not only environmental but also security problems. The

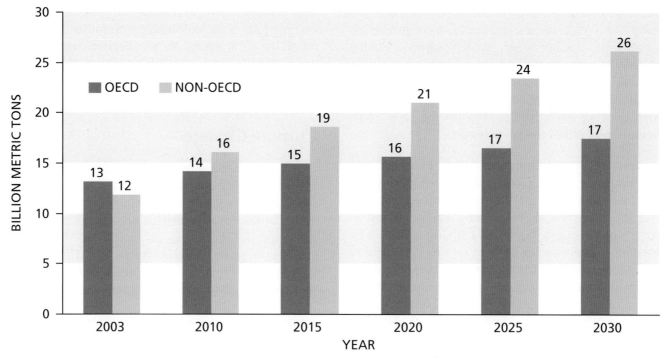

BILLION METRIC TONS

■ OECD   ▨ NON-OECD

Data Source: EIA, *International Energy Outlook 2006.*

FIGURE 4-6. *World Carbon Dioxide Emissions by Region, 2003-2030*

hardest hit countries are likely to be in the developing world, the biggest potential source of new waves of migrants and refugees.

Policy Responses and Carbon Constraints

- Policy responses to climate change, such as carbon taxes, cap-and-trade systems, and tougher efficiency and fuel standards, will affect both the supply and demand for oil and natural gas.

- Differing national responses could damage the international trading regime by distorting competition and provoking retaliation by other countries.

- It is widely agreed that significant reductions in human emissions of carbon dioxide and other greenhouse gases would require substantial innovation and the widespread deployment of new energy technologies, requiring large and sustained private and public sector investments in research, development, demonstration, and deployment.

- Many economists agree that the most cost-effective ways to reduce greenhouse gases involve broad market-based incentives to the private sector to undertake technological advances without governments mandating the technology chosen.

- Technological and policy efforts to meet energy-security and environmental goals are sometimes aligned, but often are not. For example, renewable biofuels may help meet both energy and environmental objectives despite raising food prices and creating disruptions in land and water use; whereas converting domestic coal and oil shale to liquid fuel may benefit energy security, but present significant environmental challenges.

Sustainable Development and Related Policy Challenges

Traditional concepts of economic development are being challenged by the growing movement in favor of "sustainable development." This term means different things to different people, resulting in widespread confusion over its definition. Often "sustainable development" is used simply as a call for greater attention to be paid to the environmental and social impacts of human activities. According to the United Nations' Department of Economic and Social Affairs Division for Sustainable Development, "sustainable development" is the type of investment that "meets the needs of the present without compromising

Facing the Hard Truths about Energy

the ability of future generations to meet their own needs."

Such an aim may conflict with market-based development strategies, particularly if it implies that restrictions would be placed on the behavior of economic actors, such as constraints on the use of non-renewable resources. In the energy sector, progressive adoption of "sustainable development" principles could result in increasing political pressure to move from non-renewable to renewable sources of supply—even in situations where it may make less economic sense than choosing a conventional fuel alternative. Some proponents for sustainable development reject fossil fuels completely, while others recognize they are needed until adequate alternative energy sources become widely available. Sustainable development strategies are also sometimes linked to proposed solutions to problems of energy poverty and the distribution of wealth.

Steep increases in oil prices have led to significant transfers of wealth from energy consumers to a small and increasingly concentrated group of energy producing nations. Large amounts of capital have shifted from OECD countries to non-OECD states, which may not have adequate institutional safeguards to protect against rampant corruption and misuse of these massive revenue inflows. Many resource-rich countries have no institutional capacity to distribute energy revenue equitably, or to use it to stimulate economic growth and diversity by developing and modernizing other sectors of their economies. In addition, the temptation to rely excessively on energy revenue while neglecting the rest of the economy (a condition sometimes referred to as "resource curse") can be a barrier to economic reform and a recipe for long-term economic failure.

Higher energy prices also widen the disparity in living standards between rich and poor nations. Wealthier countries have largely managed to cope with the price rise, while some developing economies have been forced to curb energy demand and to revert to use of non-commercial biomass, such as firewood. Other developing countries, however, have benefited from the current cycle of commodity price increases.

Increasingly, governments consider that these disparities in living standards reflect an unsustainable development path and may alter the way they approach natural resource development and revenue distribution. Concerns over the consequences of higher energy prices on developing and emerging or transitional countries could redirect energy investment from traditional fuels to alternative-energy technologies and services. Many countries, however, are unable to attract the latest clean-energy technologies because energy is not priced at market rates in the domestic economy.

The International Energy Agency's *World Energy Outlook 2006* estimates that over a quarter of the world's population (some 1.6 billion people) has no access to electricity. Global electrification is distributed very unevenly. The highest proportions of people without electric power live in large parts of Sub-Saharan Africa and in South Asia. Supplying electricity to these communities may drive up carbon dioxide production, further increasing concerns about climate change. Even when people live close to sources of energy production, as in the Niger Delta, they are often precluded from enjoying the potential benefits because of inadequate distribution systems, lack of needed investment, and ineffective government policies on pricing, revenue sharing, and resource regulation.

Security and Terrorism

During the past 20 years, increases in global energy demand and the elimination of uneconomic refining capacity have effectively depleted the once ample surplus in production and refining capacity. Stricter petroleum product specifications also absorbed a large share of investment capital and limited refining flexibility. This has created a tighter market in which instability, labor unrest, sabotage, or other threats to supply can drive oil prices sharply higher. In particular, global reliance on oil supply from the Persian Gulf puts a premium on security in a confined area with growing intra- and inter-state tensions emanating from the war in Iraq, Arab-Iranian rivalry, rapid social change, and religiously inspired radical groups that seek government overthrow.

Conflict in the Middle East is neither a recent phenomenon nor one that lends itself to quick solutions. While many argue that the Arab-Israeli conflict is not at the core of regional tensions, the persistence of the conflict and the polarization of opinions surrounding it keep the entire Middle East in a high state of tension. Current circumstances suggest that hostilities will persist—or perhaps even escalate—in the near term.

While overt war between countries of the Persian Gulf is unlikely, threats to and harassment of production facilities, refineries, terminals, and shipping remain a possibility. Extreme "resistance" groups seek to overturn the current order by means ranging from political activism to subversion and terrorism. Militants aim to remove many of the existing governments in the region and to drive Western powers and oil interests from the Middle East. While the likelihood of extremist groups actually taking over governments in the region is remote, there is a much greater possibility that non-governmental or para-governmental organizations could either disrupt supplies through the Strait of Hormuz or conduct a successful attack on a land-based facility.

If a radical group were to come to power in any Middle Eastern producing country, it might cease shipping oil to the United States or selling it to U.S. oil companies. Such restrictions would result in at least short-term supply disruptions that could put a small premium on oil destined for U.S. markets as other suppliers diverted their product in the global market.

Another threat could be heightened regional tensions as a result of nuclear proliferation in the Middle East. Iran's acquisition of a nuclear weapons capability, for example, could induce Saudi Arabia, Turkey, Egypt, and others to develop their own military nuclear capacity. In such a scenario, already high tensions in the region would be stoked by the threat of preemptive strikes or nuclear warfare. Should Middle East oilfields be seriously threatened, there would be sweeping consequences for world energy supplies and prices.

Other Risks and Scenarios

China and India are both concerned that the strains of unprecedented economic growth could trigger domestic political instability. Both countries must meet the energy demands of their rapidly grow-ing economies and the development expectations of extremely populous societies. Failure to deliver on these expectations could lead to social unrest, but fulfilling these demands will also create huge economic, social, political, and environmental problems. Domestic coal is the most abundant and economic resource in both countries. It is often, however, used inefficiently and is subject to infrastructure bottle-necks such as those in rail transportation. Expanded use of coal would increase greenhouse gas emissions even more rapidly.

Although most current concern centers on high oil prices, a sudden price collapse could also cause instability in parts of the Middle East and other major producing countries, such as Russia, Mexico, Nigeria, Venezuela, and Angola. In the years ahead, Middle Eastern oil producers face relatively similar challenges: undiversified extractive economies, a youthful population seeking gainful employment, and political systems that are beginning to show signs of strain in large part because of insufficiently representative governments. While all these problems are becoming more acute, current high oil prices have taken much of the political urgency out of addressing them in the near term.

Apart from the petroleum sector, economies and trade are underdeveloped in most of the major oil producing countries, although in some localized areas construction is booming and capital markets are becoming more vibrant. About 40 percent of Saudi Arabia's gross domestic product (GDP) is still directly connected to the petroleum sector, as is 60 percent of Qatar's GDP and 30 percent of Algeria's. Government revenues are even more closely tied to the energy sector: petroleum exports account for 70 to 80 percent of Saudi Arabia's state revenues, about 80 percent of Kuwait's, and 40 to 50 percent of Iran's. High oil prices thus not only create a significant income for regional producers, but the windfall revenue disproportionately aids producing governments that rely almost exclusively on oil production rather than normal taxation for their income.

How these countries manage their substantial oil and natural gas profits, how long high prices will be sustained, and how far and how quickly they may fall, are all critical questions that will determine political risks in the Middle East over the next two decades. Where elections have been held in the region, extremists have scored some striking successes. Democratic elections are not by themselves a guarantee of political stability, which requires much more fundamental changes in governance, and social and legal systems, often over many years.

In addition, radical political movements are extending their influence across borders in an unprecedented manner, thanks in part to easy access to the international media that satellite television and the internet provide. Local populations are also being radicalized by fanatical religious leaders and by indoctrination in terrorist training camps. Finally, it is difficult to achieve stability in this critical oil-producing region without real progress in an Israeli-Palestinian peace process.

Outside the Middle East, many African countries and other under-performing economies are struggling to convert their energy wealth into economic development and diversification, whether through innovative energy-development programs in cooperation with the World Bank or by increasing social requirements on energy companies. Africa currently provides the United States with about 15 percent of its imported energy and may ultimately account for over 25 percent of U.S. oil and natural gas imports. However, continued and expanded U.S. access to African energy is by no means certain as other suitors are already lining up to secure future supplies. African trade with India and especially with China is growing rapidly. China's trade with Africa doubled between 2000 and 2004 and China is now Africa's third largest trading partner after the United States and France.

Chinese and Indian companies are competing aggressively with IOCs and providing more capital to develop African resources. This is a healthy development as long as investment projects are based on economic competition and are not attached to non-economic conditions. Corruption continues to pose a challenge to stable oil and natural gas production, especially in Africa, by misallocating precious resources and by discouraging long-term investment.

In Russia, the shifting roles played by private and state companies since the Soviet Union's collapse have stemmed investment flows and economic revival of the oil and natural gas industry. These problems have been exacerbated by policy swings between support for market competition and greater government control. Current policies show a strong preference by Moscow for reestablishing state control over energy resources and to use oil and natural gas supply as geopolitical tools to increase its influence in Europe and Asia. However, the vast investment needs of Russia's energy sector could still persuade the government to become a more market-oriented global player at some point in the future, particularly as world energy prices moderate.

In the Caspian Sea region, the competing interests of Russia, China, and the European Union continue to place heavy pressure on resource development and transit decisions. Ideally, a multiple pipeline strategy would include, simultaneously, expanding capacity along the Russian route, expanding shipments to China, and dramatically increasing shipments across the Caspian Sea to Western markets—either by a shuttle-fleet of more efficient oil tankers or, more ambitiously and controversially, by seabed pipelines for oil and natural gas. In that way, oil and natural gas could be delivered to the highest-value market without political or commercial restrictions.

It remains uncertain, however, whether such a multiple-pipeline strategy can overcome significant political and financial roadblocks. The cost-benefit calculations by host and transit states, and by foreign investors, will undoubtedly play a significant role in deciding the fate of these various routes. Nevertheless, delays in resolving these transit issues have already postponed delivery of significant oil and natural gas from the Caspian Sea region to world markets. Further delays would forestall the full development of this significant oil and natural gas potential.

IMPLICATIONS FOR THE UNITED STATES

Energy Security

For more than half a century, the United States has been the leader in global economic integration and a strong advocate for the free flow of goods, services, and capital to benefit both the American and the global economies. Throughout this period, the United States has been a net importer of oil. Domestic oil production peaked in 1970. In 2030, oil and natural gas will continue to dominate primary energy demand. The notion that the United States, as the world's largest energy consumer, can truly be rid of reliance on imported oil and natural gas is politically appealing, but fanciful. "Energy independence," if it were to be pursued vigorously without taking into account economic consequences, could work at cross purposes to America's other international objectives and obligations in this increasingly interdependent world.

For globally traded commodities like oil, and increasingly for natural gas, significant supply disruptions in one part of the world affect all markets regardless of whether they seem to be directly involved. This interdependence was dramatically demonstrated by the global repercussions from

Hurricanes Katrina and Rita in 2005: storm damage to oil rigs and refineries in the Gulf of Mexico affected markets worldwide, and U.S. demand could only be met with the help of petroleum supplies from around the world. Other events that have disrupted supplies include, for example, militant activity in Iraq and Nigeria, and surges in market demand from developing countries such as China, India, and Brazil.

By the same token, in an integrated global energy market, the opening up of new resources in any particular region adds to overall global supplies and thus benefits all consumers, wherever they may be. Therefore, managing "energy *inter*dependence" is a worldwide geopolitical challenge, one in which the United States must play a constructive leadership role.

A more useful definition of energy security is required to help inform and shape the public policy debate. Such a definition would include:

- A competitive market
- Stable and diverse supply with minimal disruptions
- Low price volatility
- Adequate spare capacity and logistical infrastructure
- Diverse energy mixes
- Protection of the global environment, including climate considerations
- Flexibility to accommodate shifting demand patterns
- Transparency and reliability of commercial relationships.

Neglecting these objectives in a blind pursuit of energy self-sufficiency would risk unintended and harmful consequences for both energy suppliers and consumers alike.

As the price of energy rises, its political importance to both producing and consuming countries increases. Producers and consumers regard energy security from different perspectives. For major energy importers, supply security is a key concern because reliance on another country or third party for energy involves risk. Governments of consumer countries want to provide their citizens with energy services while protecting them from disruptions and major cost fluctuations.

Energy exporters, in turn, depend on stable demand and reliable access to consumers. Countries rich in natural resources arguably have greater control over their domestic energy security. But the ways that producer countries interpret the approaches their consumers take to secure greater energy assurance for themselves (demand-side management, promoting renewable fuels, etc.) can affect investment decisions by producer countries. These decisions, in turn, affect importing countries' energy security interests.

Energy security involves various perspectives and requires many potential solutions. These multiple possibilities make managing global energy flows extremely complex. Individual governments and companies have few tools to influence overall energy security. And yet, the interconnected nature of the global oil and natural gas markets means that decisions made by producer or consumer countries will affect the energy security of others.

Engagement and Cooperation

International cooperation is an important component of U.S. energy policy and a significant means by which Washington seeks to promote greater understanding of diverging perspectives and to foster agreement on common principles, shared priorities, and paths forward. International engagement and cooperation will become more important as geopolitical tensions continue to place stress on international energy markets and relationships between energy players.

Broad-based cooperation will ensure that global energy markets continue to function efficiently and to meet the energy needs of a growing global economy. U.S. programs should aim to:

- Expand energy production
- Improve energy efficiency
- Reduce damage to the environment caused by energy production and use
- Diversify the types, sources, and suppliers of energy
- Encourage efficient and flexible markets nationally as well as globally and avoid restrictions that impede their ability to adjust to any disruption
- Remove barriers to energy investment and trade
- Promote greater transparency in energy trade
- Invest in modernizing energy infrastructure
- Develop and deploy new technologies
- Protect global energy infrastructure.

PARTNERSHIP	GOAL	MEMBERS
Carbon Sequestration Leadership Forum	Development of improved cost-effective technologies for the separation and capture of carbon dioxide for its transport and long-term safe storage. The purpose of the CSLF is to make these technologies broadly available internationally; and to identify and address wider issues relating to carbon capture and storage.	Australia, Brazil, Canada, China, Colombia, Denmark, EC, France, Germany, Greece, India, Italy, Japan, Korea, Mexico, Netherlands, Norway, Russia, Saudi Arabia, South Africa, UK, United States
International Partnership for the Hydrogen Economy	Accelerate the transition to a hydrogen economy. The IPHE provides a mechanism for partners to organize, coordinate and implement effective, efficient, and focused international research, development, demonstration, and commercial utilization activities related to hydrogen and fuel cell technologies. The IPHE provides a forum for advancing policies, and common technical codes and standards that can accelerate the cost-effective transition to a hydrogen economy; and it educates and informs stakeholders and the general public on the benefits of, and challenges to, establishing the hydrogen economy.	Australia, Brazil, Canada, China, EC, France, Germany, Iceland, India, Italy, Japan, Korea, New Zealand, Norway, Russia, UK, United States
Generation IV	The Generation IV International Forum, or GIF, was chartered in May 2001 to lead the collaborative efforts of the world's leading nuclear technology nations to develop next-generation nuclear energy systems to meet the world's future energy needs.	Argentina, Brazil, Canada, EC (represented by EURATOM), France, Japan, Korea, South Africa, Switzerland, UK, United States
Methane to Markets	Reduce global methane emissions in order to enhance economic growth, strengthen energy security, improve air quality, improve industrial safety, and reduce emissions of greenhouse gases. The Methane to Markets Partnership is an international initiative that advances cost-effective, near-term methane recovery and use as a clean energy source.	Argentina, Australia, Brazil, Canada, China, Colombia, Ecuador, Germany, India, Italy, Japan, Mexico, Nigeria, Poland, Republic of Korea, Russia, Ukraine, UK, United States
ITER	ITER is a joint international research and development project that aims to demonstrate the scientific and technical feasibility of fusion power.	EC (represented by EURATOM), Japan, China, India, Korea, Russia, United States
Global Nuclear Energy Partnership	Develop worldwide consensus on enabling expanded use of economical, carbon-free nuclear energy to meet growing electricity demand. This will use a nuclear fuel cycle that enhances energy security, while promoting non-proliferation. It would achieve its goal by having nations with secure, advanced nuclear capabilities provide fuel services—fresh fuel and recovery of used fuel—to other nations who agree to employ nuclear energy for power generation purposes only. The closed fuel cycle model envisioned by this partnership requires development and deployment of technologies that enable recycling and consumption of long-lived radioactive waste.	Still being formed
Global Gas Flaring Reduction	The GGFR public-private partnership, a World Bank-led initiative, facilitates and supports national efforts to use currently flared gas by promoting effective regulatory frameworks and tackling the constraints on gas utilization, such as insufficient infrastructure and poor access to local and international energy markets, particularly in developing countries.	(Donors) Canada, EU, UK Foreign Commonwealth Office, Norway, United States (Countries) Algeria (Sonatrach), Angola (Sonangol), Cameroon, Chad, Ecuador, Equatorial Guinea, Indonesia, Kazakhstan, Khanty-Mansijsysk (Russian Federation), Nigeria, Norway, United States

TABLE 4-1. *Sampling of Multilateral Energy Technology Initiatives*

PARTNERSHIP	GOAL	MEMBERS
APEC – Energy Working Group	The APEC Energy Working Group (EWG) is a voluntary, regional-based forum operating under the APEC umbrella. EWG helps further APEC goals to facilitate energy trade and investment, and ensure that energy contributes to the economic, social, and environmental enhancement of the APEC community.	Australia, Brunei, Canada, Chile, China, Hong Kong, Indonesia, Japan, Republic of Korea, Malaysia, Mexico, New Zealand, Papua New Guinea, Peru, the Philippines, Russia, Singapore, Chinese Taipei, Thailand, United States, Vietnam.
Asia-Pacific Energy Partnership	Public-private partnership to develop and accelerate the deployment of cleaner and more efficient technologies and practices.	Australia, China, India, Japan, South Korea, United States
Security and Prosperity Partnership/ North America Energy Working Group	Under the SPP, the energy goals are to strengthen North America's energy markets by working together, according to our respective legal frameworks, to increase reliable energy supplies for the region's needs and development; by facilitating investment in energy infrastructure, technology improvements, production, and reliable delivery of energy; by enhancing cooperation to identify and utilize best practices, and to streamline and update regulations; by promoting energy efficiency, conservation, and technologies like clean coal.	Canada, Mexico, United States

TABLE 4-2. *Sampling of Regional Multilateral Energy-Related Activities*

International engagement takes many forms, as illustrated in Tables 4-1 and 4-2. The U.S. government engages both producer and consumer countries, as well as the private sector, to maintain open lines of communication and to seek cooperation in overcoming common energy challenges. In general, the U.S. government engages other countries through specially designated bilateral and multilateral energy dialogues, through a series of next-generation energy technology initiatives, and by integrating energy policy considerations into other related bilateral and multilateral fora.

By maintaining frequent and regular contact with major producing and consuming countries through established energy dialogues, the United States has sought to foster greater stability in global energy markets through better communication and coordination. The U.S. military has also played a large role in securing major energy transit choke points throughout the world by maintaining forward deployed positions.

Participation in institutions like the International Energy Agency creates many benefits. It helps to improve data collection and transparency, to coordinate the use of strategic stockpiles during supply disruptions, and to foster joint consideration of energy policy issues that are of particular interest to member countries. Finally, public-private, multilateral partnerships on next-generation energy technologies help to encourage research, development, and deployment of transformative energy technologies.

CONCLUSIONS

U.S. Leadership

American leadership is key to advancing free markets, international stability, and open access to energy and raw material supplies. In order to maintain and reinforce this leadership, the United States must more strongly resist both isolationism and domestic protectionism. The United States must also take the initiative to lock its economic and political principles as deeply as possible into the multilateral system.

America's prosperity rests on reliable access to stable supplies of energy from a global market. It cannot successfully pursue this goal separately from the rest of the world with a unilateral U.S. policy path. Therefore, the United States must adopt a global approach to energy security for its future national prosperity.

This means, in the immediate future, overcoming U.S. disagreements with the EU and some developing countries in global trade negotiations. In the longer term, it means strengthening institutions such as the WTO that enforce the market-based rules of the international system. It also means restoring strong political links with Europe and combating anti-Americanism around the world in more imaginative ways. And, it means doing the utmost to establish stability in the Middle East and to avoid unnecessary confrontation with China.

The U.S. government should press for large emerging consumer countries in the developing world, such as China and India, to be integrated progressively into the international energy security system—into institutions such as the International Energy Agency and the Group of Eight—in order to draw them into a decision-making process based on market principles and to enable closer monitoring of their compliance with international agreements. Irrespective of other policy differences, the United States, China, and India share vital common interests as energy importers, and cooperation among them could significantly strengthen the hand of the major consuming nations. It would also help to avert the adoption of divide-and-rule tactics by energy exporters aimed at bidding up prices and securing political objectives.

The United States should also boldly offer credible proposals for reforming international institutions, such as the United Nations and the International Monetary Fund. Multilateral institutions should be strengthened in order to enforce international rules that support not only U.S. interests but those of the rest of the world.

Energy Security

It is incumbent upon both producer and consumer countries to find common ground, or at least to agree to basic principles, for governing the energy sector to ensure a relative degree of stability for all. Tension over energy security has turned energy into a key political preoccupation for governments around the world. The challenge in responding to such short term pressures is that energy policy decisions endure for decades with profound and lasting consequences, yet they are often made to resolve immediate issues with only short-term fixes. Sustainable long-term energy policies can only be developed from a robust and healthy debate over ideas. If a policy is to be effective for an extended period, an informed general public must accept and support not just its tactical aims, but also its strategic goals.

New Policy Tools

Along with a new strategic approach, the emerging energy world requires new policy tools to influence developments. For example, the need to open energy investment markets has largely been left out of WTO and other international trade negotiations, such as for NAFTA. U.S. economic, energy, and security interests, along with those of the rest of the world, will be best served if the United States and its allies work to achieve and maintain an open, multilateral, global system to the greatest extent possible.

National Oil Companies

To achieve the expanded production required to meet growing global demand in a timely manner, NOCs should be encouraged to work cooperatively with internationally competitive oil company partners in order to encourage the use of the best technology and to adopt global standards of transparency, accountability, and contract sanctity. The U.S. government should lead a worldwide campaign against resource nationalism and protectionism in resource development.

U.S. Policy Priorities

Measures the United States can take to help achieve the above objectives include:

- An energy policy that recognizes the need for—and actively encourages—long-term investment in production both domestically and abroad.

- Promotion of market energy prices in all countries—many NOCs owe their strong positions to preferentially low product prices in their home countries. This will become increasingly unsustainable in a carbon-constrained environment.

- Continued openness in the United States to investment by foreign energy companies—especially through the Committee on Foreign Investment in the U.S. process. This is a critical bargaining chip in the U.S. government's efforts to win greater market access for American companies in producing countries.

- A firm stance opposing the carving out of energy investment and energy services from free-trade agreements.

Climate Change

Political consensus and coordinated national and international policies will be needed to facilitate long-term investments and technological advances as part of any attempt to mitigate climate change. Because the world shares a common atmosphere and because energy and other markets are interconnected, responses to climate change should be global.

Corporate Environmental Strategies

Consumers are increasingly aware of the environmental and social impacts of the products they buy. This means that energy companies must pay attention to their images as socially responsible organizations, and offer consumers the opportunity to purchase cleaner, more efficient energy or energy technologies. Companies are increasingly finding ways to turn this attention to sustainability and corporate citizenship to their competitive advantage.

A Global Response

The United States has much to gain by strengthening the international structures that promote maintaining and expanding open global markets and that prevent fragmentation of the world economy. However reluctant we and other countries may be to admit it, energy is a crucial policy area in which the interests of the United States and those of the rest of the world coincide. If the world does not respond creatively to the challenges outlined above, we risk confronting an increasing uncertain future, defined by factors beyond our control or influence.

Chapter CARBON MANAGEMENT 5

Abstract

Policies aimed at curbing carbon dioxide (CO_2) emissions will alter the energy mix, increase energy-related costs, and require reductions in demand growth. Effective carbon management will be aided by developing legal and regulatory frameworks to enable carbon capture and sequestration (CCS). As policymakers consider options to reduce CO_2 emissions, they face the challenge of creating a global framework that includes a transparent, predictable, economy-wide cost for carbon emissions.

This chapter considers climate, energy, and emissions concerns by examining the natural carbon cycle in the context of global and U.S. energy sources and uses. Various carbon management options raise new regulatory and policy implications.

An outline of the Carbon Management chapter is as follows:

• Carbon management

• Energy efficiency and demand reduction

• Transportation

• Carbon capture and sequestration.

There is growing concern that the climate is warming and that CO_2 emissions play a role. The most recent report by the Intergovernmental Panel on Climate Change (IPCC) about the physical science basis for climate change states: "Most of the observed increase in globally averaged temperatures since the mid-20th century is very likely due to the observed increase in anthropogenic greenhouse gas concentrations."[1] ("Very likely" is greater than 90 percent likelihood, according to the IPCC report.)

Moreover, initiatives in increasing number are emerging, within both the public and private sectors, aimed at reducing carbon emissions. Such a trend highlights the potential for carbon constraint to become a significant feature of future energy strategies. In particular, future carbon constraint could alter the way in which the world uses the fossil fuels that currently provide most of our energy. Since changes in fossil-fuel use could affect diverse lifestyles, economic activity, and energy supply, it is becoming increasingly important to plan for ways to accommodate carbon-constraint policies within any overall energy strategy.

To better understand the range of potential energy futures, the Demand Task Group (see Chapter One) studied in detail five publicly available worldwide energy-demand projections provided by the Energy Information Administration (EIA) and the International Energy Agency (IEA). Economic growth is the primary driver in all these projections. The expected economic growth rates were greater

---

1 The Fourth Assessment Report of the Intergovernmental Panel on Climate Change: *Climate Change 2007: The Physical Science Basis.*

than the current annual rate of 3.1 percent (1980–2000) in all the projections except for the explicitly low-growth EIA Low Economic Growth projection. Four of the projections studied are based on energy-policy assumptions that extend energy policies in effect today. The energy growth rates for these four projections range from 1.5 to 2.5 percent per year, with only the EIA Low Economic Growth projection having an energy growth rate less than the 1980–2000 energy demand growth rate of 1.7 percent per year.

Policy assumptions can play a major role in determining the outcome of energy demand projections. The IEA created the Alternative Policy scenario in an attempt to estimate future energy demand, given the major energy policies now under consideration by governments around the world. Currently, there are more than 1,400 energy-related policies either in place or proposed by various countries. The IEA first removed from the list policies already in place. From the remaining policies, it incorporated those that are likely to be implemented in the future. These additional policies included those that increased biofuels use; increased the use of other renewable energy sources; increased the use of nuclear-power generation; created an environment that promoted energy efficiency; encouraged clean-fuel technologies use; and increased the production of domestic fuel supplies.

■ Key Information: Greenhouse Gases

The earth maintains an equilibrium temperature by re-radiating the energy it receives from the sun. So-called "greenhouse gases" trap some of the re-radiated energy. Much of the debate in the past was not directed at the link between global temperature and climate change, but more towards the degree of global warming and the role of man-made greenhouse gases versus the role of natural mechanisms.

Greenhouse gases include carbon dioxide (CO_2), methane (CH_4), fluorinated gases (CFCs), sulfur hexafluoride (SF_6), and nitrous oxide (N_2O), to which human activity contributes atmospheric emissions. Of these, carbon dioxide is the most significant in its potential impact on global temperatures. The degree of warming is linked to the total volume of CO_2 in the atmosphere; since the beginning of the industrial revolution, the amount of CO_2 in the atmosphere has risen by about a third, from around 2,100 billion tons to around 2,750 billion tons. These figures are usually expressed as concentrations of CO_2 in parts per million of the total mass of the atmosphere. The pre-industrial levels of CO_2 were about 280 parts per million and current levels are rising through 380 parts per million. In order to stabilize the concentration of CO_2 and other greenhouse gases in the atmosphere, annual global emissions would have to be brought under control and then made to decline year after year.

Any approach to reducing the growth of the levels of greenhouse gases in the atmosphere must include either reducing the emissions of CO_2 to the atmosphere or enhancing the sinks for CO_2. The former can only be achieved by reducing the amount of fossil fuel burned or by capturing the produced CO_2 and preventing it from reaching the atmosphere. Enhancing carbon sinks can be achieved by increasing the mass of carbon tied up in the biosphere. For example, growing more trees in forests, attempting to induce the growth of algae blooms in oceans, or using more no-till farming methods (increasing carbon uptake in soils) could reduce the levels of CO_2 in the atmosphere.

Other greenhouse gases also can be curtailed. Agricultural practices such as reduced use of fertilizer (reducing nitrous oxide emissions), and collecting and flaring or burning methane from livestock waste, landfills, and coal mines could also play a role in offsetting future greenhouse gas emissions. In addition, reducing leakage of sulfur hexafluoride from utility transmission and distribution equipment, and destroying or avoiding production of fluorinated gases and nitrous oxide could also help control greenhouse gases.

Facing the Hard Truths about Energy

The combined results of the five projections can be summarized as follows:

- Generally the projected world oil share of energy demand is lower in the future, while the natural gas and coal shares are higher.

- The projected nuclear share of world energy demand is lower in all cases except the Alternative Policy Case, where it is about the same as in 2000.

- Global CO_2 emissions were 24 billion metric tons in 2000, growing to a projected range between 34 (Alternative Policy Case) and 51 (High Economic Growth Case) billion metric tons in 2030.

- Projected U.S. energy demand growth rate is higher in the future than in the past in all but the Alternative Policy Case.

- Projected energy shares align in essentially the same way in the United States as in the rest of the world.

- The U.S. rate of growth of CO_2 emissions is projected to increase more slowly in the future than in the past, except in the High Economic Growth Case where emissions may grow more rapidly than in the past.

In light of these projections and the likelihood that some carbon constraint will emerge, and the assumption that the world will want to continue to use fossil fuels for a large fraction of energy requirements in the foreseeable future, it is important that governments and industries plan to accommodate a carbon constraint in their energy strategies. It is unlikely that the continued use of oil, natural gas, and coal, could remain unaffected in a carbon-constrained world.

CARBON MANAGEMENT

By its nature, climate change is global. The interrelation between energy and other markets requires that an effective response to climate change also, ultimately, be global. Carbon emissions from burning fossil fuels, combined with those from changing land use, augment the large natural flux of carbon between the atmosphere, the land, and the oceans (see Figure 5-1). Rapid mixing in the atmosphere ensures that CO_2 emitted anywhere in the world is quickly distributed about the globe, and since the start of the industrial era, the mass of CO_2 in the world's atmosphere has risen by a third.

Without international cooperation in the coming decades, achieving significant reductions in CO_2 emissions would be elusive, and disparity in national responses would create challenges to the international trade regime as different nations sought to address and prioritize what they saw to be their own particular concerns.

Approaches to reducing CO_2 emissions could include the following elements:

- Energy efficiency and demand reduction
  - Better and more efficient use of energy in all sectors, including transportation, buildings, industrial energy use, and power generation
  - Improved efficiency will need to be translated into reduced energy demand rather than solely into increased performance

- Use of lower-carbon fuels
  - Shift from coal to natural gas

- Use of non-carbon based power ("decarbonization")
  - Nuclear power
  - Wind power
  - Solar power
  - Ocean and geothermal power

- Use of "carbon neutral" energy sources
  - Biomass to augment power generation
  - Biofuels to augment hydrocarbons used for transportation

- Carbon capture and sequestration
  - Preventing the release to the atmosphere of CO_2 generated by the combustion of fossil fuels.

Innovation and deployment of new energy technologies in global energy systems could improve the potential for significant reductions in CO_2 emissions while maintaining the desired level of economic activity. This would require substantial private- and public-sector investments in research, development, demonstration, and deployment. The most cost-effective CO_2 policies would involve broad, technology neutral, market-based mechanisms to create incentives for the private sector to undertake these technology changes.

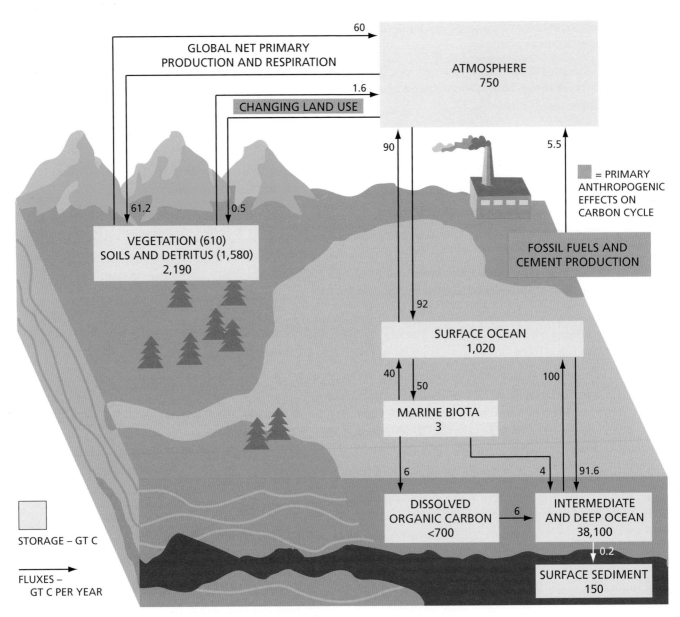

Source: OSTP NanoEnergy Brief, 10 August 2005, available at www.er.doe.gov/bes/presentations/OSTP_NanoEnergyBrief_10AUG05.pdf (based on D. Schimel, D. Alves, I. Enting, M. Heimann, F. Joos, D. Raynaud, and T. Wigley, 1996: "CO$_2$ and the Carbon Cycle").

FIGURE 5-1. *The Global Carbon Cycle, with 1990s Carbon Fluxes in Gigatons of Carbon (GT C) per Year*

The Continued Use of Domestic Energy Resources under Carbon Constraint

Currently, fossil fuels (oil, natural gas, and coal) provide more than 80 percent of the world's energy needs. In terms of global CO$_2$ emissions from fossil fuels, oil accounts for 39 percent of these emissions and natural gas for 20 percent, while coal accounts for the remaining 41 percent.[2] Within the United States, fossil fuels

2 International Energy Agency, *World Energy Outlook 2006*.

similarly provide more than 80 percent of the nation's energy needs, as shown in Figure 5-2, which details the distribution both of the sources and the uses of the national energy budget in units of 10^{15} Btu (quads) (where 1 quad = 293 billion kilowatt-hours). The figure reveals both the degree of dependence on fossil fuels and the amount of energy lost, which in turn provides some measure of the potential scope for efficiency improvements.

Absent societal and market responses to climate change, oil, natural gas, and coal would continue to

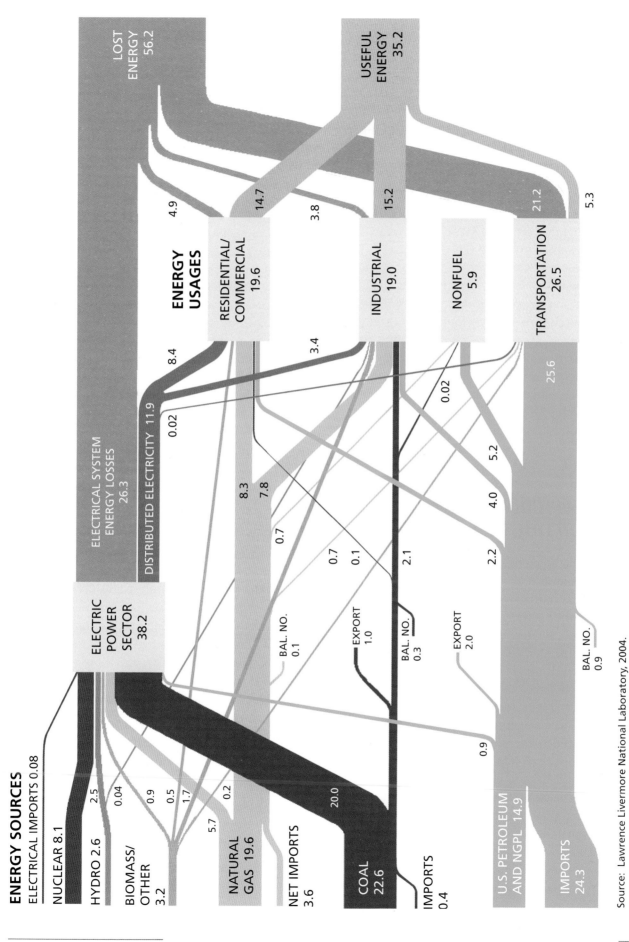

ENERGY SOURCES

ELECTRICAL IMPORTS 0.08

NUCLEAR 8.1

HYDRO 2.6 — 2.5

BIOMASS/OTHER 3.2 — 0.04, 0.9, 0.5, 1.7

NATURAL GAS 19.6 — 5.7, 0.2

NET IMPORTS 3.6

COAL 22.6 — 20.0

IMPORTS 0.4

U.S. PETROLEUM AND NGPL 14.9

IMPORTS 24.3

ELECTRIC POWER SECTOR 38.2

ELECTRICAL SYSTEM ENERGY LOSSES 26.3

DISTRIBUTED ELECTRICITY 11.9

LOST ENERGY 56.2

USEFUL ENERGY 35.2

ENERGY USAGES

RESIDENTIAL/COMMERCIAL 19.6 — 4.9, 14.7, 8.4

INDUSTRIAL 19.0 — 3.8, 15.2, 3.4

NONFUEL 5.9

TRANSPORTATION 26.5 — 21.2, 5.3

8.3, 7.8, 0.02, 0.7, 0.02, 5.2, 4.0, 2.2, 25.6, 0.9, 2.1

BAL. NO. 0.1

EXPORT 1.0

BAL. NO. 0.3

EXPORT 2.0

BAL. NO. 0.9

0.7, 0.1

Source: Lawrence Livermore National Laboratory, 2004.

***FIGURE 5-2.** U.S. Energy Sources and Uses in 2002 (Quadrillion Btu per Year)*

play a major role in energy supply over the next three decades and beyond. In particular, because of its high energy density, and the convenience of using a liquid fuel, petroleum would continue to dominate transportation. Conventional oil, heavy oils, and, to a lesser extent, biofuels and liquid fuels derived from natural gas and coal would ensure continuity of supply for transportation at relatively low cost. At the same time, heat and power would be dominated by coal and natural gas from domestic resources.

The question arises: What happens to this projection if there is significant constraint on CO_2 emissions? Given that most energy-related CO_2 emissions come from fossil fuels, the use of these resources cannot remain unaffected in a carbon-constrained world. A combination of improved efficiency, demand reduction, decarbonization, and CCS would be needed to reduce emissions. CCS would strongly determine the extent to which we could continue to use a variety of fossil fuels, and in particular it would enable the continued use of the large domestic U.S. coal reserves while still reducing CO_2 emissions. Similarly, incorporating CCS, China and India could reduce their CO_2 emissions while continuing to use their own substantial coal reserves.

ENERGY EFFICIENCY AND DEMAND REDUCTION

Improving the efficiency of energy use within the industrial, commercial, domestic, and transportation sectors has the potential to reduce energy use without reducing economic activity, and to reduce the associated CO_2 emissions. However, to achieve this, incentives would be needed to encourage investments in higher-efficiency capital and to encourage using newly gained efficiency to actually reduce demand. Key to stimulating long-term investment by the private sector in more energy-efficient capital would be a steady, predictable, long-term increase in the cost of CO_2 emissions. This would be enhanced by government incentives to economically retire older, high-CO_2 emitting plants as well as to invest in newer, low-emissions capital. Incentives in the building sector, both commercial and domestic, would be needed to encourage the use of higher-efficiency construction techniques and efficient cooling and heating systems, which often come at a higher initial cost with a long "pay-back" period.

TRANSPORTATION

While CCS can address CO_2 emissions from coal and the extra emissions associated with producing unconventional oil, it cannot address the tail-pipe emissions produced when using hydrocarbon fuels for transportation. If we wished, in a carbon-constrained world, to continue significant use of gasoline and diesel as transportation fuels, and at the same time to reduce CO_2 emissions, then other approaches would be needed. The appropriate measures to achieve such reductions would focus largely on a combination of improved engine efficiency and on regulatory mechanisms to reduce demand.

There is potential to almost double the efficiency of existing gasoline- and diesel-powered vehicles. And there are technologies to augment internal-combustion engines in cars using electric hybrids and plug-in electric hybrids, which are already available. So long as the centralized electricity generating plants control CO_2 emissions, then the electrification of cars helps reduce overall CO_2 emissions as well as reduce the requirements for oil imports. Examples of such solutions include integrated coal-fired power with CCS or alternative low-carbon electricity sources such as nuclear, wind, or other renewables.

However, technical efficiency improvements may not, by themselves, lead to a reduction in the demand for hydrocarbon fuels. Over the past two decades, light-duty vehicle efficiency improvements in the United States have been countered by increased miles driven and heavier, higher-performance vehicles. Active policies to reduce demand for transportation fuel would be an important element in any portfolio of strategies to reduce CO_2 emission in a carbon-constrained world. Demand reduction could be achieved by combining approaches that reflect the following considerations:

- Reducing carbon emissions from transportation would have key importance in a carbon-constrained world.

- Public education, particularly of the next generation of consumers, would play an important role in long-term strategies to reduce demand.

- Improved engine efficiency enables demand reduction, especially if accompanied by other mechanisms to reduce demand.

- Increasing fuel price is unlikely to be sufficient by itself. A combination of increased price and regulation would probably be necessary to reduce demand effectively.

- Government incentives to increase the use of public transport would help reduce demand for transportation fuel.

- Congestion charges and high-occupancy vehicle (HOV) systems would further help reduce fuel demand.

- Government incentives to retire older, less-efficient vehicles would help reduce fuel demand, and programs to audit the energy efficiency of the existing fleet would be an effective complement to such incentives.

CARBON CAPTURE AND SEQUESTRATION

In a carbon-constrained world, CCS would allow us to sustain many of the benefits of using hydrocarbons. Even where the CO_2 generated by burning hydrocarbons cannot be captured easily, as with using oil for transportation, sequestering CO_2 from other sources (such as coal-fired power stations) can help create—to some degree—the margin needed to allow for the volumes of CO_2 that escape capture. Fossil fuels are likely to remain an important part of the energy mix, because of the continuing competitive (direct) cost of hydrocarbons, and the huge investment already made in infrastructure to deliver them. Therefore, the combination of fossil fuel use with CCS is likely to be emphasized as a strong complement to strategies involving alternative, non-hydrocarbon, energy-supply sources, and to measures designed to encourage more efficient energy use. Here we compile key questions about the potential for CCS technology.

What is the Contribution of CCS to Maintaining Energy Supply from Fossil Fuels?

In a carbon-constrained world, CCS would play a key role in allowing the continued use of coal and the growing use of unconventional oil. By providing a means for dealing with a significant fraction of the CO_2 emissions from fossil fuels, CCS would allow us to retain fuel diversity for many decades. CCS would be implemented largely in association with burning coal,

which, worldwide, now accounts for 41 percent of all CO_2 emissions from fossil fuels. At the same time, chemical plants and centralized power generation using natural gas or oil could also incorporate CCS.

The growing need to provide transportation will increase the pressure to move towards other fossil sources for liquid fuels, such as unconventional oil (heavy oil, shale oil, tar sands) and coal-to-liquids (CTL) technologies. Since exploiting these resources comes with a significantly heavier CO_2 burden than with conventional oil and natural gas, then in a carbon-constrained world, CCS would become increasingly important. CCS can be directly applied to the extraction of unconventional oil and to the CTL process, and has the potential to mitigate the extra CO_2 burden beyond that from using these fuels for transportation. This facilitates their use under carbon constraint.

CCS also has application to disposal of petroleum coke (petcoke), which is the "bottom of the barrel" residue produced by the world's refineries. Petcoke is similar to coal as a fuel, but petcoke's generally higher sulfur level can be a significant challenge to its use for power generation. However, gasification, along with CCS, makes it possible to burn polluting fuels like petcoke because removing pollutants from a high-pressure gas stream is much cheaper than from a stack. Petcoke-fueled power, combined with CCS, has the potential to transform a costly problem into a profitable technology.

What is the Level of Readiness for Large Scale CCS?

The technologies for capturing CO_2 from pre- and post-combustion gas streams are available. However, their costs are somewhat uncertain and constraints remain on the levels of oxygen, particulates, and sulfur oxides for effective extraction using conventional amine solvents. Current capture technologies also prefer steady-state conditions that do not always prevail in the power-generation industry. Similar concerns apply to the more sophisticated pre-combustion capture. However, broadly speaking, the capture technologies exist and are not critically dependent on new technological breakthroughs. The same is true for CO_2 sequestration technologies; the oil industry has extensive experience with pumping liquids into subsurface formations and evaluating the security of these formations for storage. Currently, several pilot projects have successfully demonstrated sequestration of CO_2 in volumes amounting to millions of tons.

Still missing is the demonstration of fully integrated CCS at commercial scale, along with an established legal and regulatory environment that will enable and encourage CCS. There is, we believe, a strongly growing need within the United States to implement full-scale integration of power generation and CCS. Elsewhere, there are efforts to create just such integration. China, in particular, with funding from the European Union, plans a full-scale plant with CCS within the next five years. The United States should not delay such implementation while awaiting further research. We recommend that the United States achieve the necessary refinements in the largely existing technologies by accelerating full-scale implementation. Further, the United States should share its experience with other nations.

Does the Capacity for Underground Storage Exist?

It is very likely that there is ample storage space in subsurface formations to store enough CO_2 to substantially alleviate atmospheric emissions. What is less well known is the distribution and availability of these storage resources. While exhausted oil and natural gas reservoirs will provide room for considerable amounts of CO_2, it will probably be necessary to also use deep saline formations, depending, for example, on the siting requirements for power stations with CCS. Subsurface storage space will become a resource, with its own supply curve, and we recommend that the United States extend activities by the Carbon Sequestration Regional Partnerships and conduct, at a federal level, a full survey of the nation's potential sequestration sites. A preliminary map of potential U.S. storage sites is shown in Figure 5-3. Other nations should be encouraged to do the same.

What is the Cost of CCS Compared to Other Approaches to Carbon Mitigation?

CCS represents a competitive way to address a substantial fraction of the potential need for carbon mitigation; the IPCC Special Report on Carbon Dioxide Capture and Storage points out that including CCS in a mitigation portfolio could achieve suitable stabilization of CO_2 concentrations in the atmosphere at a lower cost than otherwise.[3] The IPCC report observes: "Models indicate that CCS systems will be competitive with other large-scale mitigation options such as nuclear power and renewable energy technologies. These studies show that including CCS in a mitigation portfolio could reduce the cost of stabilizing CO_2 concentrations by 30 percent or more. One aspect of the cost competitiveness of CCS technologies is that they are compatible with most current energy infrastructures."

Current estimates for the cost of CCS implementation on coal and natural gas fired power plants are about $40/ton of CO_2. This includes the cost to capture the CO_2, compress it to supercritical (liquid) form, and inject it in the subsurface for sequestration. To put this cost in perspective, $40/ton of CO_2 equates to between 2 and 4 cents per kilowatt-hour depending on the fuel source, with gas at the lower end of the range and coal at the upper end.

Efforts to reduce CCS costs would focus on capture technology, which today accounts for about half the cost. There is considerable scope for improving the current capture technologies, and for implementing new ones. Nonetheless, research in these areas should parallel implementing current technologies, and should not serve as a reason to delay a rapid start on full-scale CCS.

What is the Role of CO_2-Based Enhanced Oil Recovery (CO_2-EOR) in CCS?

Large volumes of naturally occurring CO_2 obtained from underground deposits are currently used by the oil industry to enhance the recovery of oil from mature reservoirs.[4,5] This CO_2-EOR is currently conducted without regard to storing the CO_2 "downhole." However, with relative ease present technology could

---

3   Intergovernmental Panel on Climate Change, *IPCC Special Report on Carbon Dioxide Capture and Storage*, 2005, Interlachen, http://www.ipcc.ch/.

4   Melzer LS (ed.), "CO2 Sourcing for Enhanced Oil Recovery," The University of Texas of the Permian Basin's Center for Energy and Economic Diversification Short Course #13 on Carbon Dioxide Flooding, Presented at the Annual CO2 Flooding Conference, Midland, Texas, December 6, 2004.

5   Bliss K, "Final Report for DOE Award No. DE-FC26-03NT41994, Admendment No. A000," report submitted by the Interstate Oil and Gas Compact Commission, Oklahoma City, OK (January 24, 2005): 31, available at http://www.iogcc.state.ok.us/PDFS/CarbonCaptureandStorageReportandSummary.pdf.

Facing the Hard Truths about Energy

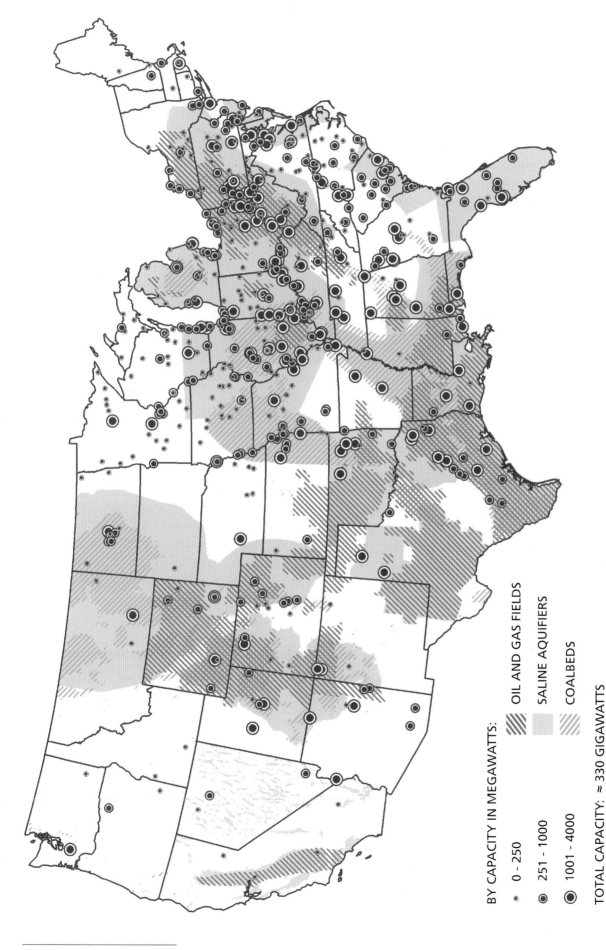

BY CAPACITY IN MEGAWATTS:

· 0 - 250

⊙ 251 - 1000

⦿ 1001 - 4000

OIL AND GAS FIELDS

SALINE AQUIFERS

COALBEDS

TOTAL CAPACITY: ≈ 330 GIGAWATTS

Note: For further information on and maps of carbon sources and potential sequestration sites, see www.natcarb.org.

FIGURE 5-3. *U.S. Coal-Fired Power Plants (2000) and Potential Sequestration Sites*

be modified to emphasize such storage. In a carbon-constrained world, we could also expect rising pressure to use anthropogenic CO_2 to drive this recovery enhancement, which would lead to a net reduction in atmospheric CO_2. While the likely extent of CO_2-EOR provides a relatively small fraction of the capacity needed for CO_2 sequestration, it does offer a strong technology bridge to carbon-sequestration technologies and should be encouraged as an important element of a CCS strategy. Government incentives for CO_2 storage in association with CO_2-EOR, and new arrangements for developing suitable infrastructure for commercial use of anthropogenic CO_2 for EOR with storage, could help CO_2-EOR for storage succeed, particularly as CO_2 becomes increasingly available (and increasingly cheap) under a wide-scale adoption of CCS.

Regulation

The technological hurdles to effectively implementing CCS are surmountable. However, the regulatory framework within which CCS is deployed will play an important role in determining CCS's future. The legislative framework within which CCS is conducted will have a major impact on how rapidly the technology is implemented. And legislation will ultimately determine whether CCS can effectively mitigate carbon emissions and facilitate using future hydrocarbon supplies.

During a 2006 G8 forum on carbon sequestration,[6] more than 120 participants from 15 nations identified

6   G8 International Energy Agency (IEA) & Carbon Sequestration Leadership Forum (CSLF) First Workshop on Near Term Opportunities, held 22–23 August 2006, San Francisco.

5 critical areas of regulation that need to be resolved in order to facilitate the near-term deployment of CCS:

- Ownership and liability of CO_2 at every step along the "value chain"

- Regulatory treatment of CO_2 and other gases in the CO_2 stream

- Monitoring, verification, and remediation

- Property rights and intellectual property

- Jurisdictional and trans-boundary issues.

Moreover, the roles of federal and state governments, regarding which authority is responsible for which regulation or permitting process, need clarification. Such clarification will help attract commercial players into the carbon capture and storage market. Participants of the G8 forum felt that "progress cannot be made on near term opportunities if this issue is not resolved."

CCS Conclusion

In summary, CCS would greatly facilitate the sustained use of oil, natural gas, and coal to meet U.S. energy demands in a carbon-constrained world. Moreover, it would reduce the pace at which we would otherwise need to develop and employ alternative energy sources. CCS is viable and its introduction is not limited by any need for significant technological breakthroughs.

Chapter 6 RECOMMENDATIONS

Abstract

The NPC study participants developed recommendations in the following five strategic areas. Study participants believe that implementing these five strategies will enable industry and government to more adequately prepare for the hard energy truths facing the United States and the world.

The NPC makes the following policy recommendations by strategy.

- Moderate demand by increasing energy efficiency

- Expand and diversify U.S. energy supply

- Strengthen global and U.S. energy security

- Reinforce capabilities to meet new challenges

- Address carbon constraints

■ Moderate Demand by Increasing Energy Efficiency

Improve Vehicle Fuel Economy

The NPC makes the following recommendations to increase vehicle fuel economy:

- Improve car and light-truck fuel economy standards at the maximum rate possible by applying economic, available technology.

  - Update the standards on a regular basis.

  - Avoid further erosion of fuel economy standards resulting from increased sales of light trucks, or, alternatively, adjust light-truck standards to reflect changes in relative light-truck and car market shares.

Potential Effect: 3-5 million barrels of oil per day in the United States from the increased base in 2030.

Reduce Energy Consumption in the Residential and Commercial Sectors

Building Energy Codes
Appliance and Equipment Standards

The NPC makes the following recommendations to improve efficiency in the residential and commercial sectors:

- Encourage states to implement and enforce more aggressive energy efficiency building codes, updated on a regular basis.

- Establish appliance standards for new products.

- Update federal appliance standards on a regular basis.

Potential Effect: 7-9 quadrillion Btu per year by 2030 in the United States, including 2-3 quadrillion Btu per year of natural gas (5-8 billion cubic feet per day),

4-5 quadrillion Btu per year of coal, and ~1 quadrillion Btu per year (0.5 million barrels per day) of oil.

Increase Industrial Sector Efficiency

The NPC makes the following recommendations to improve efficiency in the industrial sector:

- The Department of Energy should conduct and promote research, development, demonstration, and deployment of industrial energy efficiency technologies and best practices.

- The research and development tax credit should be permanently extended to spur private research and development investments.

Potential Effect: 4-7 quadrillion Btu per year by 2030 in the United States, about equal parts coal, gas, and oil.

■ Expand and Diversify U.S. Energy Supply

Understanding the Range of Production Forecasts

Recommendations for improved understanding of forecasts and data are discussed specifically in the section "Improve the Quality of Energy Data and Information" later in this chapter.

Reduce Declines in U.S. Conventional Oil and Natural Gas Production

The NPC makes the following recommendations to promote enhanced oil recovery (EOR) from existing reservoirs:

- Support regulatory streamlining and research and development programs for marginal wells.

- Expedite permitting of EOR projects, pipelines, and associated infrastructure.

Potential Effect: An additional 90 to 200 billion barrels of recoverable oil in the United States alone, which could help slow the current decline in production

Increase Access for New Energy Development

The NPC makes the following recommendations to expand access to the most favorable U.S. oil and natural gas basins:

- Conduct national and regional basin-oriented resource and market assessments to identify opportunities for increasing oil and natural gas supply.

- Use technology and operational advancements to allow environmentally responsible development of high potential onshore and offshore areas currently restricted by moratoria or access limitations.

Potential Effect: Material increases to current production within 5 to 10 years from currently inaccessible areas could approach 40 billion barrels of oil and 250 trillion cubic feet of natural gas with current technology.

The NPC makes the following recommendations to increase unconventional oil and natural gas production:

- Accelerate U.S. oil shale and oil sands research and development and leasing.

- Accelerate U.S. unconventional natural gas leasing and development.

Potential Effect: Double U.S. unconventional natural gas production to more than 10 billion cubic feet per day, increasing total U.S. natural gas production by about 10 percent.

Diversify Long-Term Energy Production

Accelerate the Development of Energy from Biomass

The NPC makes the following recommendations to accelerate development of biomass energy sources at large commercial scale:

- Support research into second-generation biofuel crops that have lower input requirements or are suited to more marginal lands.

- Promote agricultural policies that enhance global production of both food crops and biomass for fuel.

- Support policies that promote the development of the infrastructure for harvesting, storing, and transporting energy crops, and facilitate the integration of biofuels into the national transportation fuel supply.

Potential Effect: Increase U.S. production by up to 4 million barrels per day of oil-equivalent liquids[1]

Enable the Long-Term Environmental Viability of Coal for Power, Fuel, and Feedstock

Recommendations for maintaining coal's long-term viability are discussed specifically in the section "Address Carbon Constraints" later in this chapter.

Expand Domestic Nuclear Capability

The NPC makes the following recommendations to expand the domestic technical and industrial capabilities of the nuclear energy/power industry:

- Implement the recommendation by the National Commission on Energy Policy[2] to provide $2 billion over ten years from federal energy research, development, demonstration, and deployment budgets for demonstration of one to two new advanced nuclear facilities.

- Fulfill existing federal commitments on nuclear waste management.

Potential Effect: Reestablish U.S. leadership capability. Maintaining a viable nuclear energy option will increase policy choices in future carbon-constrained circumstances.

---

1 The "Billion Ton Study" – *Biomass as a Feedstock for a Bioenergy and Bioproducts Industry: The Technical Feasibility of a Billion-Ton Annual Supply*, USDA and USDOE, April 2005, available at http://www.osti.gov/bridge

2 See www.energycommission.org/files/contentFiles/report_non-interactive_44566feaabc5d.pdf, page IV

■ Strengthen Global and U.S. Energy Security

The NPC makes the following recommendations to promote global and U.S. energy security:

- Integrate energy policy into trade, economic, environmental, security, and foreign policies by having the Department of Energy share an equal role with the Departments of Defense, State, Treasury, and Commerce on policy issues relating to energy and energy security.

- Continue to develop the international energy marketplace by expanding the energy dialogue with major consuming and producing nations, including China, India, Canada, Mexico, Russia, and Saudi Arabia.

- Promote an effective global energy marketplace by sustaining and intensifying efforts to encourage global adoption of transparent, market-based approaches to energy through multilateral and international institutions—including the World Trade Organization, G8, Asia-Pacific Economic Cooperation (APEC), IEA, International Energy Forum, and the Joint Oil Data Initiative (JODI).

- Assist and encourage global adoption of energy efficiency technologies through technology transfer programs and lend-lease arrangements.

Potential Effect: Restricted resource access and curtailed production could put potential 2030 global liquid (25-35+ million barrels per day) and gas (150-200+ billion cubic feet per day) incremental growth at risk.

■ Reinforce Capabilities to Meet New Challenges

Develop a Comprehensive Forecast of U.S. Infrastructure Requirements

The NPC makes the following recommendations to improve understanding of infrastructure needs to meet future U.S. energy system growth:

- The Department of Energy (DOE) should develop an integrated study of the energy infrastructure needs to 2030.

- The EIA should incorporate infrastructure-related data into its energy information collection system.

Rebuild U.S. Science and Engineering Capabilities

The NPC makes the following recommendation to enhance U.S. science and technical education programs:

- Provide support to those seeking engineering and other technical degrees, both undergraduate and graduate, by increasing scholarships and research funding at universities and support for technical schools.

The NPC makes the following recommendation to make it easier for retirees to continue working as consultants, teachers, and coaches:

- Modify the U.S. tax code and retirement plan regulations to allow part-time work after retirement without penalty.

The NPC makes the following recommendation to increase the supply of trained energy professionals in the United States:

- Increase student and immigration quotas for trained professionals in energy and technical fields.

Create Research and Development Opportunities

The NPC makes the following recommendations to expand research and development opportunities to support long-term study goals:

- Review the current DOE research and development portfolio to refocus spending on innovative, applied research in areas such as EOR, unconventional oil and natural gas, biofuels, nuclear energy, coal-to-fuels, and CCS.

- Maintain a fundamental research budget in the DOE Office of Science to support novel technologies.

- Focus and enhance research in the U.S. universities and National Laboratories.

- Encourage DOE, Department of Defense, and industry cooperation in innovative areas of development, such as advanced materials and metocean information and analyses.

Improve the Quality of Energy Data and Information

The NPC makes the following recommendations to enhance the quality of energy data and information:

- Expand data collected by EIA and IEA to provide additional sources of production and consumption data for inclusion in annually prepared public domain energy outlooks.

- Expand funding for data collection and analysis of energy transportation systems to enable informed infrastructure decisions.

The NPC makes the following recommendations to update publicly available global endowment and resource estimates:

- The USGS should conduct a comprehensive geological assessment of U.S. and global oil and natural gas endowment and recoverable resources.

  - Incorporate wider participation of industry and international experts and current data.

- The USGS should conduct a new, comprehensive survey of U.S. and global recoverable coal resources and reserves using common analysis and reporting methodologies.

- The U.S. Departments of Energy and Agriculture should conduct a global biomass resource assessment.

Potential Effect: Timely and better informed policy decisions based on shared understanding of critical resource data

---

■ Address Carbon Constraints

Enable Carbon Capture and Sequestration

The NPC makes the following recommendations to enable long-term environmental viability of coal for both power and fuel:

- Establish a legal and regulatory framework that is conducive to CCS.

  - Provide regulatory clarity for land use and liability policies.

  - Provide access to federal lands for storage.

- Enable full scale CCS and clean coal technology demonstration.

  - Organize efforts between the power and oil/natural gas industries.

- Undertake a national CO_2 sequestration capacity assessment.

  - Build on the existing efforts being undertaken by the DOE Regional Partnerships.

  - Encourage global application.

- Continue federal research and development support for advanced coal-to-fuel technologies.

Potential Effect: Maintaining coal's projected 30 percent contribution (54 quadrillion Btu per year in 2005) to the future U.S. energy mix, including potential coal-to-liquids production, even in carbon-constrained circumstances.

As policymakers consider actions to reduce CO_2 emissions, the NPC recommends including:

- An effective global framework for carbon management incorporating all major emitters of CO_2 and focusing particularly on opportunities for U.S.–China cooperation.

- A U.S. mechanism for setting an effective cost for emitting CO_2 that is:

  - Economy-wide, market-based, visible, transparent, applicable to all fuels.

  - Predictable over the long term for a stable investment climate.

- A credit for CO_2 used in enhanced oil and natural gas recovery.

Chapter
METHODOLOGY 7

Abstract

The global oil and gas study prepared by the National Petroleum Council (NPC) is unique in scope and participation. The complexity and scale of integrated energy markets, and the long lead-times necessary to make material changes required a study that took a long-term, comprehensive view of supply, demand, infrastructure, technology, and geopolitics. To achieve this, more than 350 expert participants from diverse backgrounds and organizations joined in a comprehensive work effort based on sound data and science. The effort included analysis of multiple public and aggregated proprietary energy outlooks, and required subgroups to address themes as diverse as deepwater exploration, renewable energy, transportation efficiency, and human resources. In addition, more than 1,000 persons and groups actively involved with energy issues provided feedback through a formal outreach program. The study includes core strategies and key recommendations for policymakers. When developing findings and recommendations, the study leadership sought to balance economic, security, and environmental perspectives.

This chapter describes how the study was organized and conducted. It describes the participants and expert task groups, identifies cross-cutting topics that emerged, details the data streams used for analyses, and explains how a data warehouse was created. An important feature of the report is a survey of 24 parallel studies that were recently published. The full report will be distributed broadly to government and public audiences.

The outline for this chapter is as follows:

- Guiding Principles

- Study Organization

  – Task Groups

  – Cross-Cutting Groups

  – Integration Team

- Information Management

  – An Analytical Approach

  – Storing Information—The Data Warehouse

  – Public Data and Information

  – Proprietary Data and Information

  – Parallel Studies

- Summary.

This report originated in late 2005, when Secretary of Energy Samuel Bodman requested that the NPC undertake a study on the ability of global oil and natural gas supply to keep pace with growing world demand. The Secretary suggested three questions that might be considered:

- What does the future hold for global oil and natural gas supply?

- Can incremental oil and natural gas supplies be brought on-line, on-time, and at a reasonable price to meet future demand without jeopardizing economic growth?

- What oil and gas supply strategies and/or demand-side strategies does the Council recommend the U.S. pursue to ensure greater economic stability and prosperity?

Accepting the Secretary's request, the NPC formed the Committee on Global Oil and Gas with Lee Raymond, former Chairman and Chief Executive Officer of Exxon Mobil Corporation, as its Chair. Clay Sell, the Deputy Secretary of Energy, was designated by Secretary Bodman to serve as the study's Government Cochair. From the 54 NPC members of the Committee on Global Oil and Gas, Mr. Raymond appointed four as Vice Chairs for specific areas of the study. These six served as an "Executive Committee" to oversee the study process. A Coordinating Subcommittee (CSC) was created to guide and focus this ambitious undertaking. Additionally, four task groups and 36 subgroups assisted in the conduct of the study. The study organization is described more fully in the Preface and is outlined in Figure 7-1. The rosters of all the study groups are in Appendix B.

The CSC included members from government, industry and non-governmental organizations to provide a wide range of skills and viewpoints, as shown in Figure 7-2.

GUIDING PRINCIPLES

The CSC's first task was to set the study's boundaries and guiding principles. First, the study leadership recognized that this undertaking would be incomplete without examining all the dimensions of the energy debate including alternative energy sources. Second, the CSC decided the study would not create a new forecast of demand, supply, or price offering yet another perspective on the uncertain energy outlook. Rather, the study would analyze existing projections and outlooks to identify underlying assumptions, understand why they differ, and thereby identify critical factors governing the future of oil and gas to 2030. Third, the CSC decided to consider and balance other points of view, including economic, environmental, and security goals. These

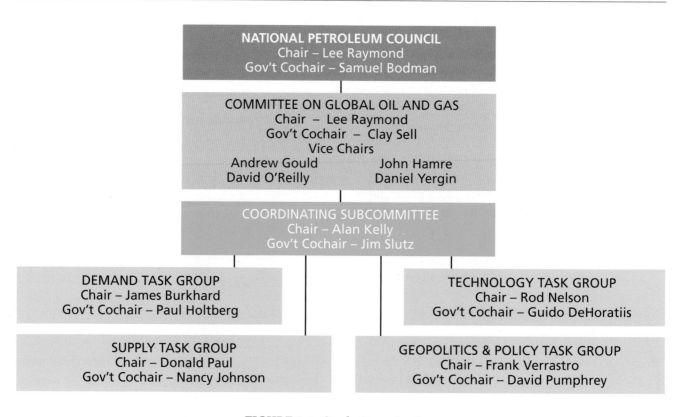

FIGURE 7-1. *Study Organization*

Facing the Hard Truths about Energy

U.S. DEPT. OF ENERGY

DEUTSCHE BANK

ALLIANCE TO
SAVE ENERGY

RESOURCES
FOR THE FUTURE

CERA

Chevron

CSIS

ExxonMobil

Schlumberger

JPMorgan

MARATHON

FLUOR.

AEP AMERICAN
ELECTRIC
POWER

SHELL

FIGURE 7-2. *Diverse Leadership*

three decisions enabled the NPC to create an original study with broad perspective.

The following guiding principles were pursued throughout the study:

- This is not another energy forecast of demand, supply, or price.

- Experts will gather and analyze public and aggregated proprietary data.

- Study teams will solicit input from a broad range of interested parties.

- Analyses will emphasize long-term conditions, not near-term volatility.

- Recommendations will be supported by sound data and science.

- Participants will comply fully with antitrust laws and regulations.

The study was designed in full compliance with both the letter and the spirit of all applicable laws and regulations, including but not limited to antitrust laws and the Federal Advisory Committee Act, in mind. Specifically, an independent accounting firm aggregated and removed all identifying information from all proprietary projection data provided by companies and consultants. More generally, the study was conducted in strict compliance with comprehensive antitrust guidelines governing all participants' conduct throughout all stages of the study, including data analysis, outreach sessions, meetings among the various participants, and preparation of this report. These guidelines ensured that no individually identifiable sensitive competitive information was exchanged during the study and effectively precluded any opportunities for anticompetitive agreement. An Antitrust Advisory Subgroup provided guidance to the study.

The study leadership was committed to receiving views and information from a broad range of interested parties, and focused outreach efforts to countries and organizations involved with energy. The effort included:

- More than 350 participants from diverse backgrounds

- Dialogue with more than 1,000 persons and groups with energy interests

- Department of Energy support to approach 19 key countries for information.

Figure 7-3 illustrates the diverse backgrounds of study participants.

The Coordinating Subcommittee defined a timeline for the entire study, which continued for more than 18 months. To ensure real-time communications, and to assess progress, representatives from the CSC, including Department of Energy and legal advisors, created a study website for posting all deliverables, analyses and status updates. Monthly meetings were scheduled for the CSC and Task Groups, supplemented by weekly teleconferences to review work products and commitments. The NPC Execu-

tive Committee participated in periodic reviews to receive updates and provide guidance. Finally, the CSC leadership provided regular status reports to all participants.

STUDY ORGANIZATION

Task Groups

As the scope of the study evolved, four core groups of subject matter experts were assembled into specialized Task Groups: Demand, Supply, Technology, and Geopolitics & Policy. These Task Groups became the focus of the study's research and analytical efforts. The CSC guided the Task Groups to respond to a series of comprehensive framing questions through an extensive analysis of available reports and publications. The teams developed a broad range of integrated summary observations and findings, which eventually underpinned the agreed strategies and recommendations in the report. Supporting the Task Groups were numerous cross-cutting subgroups that examined specific topics to complement key subject areas. The membership of each of the cross-cutting groups is also found in Appendix B and a simplified diagram of Task Group interrelationships is shown in Figure 7-4.

While the four Task Groups were charged with specific, separate project objectives, the teams' efforts were fully aligned and integrated as depicted in Figure 7-4. Individual subject matter experts selected for this study were not only experienced at interpreting and analyzing Task Group-specific information, but also had sufficient breadth of knowledge to communicate and share information across the team boundaries. Extensively detailed topic papers prepared by each Task Group are also made available to supplement this report. A listing of the topic papers can be found in Appendix E.

Demand Task Group

The Demand Task Group analyzed the range of projections for world energy demand to 2030, key "drivers" underlying the demand projections such as economic activity and demographics, and the relationship of historical performance to future projections. The group analyzed the potential effect of energy efficiency measures on demand, ways that environmental concerns might alter the energy mix, and how fuel-use patterns might evolve. The group

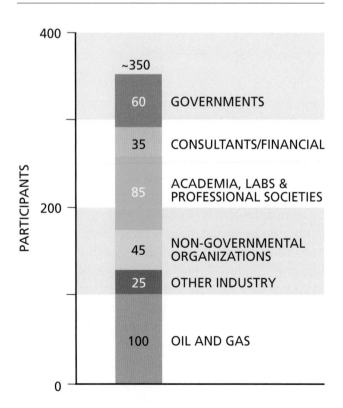

FIGURE 7-3. *Diverse Backgrounds of Participants*

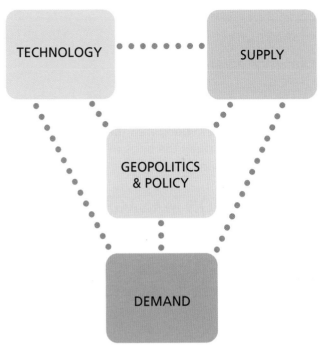

FIGURE 7-4. *Task Group Interrelationships*

also worked with the Supply Task Group to address critical infrastructure implications posed by differing fuel use.

The Demand Task Group organized its activities into six subgroups: Demand Data Evaluation, Electric Generation Efficiency, Coal Impact, Industrial Efficiency, Cultural/Social/Economic Trends, and Residential/Commercial Efficiency. The subgroups prepared topic papers that summarized input, analyses, and findings. After identifying the most significant issues, the group developed potential demand moderation strategies as a step toward formulating recommendations. The Demand Task Group's analyses and conclusions are summarized in Chapter One of this report.

Supply Task Group

To guide its assessment of the global supply of energy, the Supply Task Group considered how the energy supply/capacity mix may change and evolve over the next 25 years. The group considered a wide variety of outlooks for future oil and gas supply/capacity, and assessed the key factors that drive supply changes. The group asked what additional data could help reduce the uncertainty associated with the global energy endowment and the timing for converting it into production capacity—resource endowment, infrastructure, geopolitics, technology progress/utilization, for example. The group examined how coal might fit into the future energy mix, weighing ample supply against environmental consequences and the likely costs to address carbon constraints. Significantly, the group examined the range of outlooks for non-hydrocarbon energy supplies such as nuclear, hydro, wind, solar, biomass, and bio-liquids, noting the opportunities and challenges associated with each energy source.

The Supply Task Group formed nine subgroups organized into three functional groups to conduct its analyses: Data Interpretation/Database, Endowment, and Energy Infrastructure and Delivery. The results of the Supply Task Group's work are summarized in Chapter Two of this report.

Technology Task Group

The Technology Task Group focused on the examination of technological advances that may influence future energy use or sources. The more than 120 subject-matter experts who participated in the Technology Task Group were identified and organized into 14 subgroups around technical themes. The Technology Task Group then examined specific technical subjects as they related to these broad topics: transportation efficiency, nuclear, unconventional gas, heavy oil, coal-to-liquids/coal-to-gas, technology development and deployment, carbon management, shale oil/hydrates, exploration, deepwater, conventional/EOR/arctic, and human resources. In particular, the team was requested to address time horizons for potential technology deployment, research budgets, and the science and engineering capabilities required to support development.

The results of the discussion, debate, and insights provided by the Technology Task Group are in Chapter Three of this report and integrated with the analyses found in the Supply and Demand chapters.

Geopolitics & Policy Task Group

The Geopolitics & Policy Task Group operated as two distinct teams as the study progressed. During the study analysis phase, the Geopolitics Team assessed how sovereign national, regional, and global policy decisions might affect global supply and demand outlooks. The Geopolitics Team included regional scholars as well as industry, academic and NGO participants. Topics addressed included broad issues such as governance, security, globalism, and climate and the environment. The Geopolitics chapter reflects the integrated content of those working documents and the discussion, debate and insights provided by the group at large.

The Policy team was formed toward the conclusion of the study and included representatives of other study teams involved in the effort as well as a contingent of outside experts drawn from the policy community. The group was used primarily to analyze and vet the various study findings and policy recommendations advanced by the Task Groups. Final selection of the most significant recommendations was performed by the CSC and working groups made up of its members.

Cross-Cutting Groups

Each Task Group began by posing a set of framing questions to guide its work. These framing questions highlighted a need for a number of cross-cutting groups to focus on topics of concurrent interest to several Task Groups. The cross-cutting groups were staffed by subject matter experts typically from two or more Task Groups. Subjects investigated included macroeconomics, gas-to-liquids/coal-to-liquids, biofuels/renewables, infrastructure, parallel studies, carbon management, refining, transportation, nuclear power, and coal.

Integration Team

The Task Groups shared information through the cross-cutting groups and by arranging overlapping membership. Even with these ongoing linkages, a broader effort was necessary to prepare integrated views of the global energy picture. An Integration Team was formed to summarize observations and findings, and to extract key conclusions. This team included members from the CSC and Task Groups, and identified the following overarching themes for review with the Policy Team and the full CSC.

- Economic growth, energy demand, and demand moderation
- Fossil energy supply and delivery
- Non-fossil energy supply and delivery
- Energy security and interdependence

- Carbon management
- Infrastructure
- Industry capacity
- Technology.

Through a process of reviews, the findings and observations were refined into the "hard truths" of this study, and formed the basis of proposed strategies and recommendations.

INFORMATION MANAGEMENT

An Analytical Approach

While the study scope was evolving, the Task Groups began assembling data for their analyses. As illustrated in Figure 7-5, the data streams used by the Task Groups for their analysis drew on public and proprietary information. In addition, a number of recent parallel studies from the energy sector were reviewed for relevant information and data.

Storing Information— The Data Warehouse

To make the study's broad-ranging and original sources easily available to all participants, a data warehouse was developed. This provided for centralized management of the multidimensional data collected. By the time it concluded, the study had compiled and used nearly 100 energy forecasts or outlooks. These forecasts and several hundreds of papers/documents on various aspects of the energy sector were used in the interpretations that formed the basis of the study findings and recommendations.

As an organizing feature, a digital survey questionnaire was developed to collect a consistent set of

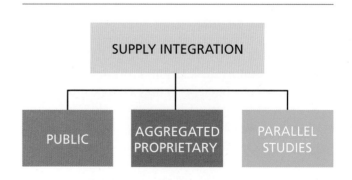

FIGURE 7-5. *Multiple Data Sources*

Facing the Hard Truths about Energy

historical and forecast data for all data streams. The survey captured both numeric data and the assumptions used in individual energy outlooks.

The data request was very comprehensive although not all of the respondents completed all aspects of the survey. Data were requested at the world, regional and also key country levels. The regions surveyed were organized in these broad headings: North America, Central and South America, OECD, Non-OECD Europe and Asia/Oceania, the Middle East, and Africa.

The data warehouse was designed to be the main analytical tool for the Task Groups, accepting all data collected from the survey questionnaire and other data sources. As the survey data were multi-dimensional, Oracle OLAP database technology was used and the collection was organized using 7 dimensions:

1. Time *(year)*

2. Geography *(country or geographic region)*

3. Energy type *(e.g., oil, gas, coal, nuclear, renewable)*

4. Energy sector *(e.g., commercial, residential)*

5. Case type *(e.g., business as usual, alternative energy policy)*

6. Units *(applicable unit of measure)*

7. Source *(e.g., public, proprietary)*

Once in the data warehouse, selected values or ranges of values for any or all dimensions could be applied as a filter to enable analysis.

The questionnaire collected high-level assumptions, oil and natural gas endowment, oil production, natural gas production, coal energy supply, the methodology used by the different outlooks, economic/demographic information, energy prices, total energy consumption, energy production and electricity generation, and environmental information. Additional supply data were developed for liquefied natural gas and gas-to-liquids, infrastructure, and biomass/biofuels.

The review process produced supply data sets associated with the key documents that were identified and collected. These data sets cover a wide range of views, including low-end projections, mid-

range and reference cases, and high-end forecasts. Each data set generated represents a unique and consistent forecast. Several organizations provided multiple scenarios, each of which was documented as a separate case for evaluation.

The contents of the Data Warehouse and a viewer application are available on the CD that accompanies this report (see Appendix E).

Public Data and Information

Each of the Task Groups searched the literature for integrated, global energy supply/demand forecasts that extended until at least 2030 and were in the public domain. Five forecasts were found that met these criteria, three from the U.S. Energy Information Administration and two from the International Energy Agency (Table 7-1).

To capture an even more comprehensive set of forecasts, the study identified a "wide net" of additional public sources. About 80 additional organizations and individuals were enlisted to participate by contributing data in a standard survey format. Among the sources for the wide-net data were: DOE, National Coal Council, OPEC, Greenpeace, Pew, SAIC, Natural Resources Defense Council, Climate Change Science Program, European Commission, and the Association for the Study of Peak Oil.

Energy Information Administration
International Energy Outlook 2006

- Reference Case

- High Case (economic growth, oil price)

- Low Case (economic growth, oil price)

International Energy Agency
World Energy Outlook 2006

- Reference Case

- Alternative Policy Case

TABLE 7-1. *Integrated, Global Energy Supply/Demand Forecasts*

In addition to the data gathered from other public domain sources, Energy Secretary Bodman sent letters in October 2006 to 19 governments, advising them of the study and seeking their participation, comments, and contributions. The countries were Australia, Azerbaijan, Brazil, Canada, Peoples Republic of China, Germany, India, Indonesia, Japan, Kazakhstan, Kuwait, Mexico, Nigeria, Norway, Qatar, Russia, Saudi Arabia, United Arab Emirates, and United Kingdom.

Proprietary Data and Information

To supplement and test the major public domain projections, an analysis of aggregated proprietary information was also undertaken. The "National Petroleum Council Survey of Global Energy Supply/Demand Outlooks" was sent to 34 international oil companies and consulting groups that were believed to make this type of projection. No study participant had access to individual, proprietary survey responses or knew which organizations were among the respondents. A list of organizations to which the survey was sent is shown in Table 7-2.

In addition to quantitative data, the questionnaire also requested high-level assumptions, oil and natural gas endowment, oil production, natural gas production, coal energy supply, the methodology used by the different outlooks, economic/demographic information, energy prices, total energy consumption, energy production and electricity generation, and environmental information. Additional supply data were developed for liquefied natural gas and gas-to-liquids, infrastructure, and biomass/biofuels.

Because of the commercial value of these data, and to ensure strict compliance with all antitrust requirements, the data were collected and aggregated by an independent accounting firm, Argy, Wilze and Robinson (AWR), which was charged with maintaining the anonymity and confidentiality of the responses. No one outside this independent third-party organization had access to individual, proprietary survey responses or even knew which organizations were among the respondents.

As the aggregator of the proprietary data, AWR was tasked with:

- Receiving the survey responses from responding organizations.

International Oil Companies

BP

Chevron

ConocoPhillips

Eni S.p.A.

Exxon Mobil Corporation

Marathon Oil Company

PetroCanada

Reliance Industries Limited

Repsol

Shell

Total S.A.

Valero

Consultants and Others

Barclays Capital

Bernstein Research Group

Cambridge Energy Research Associates

Caterpillar Inc.

Chemical Data Inc.

CRA International, Inc.

Deutsche Bank

Global Insight, Inc.

Goldman, Sachs & Co.

Jacobs Consultancy Inc.

Lawrence Berkeley National Laboratory

McKinsey Global Institute

Oak Ridge National Laboratory

PFC Energy

PIRA Energy Group

Probe Economics, Inc

Purvin & Gertz, Inc.

Rocky Mountain Institute

Simmons and Company International

SRI International

Wood Mackenzie Ltd.

Ziff Energy Group

TABLE 7-2. *Recipients of the NPC Survey of Global Energy Supply/Demand Outlooks*

Facing the Hard Truths about Energy

- Clarifying with the survey respondent any responses that appeared inconsistent or incorrectly entered. The NPC required that the aggregator also engage an independent technical expert, who operated under the same confidentiality requirements as any other employee of the aggregator, to assist in reviewing the survey responses.

- Provided that at least three responses were received from a group of respondents (i.e., International Oil Companies or Consultants), preparing a report for that group of the aggregated survey data and the individual qualitative responses after suitable editing to preclude identifying any specific response with a specific respondent.

- Submitting a draft report of the aggregated and de-identified responses to the NPC's outside antitrust counsel as an additional check to ensure compliance with the reporting guidelines.

- Following up as necessary and issuing an amended final report if the NPC requested that specific items in the report be clarified.

The data were aggregated separately for the International Oil Companies and the Consulting Companies, and again for combined groupings.

For each of the groups separately, provided at least three responses were received for each group, AWR reported:

- The highest values for each quantitative response (where at least three values were reported) and associated qualitative responses.

- The lowest values for each quantitative response (where at least three values were reported) and associated qualitative responses.

- The average values for each quantitative response (where at least three values were reported) and associated qualitative responses.

Then, for all the responses combined, AWR reported:

- For the two responses with the highest total global energy use in 2030, a report of the average of all quantitative responses where two responses were reported, and all qualitative responses.

- For the two responses with the lowest total global energy use in 2030, a report of the average of all quantitative responses where two responses were reported, and all qualitative responses.

- For all responses, a report of the average of all quantitative responses where at least two responses were reported, and all qualitative responses.

Following completion of its report, AWR was required to destroy all survey responses, working papers, notes, and any other record of the survey responses, keeping only the survey report.

As a result of the proprietary data collection, 29 cases from 21 respondents were incorporated into the 9 aggregations that now reside in the data warehouse—International Oil Companies (low, average, and high energy use); Consulting Companies (low, average, and high energy use), and the combined low, average, and high responses from all the International Oil Company and Consultant respondents. The response rate for the International Oil Companies was 75 percent or greater, with the response rate from the Consulting Companies less than 75 percent.

Parallel Studies

A parallel studies process examined numerous other recent public reports that addressed various aspects of energy policy to inform the work of the NPC study's Coordinating Subcommittee. (Appendix D provides summaries of these parallel studies.) The reports included are shown in Table 7-3.

SUMMARY

The NPC study, *Facing the Hard Truths about Energy*, differs from most of the parallel studies we reviewed by its depth of analysis, its breadth of sources and participants, and its balanced perspectives. The methodology adopted by the study team included a comprehensive review of multiple supply and demand outlooks to 2030. This effort was further extended by the Task Groups and cross-cutting groups to include assessments of technology, infrastructure, alternative energy sources, security, and the environment. This methodology enabled the team to create and recommend a core set of five strategies for the nation to pursue. Solutions to the energy challenges will depend on the cooperation of government and industry, in the United States and around the world, to create the necessary opportunities for a balanced future—including economic, security, and environmental goals.

National Commission on Energy Policy	Stern Review Report
Energy Security Leadership Council	Global Roundtable on Climate Change
Business Roundtable Energy Task Force	World Energy Technology Outlook – 2050
National Association of Manufacturers	2000-2050 North American Transportation Energy Futures
Council on Foreign Relations	
Alliance for Energy and Economic Growth	UN Foundation (Scientific Expert Group)
World Energy Council/US Energy Association	CNA – National Security and the Threat of Climate Change
IEA World Energy Outlook 2006	
U.S. DOE/EIA International Energy Annual 2006	MIT – The Future of Coal in a Carbon-Constrained World
ExxonMobil Outlook for Energy	EPRINC – Ethanol and U.S. Energy Security
NETL Oil Peaking Study	U.S. Climate Action Partnership
U.S. Government Accountability Office	Council of the Americas – Energy Action Group
American Enterprise Institute	OPEC Secretariat – World Oil Outlook 2007
Intergovernmental Panel on Climate Change	Energy Charter – Oil & Gas Pricing Study

TABLE 7-3. *Studies Examined*

Appendices

The Secretary of Energy
Washington, DC 20585

October 5, 2005

Mr. Lee Raymond
Chairman, National Petroleum Council
1625 K Street, NW
Washington, DC 20006

Dear Mr. Raymond:

Perspectives vary widely on the ability of supply to keep pace with growing world demand for oil and natural gas, the point in time at which global oil production will plateau and then begin to decline ("peak oil"), the implications these may have for the U.S. and world economy, and what steps should be taken to achieve more positive outcomes.

Accordingly, I request the National Petroleum Council conduct a study on global oil and natural gas supply. Key questions to be addressed in the study may include:

- What does the future hold for global oil and natural gas supply?

- Can incremental oil and natural gas supply be brought on-line, on-time, and at a reasonable price to meet future demand without jeopardizing economic growth?

- What oil and gas supply strategies and/or demand side strategies does the Council recommend the U.S. pursue to ensure greater economic stability and prosperity?

For the purposes of the study, I am designating Under Secretary David Garman to represent me and to provide the necessary coordination between the Department of Energy and the National Petroleum Council. He will also provide coordination with the Department of State, other Federal agencies, and international organizations as required.

I look forward to reviewing the Council's proposed study committee and detailed study plan.

Sincerely,

Samuel W. Bodman

DESCRIPTION OF THE NATIONAL PETROLEUM COUNCIL

In May 1946, the President stated in a letter to the Secretary of the Interior that he had been impressed by the contribution made through government/industry cooperation to the success of the World War II petroleum program. He felt that it would be beneficial if this close relationship were to be continued and suggested that the Secretary of the Interior establish an industry organization to advise the Secretary on oil and natural gas matters.

Pursuant to this request, Interior Secretary J. A. Krug established the National Petroleum Council (NPC) on June 18, 1946. In October 1977, the Department of Energy was established and the Council was transferred to the new department.

The purpose of the NPC is solely to advise, inform, and make recommendations to the Secretary of Energy on any matter requested by the Secretary, relating to oil and natural gas or the oil and gas industries. Matters that the Secretary would like to have considered by the Council are submitted in the form of a letter outlining the nature and scope of the study. The Council reserves the right to decide whether it will consider any matter referred to it.

Examples of studies undertaken by the NPC in the last 20 years include:

- *Factors Affecting U.S. Oil & Gas Outlook* (1987)

- *Petroleum Storage & Transportation* (1989)

- *Industry Assistance to Government – Methods for Providing Petroleum Industry Expertise During Emergencies* (1991)

- *Petroleum Refining in the 1990s – Meeting the Challenges of the Clean Air Act* (1991)

- *The Potential for Natural Gas in the United States* (1992)

- *U.S. Petroleum Refining – Meeting Requirements for Cleaner Fuels and Refineries* (1993)

- *The Oil Pollution Act of 1990: Issues and Solutions* (1994)

- *Marginal Wells* (1994)

- *Research, Development, and Demonstration Needs of the Oil and Gas Industry* (1995)

- *Future Issues – A View of U.S. Oil & Natural Gas to 2020* (1995)

- *U.S. Petroleum Product Supply—Inventory Dynamics* (1998)

- *Meeting the Challenges of the Nation's Growing Natural Gas Demand* (1999)

- *U.S. Petroleum Refining—Assuring the Adequacy and Affordability of Cleaner Fuels* (2000)

- *Securing Oil and Natural Gas Infrastructures in the New Economy* (2001)

- *Balancing Natural Gas Policy—Fueling the Demands of a Growing Economy* (2003)

- *Observations on Petroleum Product Supply* (2004).

The NPC does not concern itself with trade practices, nor does it engage in any of the usual trade association activities. The Council is subject to the provisions of the Federal Advisory Committee Act of 1972.

Members of the National Petroleum Council are appointed by the Secretary of Energy and represent all segments of the oil and natural gas industries and related interests. The NPC is headed by a Chair and a Vice Chair, who are elected by the Council. The Secretary of Energy serves as the NPC's Government Cochair. The Council is supported entirely by voluntary contributions from its members.

Additional information on the Council's origins, operations, and reports can be found at www.npc.org.

NATIONAL PETROLEUM COUNCIL
MEMBERSHIP

2006-2007

Jacob Adams	Director	Arctic Slope Regional Corporation
George A. Alcorn, Sr.	President	Alcorn Exploration, Inc.
Robert O. Anderson		Roswell, New Mexico
Thurmon M. Andress	Managing Director	BreitBurn Energy LP
Philip F. Anschutz	Chairman and Chief Executive Officer	The Anschutz Corporation
Gregory L. Armstrong	Chairman and Chief Executive Officer	Plains All American Pipeline, L.P.
Robert G. Armstrong	President	Armstrong Energy Corporation
Gregory A. Arnold	President and Chief Executive Officer	Truman Arnold Companies
Ralph E. Bailey	Chairman	Fuel-Tech N.V.
Fredrick J. Barrett	Chairman and Chief Executive Officer	Bill Barrett Corporation
Michel Bénézit	President, Refining and Marketing	Total S.A.
Robert W. Best	Chairman of the Board, President and Chief Executive Officer	Atmos Energy Corporation
Alan L. Boeckmann	Chairman and Chief Executive Officer	Fluor Corporation
Donald T. Bollinger	Chairman of the Board and Chief Executive Officer	Bollinger Shipyards, Inc.
John F. Bookout		Houston, Texas
Ben M. Brigham	Chairman, President and Chief Executive Officer	Brigham Exploration Company
Jon S. Brumley	President and Chief Executive Officer	Encore Acquisition Company
John E. Bryson	Chairman	Edison International
Philip J. Burguieres	Chief Executive Officer	EMC Holdings, L.L.C.
Frank M. Burke, Jr.	Chairman and Chief Executive Officer	Burke, Mayborn Company, Ltd.
Kateri A. Callahan	President	Alliance to Save Energy
Robert B. Catell	Chairman and Chief Executive Officer	KeySpan
Clarence P. Cazalot, Jr.	President and Chief Executive Officer	Marathon Oil Corporation
William M. Cobb	2008 President-Elect	Society of Petroleum Engineers
June Ressler Coldren	President and Chief Executive Officer	Cenergy Corporation
William A. Custard	President and Chief Executive Officer	Dallas Production, Inc.
Patrick D. Daniel	President and Chief Executive Officer	Enbridge Inc.
Peter A. Darbee	President and Chief Executive Officer	PG&E Corporation
Charles D. Davidson	Chairman, President and Chief Executive Officer	Noble Energy, Inc.
Barry E. Davis	President and Chief Executive Officer	Crosstex Energy, Inc.
Chadwick C. Deaton	Chairman and Chief Executive Officer	Baker Hughes Incorporated
Claiborne P. Deming	President and Chief Executive Officer	Murphy Oil Corporation
Cortlandt S. Dietler	Former Chairman	TransMontaigne Inc.
David F. Dorn		Denver, Colorado
Laurence M. Downes	Chairman and Chief Executive Officer	New Jersey Resources Corporation
Dan L. Duncan	Chairman	Enterprise Products Partners L.P.

Stephen A. Holditch	Noble Endowed Chair and Head of the Harold Vance Department of Petroleum Engineering	Texas A&M University
John R. Huff	Chairman of the Board	Oceaneering International, Inc.
Roy M. Huffington	Chairman of the Board and Chief Executive Officer	Roy M. Huffington, Inc.
Dudley J. Hughes	President	Hughes South Corporation
Ray L. Hunt	Chief Executive Officer	Hunt Oil Company
Hillard G. Huntington	Executive Director, Energy Modeling Forum	Stanford University
John R. Hurd	General Partner	Hurd Enterprises, Ltd.
Ray R. Irani	Chairman, President and Chief Executive Officer	Occidental Petroleum Corporation
Eugene M. Isenberg	Chairman and Chief Executive Officer	Nabors Industries, Inc.
Mark A. Jackson	Former Chairman of the Board and President	Noble Corporation
Peter M. Johnson	President	Sinclair Oil Corporation
Robert J. Johnson	President	National Association of Black Geologists and Geophysicists
A. V. Jones, Jr.	Chairman	Van Operating, Ltd.
Jon Rex Jones	Chairman	Jones Management Corp.
Jerry D. Jordan		Columbus, Ohio
Fred C. Julander	President	Julander Energy Company
W. Robert Keating	Commissioner, Department of Public Utilities	Commonwealth of Massachusetts
Richard C. Kelly	Chairman, President and Chief Executive Officer	Xcel Energy Inc.
Richard D. Kinder	Chairman and Chief Executive Officer	Kinder Morgan Inc.
Henry G. Kleemeier	Executive Vice President and Chief Operating Officer	Kaiser-Francis Oil Company
Harold M. Korell	Chairman, President and Chief Executive Officer	Southwestern Energy Company
Harold N. Kvisle	President and Chief Executive Officer	TransCanada Corporation
David L. Kyle	Chairman, President and Chief Executive Officer	ONEOK, Inc.
Stephen D. Layton	President	E&B Natural Resources
Virginia B. Lazenby	Chairman and Chief Executive Officer	Bretagne LLC
David J. Lesar	Chairman of the Board, President and Chief Executive Officer	Halliburton Company
Michael C. Linn	President and Chief Executive Officer	Linn Energy, LLC
Andrew N. Liveris	President and Chief Executive Officer	The Dow Chemical Company
Robert L. Long	President and Chief Executive Officer	Transocean Inc.
Daniel H. Lopez	President	New Mexico Institute of Mining and Technology
William D. McCabe	Principal	McCabe & Associates

Aubrey K. McClendon	Chairman of the Board and Chief Executive Officer	Chesapeake Energy Corporation
W. Gary McGilvray	President and Chief Executive Officer	DeGolyer and MacNaughton
James T. McManus, II	President and Chief Executive Officer	Energen Corporation
Cary M. Maguire	President	Maguire Oil Company
Steven J. Malcolm	Chairman, President and Chief Executive Officer	The Williams Companies, Inc.
Robert A. Malone	Chairman and President	BP America Inc.
Charles J. Mankin	Director	Oklahoma Geological Survey
Timothy M. Marquez	Chairman and Chief Executive Officer	Venoco, Inc.
Donald L. Mason	Commissioner	The Public Utilities Commission of Ohio
F. H. Merelli	Chairman, President and Chief Executive Officer	Cimarex Energy Co.
Augustus C. Miller	Chairman and Chief Executive Officer	Miller Oil Co., Inc.
C. John Miller	Chief Executive Officer	Miller Energy, Inc.
David B. Miller	Senior Managing Director	EnCap Investments L.P.
Merrill A. Miller, Jr.	President and Chief Executive Officer	National Oilwell Varco, Inc.
Michael G. Morris	Chairman, President and Chief Executive Officer	American Electric Power Co., Inc.
Robert A. Mosbacher	Chairman	Mosbacher Energy Company
James J. Mulva	Chairman of the Board and Chief Executive Officer	ConocoPhillips
John Thomas Munro	President	Munro Terminal Corporation
David L. Murfin	President	Murfin Drilling Co., Inc.
Mark B. Murphy	President	Strata Production Company
William C. Myler, Jr.	President	The Muskegon Development Co.
Scott A. Neitzel	Vice President – Energy Supply	Madison Gas and Electric Company
Richard S. Neville	President	Western Petroleum Company
J. Larry Nichols	Chairman of the Board and Chief Executive Officer	Devon Energy Corporation
John W. B. Northington	Principal	Northington Strategy Group
Erle Nye	Chairman Emeritus	TXU Corp.
Christine J. Olson	Chairman and Chief Executive Officer	S. W. Jack Drilling Company
David J. O'Reilly	Chairman of the Board and Chief Executive Officer	Chevron Corporation
C. R. Palmer	Chairman Emeritus	Rowan Companies, Inc.
Mark G. Papa	Chairman and Chief Executive Officer	EOG Resources, Inc.
Paul H. Parker	Executive Vice President	Center for Resource Management
Robert L. Parker, Sr.	Chairman of the Board	Parker Drilling Company
A. Glenn Patterson	Advisor	Patterson–UTI Energy, Inc.
Ralph R. Peterson	Chairman and Chief Executive Officer	CH2M HILL Companies, Ltd.

Douglas B. Petno	Managing Director and Energy Group Head	J.P. Morgan Securities Inc.
Hilda Pinnix-Ragland	Former Chairman	American Association of Blacks in Energy
L. Frank Pitts	Owner	Pitts Oil Company
Keith O. Rattie	Chairman, President and Chief Executive Officer	Questar Corporation
Lee R. Raymond	Retired Chairman and Chief Executive Officer	Exxon Mobil Corporation
Corbin J. Robertson, Jr.	President	Quintana Minerals Corporation
Douglas L. Rock	Chairman, President and Chief Executive Officer	Smith International, Inc.
James E. Rogers	Chairman, President and Chief Executive Officer	Duke Energy Corporation
Peter R. Rose	Past President	American Association of Petroleum Geologists
Robert E. Rose	Chairman of the Board	GlobalSantaFe Corporation
Henry A. Rosenberg, Jr.	Chairman of the Board	Crown Central LLC
Richard M. Schaeffer	Chairman of the Board	New York Mercantile Exchange, Inc.
Christopher T. Seaver	Former President	Hydril Company LP
S. Scott Sewell	President	Delta Energy Management, Inc.
Bobby S. Shackouls	Immediate Past Chair	National Petroleum Council
Mayo A. Shattuck III	Chairman of the Board, President and Chief Executive Officer	Constellation Energy Group, Inc.
Diane S. Shea	Former Executive Director	National Association of State Energy Officials
R. Gordon Shearer	President and Chief Executive Officer	HESS LNG LLC
Scott D. Sheffield	Chairman and Chief Executive Officer	Pioneer Natural Resources Company
Adam E. Sieminski	Chief Energy Economist, Global Markets/Commodities	Deutsche Bank AG
Matthew R. Simmons	Chairman of the Board	Simmons and Company Int'l.
Sam R. Simon	President and Chief Executive Officer	Atlas Oil Company
Bob R. Simpson	Chairman and Chief Executive Officer	XTO Energy Inc.
Robert C. Skaggs, Jr.	President and Chief Executive Officer	NiSource Inc.
Zin E. Smati	President and Chief Executive Officer	SUEZ Energy North America, Inc.
Bruce A. Smith	Chairman, President and Chief Executive Officer	Tesoro Corporation
John R. Smith	Immediate Past Chairman	The Energy Council
Robert D. Somerville	Chairman and Chief Executive Officer	American Bureau of Shipping & Affiliated Companies
Richard H. Straeter	President	Continental Resources of Illinois, Inc.
Dean E. Taylor	Chairman, President and Chief Executive Officer	Tidewater Inc.

Branko Terzic	Global and U.S. Regulatory Policy Leader, Energy and Resources	Deloitte Services LP
Carl F. Thorne	Non-Executive Chairman	ENSCO International Incorporated
Rex W. Tillerson	Chairman, President and Chief Executive Officer	Exxon Mobil Corporation
Scott W. Tinker	Director, Bureau of Economic Geology and State Geologist of Texas	The University of Texas
David A. Trice	Chairman of the Board and Chief Executive Officer	Newfield Exploration Company
Diemer True	Chairman	Diamond Oil, LLC
H. A. True, III	Partner	True Oil LLC
W. Bruce Valdez	Executive Director	Southern Ute Growth Fund
Paul G. Van Wagenen	Chairman, President and Chief Executive Officer	Pogo Producing Company
Philip K. Verleger, Jr.	President	PKVerleger, L.L.C.
John B. Walker	President and Chief Executive Officer	EnerVest Management Partners, Ltd.
L. O. Ward	Chairman and Chief Executive Officer	Ward Petroleum Corporation
Kelcy L. Warren	Co-Chairman and Co-Chief Executive Officer	Energy Transfer Partners, L.P.
Rebecca W. Watson	Partner	Hogan & Hartson, L.L.P.
J. Robinson West	Chairman	PFC Energy, Inc.
Leon E. Westbrock	Executive Vice President and Chief Operating Officer, Energy	CHS Inc.
C. John Wilder	Chairman, President and Chief Executive Officer	TXU Corp.
Bruce W. Wilkinson	Chairman of the Board and Chief Executive Officer	McDermott International, Inc.
Clayton W. Williams	Chairman, President and Chief Executive Officer	Clayton Williams Energy, Inc.
Barry A. Williamson	Attorney At Law	Austin, Texas
Mary Jane Wilson	President and Chief Executive Officer	WZI Inc.
Patricia A. Woertz	Chairman, Chief Executive Officer and President	Archer Daniels Midland Company
George M. Yates	President and Chief Executive Officer	HEYCO Energy Group, Inc.
John A. Yates	President	Yates Petroleum Corporation
Daniel H. Yergin	Chairman	Cambridge Energy Research Associates
Henry Zarrow	Vice Chairman	Sooner Pipe, L.P.

APPENDIX B
STUDY GROUP ROSTERS

STUDY PARTICIPATION

Study group and outreach participants contributed in a variety of ways, ranging from full-time work in multiple study areas, to involvement on a specific topic, to reviewing proposed materials, or to participating solely in an outreach session. Involvement in these activities should not be construed as endorsement or agreement with all the statements, findings, and recommendations in this report. Additionally, while U.S. government participants provided significant assistance in the identification and compilation of data and other information, they did not take positions on the study's policy recommendations.

As a federally appointed and chartered advisory committee, the National Petroleum Council is solely responsible for the final advice provided to the Secretary of Energy. However, the Council believes that the broad and diverse study group and outreach participation has informed and enhanced its study and advice. The Council is very appreciative of the commitment and contributions from all who participated in the process.

This appendix lists the individuals who served on this study's Committee, Coordinating Subcommittee, Task Groups, and Subgroups as a recognition of their contributions. In addition, the National Petroleum Council wishes to acknowledge the numerous other individuals and organizations who participated in some aspects of the work effort through workshops, outreach meetings, and other contacts. Their time, energy, and commitment significantly enhanced the study and their contributions are greatly appreciated.

COMMITTEE ON GLOBAL OIL AND GAS

Chair
Lee R. Raymond   Retired Chairman and Chief Executive Officer   Exxon Mobil Corporation

Government Cochair
Jeffrey Clay Sell   Deputy Secretary of Energy   U.S. Department of Energy

Vice Chair – Demand
Daniel H. Yergin   Chairman   Cambridge Energy
                                                                          Research Associates

Vice Chair – Supply
David J. O'Reilly   Chairman of the Board and   Chevron Corporation
                              Chief Executive Officer

Vice Chair – Technology
Andrew Gould   Chairman and Chief Executive Officer   Schlumberger Limited

Vice Chair – Geopolitics & Policy
John J. Hamre   President and Chief Executive Officer   Center for Strategic &
                                                                          International Studies

Secretary
Marshall W. Nichols   Executive Director   National Petroleum Council

Members
Michel Bénézit   President, Refining and Marketing   Total S.A.
Alan L. Boeckmann   Chairman and Chief Executive Officer   Fluor Corporation
John F. Bookout   Houston, Texas
Kateri A. Callahan   President   Alliance to Save Energy
Robert B. Catell   Chairman and Chief Executive Officer   KeySpan
Clarence P. Cazalot, Jr. President and Chief Executive Officer   Marathon Oil Corporation
William M. Cobb   2008 President-Elect   Society of Petroleum Engineers
Chadwick C. Deaton   Chairman and Chief Executive Officer   Baker Hughes Incorporated
Claiborne P. Deming   President and Chief Executive Officer   Murphy Oil Corporation
Randall K. Eresman   President and Chief Executive Officer   EnCana Corporation
Stephen E. Ewing   Former Vice Chairman   DTE Energy
William L. Fisher   Professor and Barrow Chair,   The University of Texas
                              Jackson School of Geosciences
Robert W. Fri   Visiting Scholar   Resources for the Future Inc.
Lawrence J. Goldstein   Director   Energy Policy Research
                                                                          Foundation, Inc.
Charles W. Goodyear   Chief Executive Officer   BHP Billiton Plc
James T. Hackett   Chairman, President and   Anadarko Petroleum Corporation
                              Chief Executive Officer

John B. Hess	Chairman, President and Chief Executive Officer	Hess Corporation
John D. Hofmeister	President and U.S. Country Chair	Shell Oil Company
Stephen A. Holditch	Noble Endowed Chair and Head of the Harold Vance Department of Petroleum Engineering	Texas A&M University
Roy M. Huffington	Chairman of the Board and Chief Executive Officer	Roy M. Huffington, Inc.
Ray L. Hunt	Chief Executive Officer	Hunt Oil Company
Ray R. Irani	Chairman, President and Chief Executive Officer	Occidental Petroleum Corporation
Richard D. Kinder	Chairman and Chief Executive Officer	Kinder Morgan Inc.
Harold N. Kvisle	President and Chief Executive Officer	TransCanada Corporation
David J. Lesar	Chairman of the Board, President and Chief Executive Officer	Halliburton Company
Michael C. Linn	President and Chief Executive Officer	Linn Energy, LLC
Andrew N. Liveris	President and Chief Executive Officer	The Dow Chemical Company
W. Gary McGilvray	President and Chief Executive Officer	DeGolyer and MacNaughton
Robert A. Malone	Chairman and President	BP America Inc.
Michael G. Morris	Chairman, President and Chief Executive Officer	American Electric Power Co., Inc.
Robert A. Mosbacher	Chairman	Mosbacher Energy Company
James J. Mulva	Chairman of the Board and Chief Executive Officer	ConocoPhillips
J. Larry Nichols	Chairman of the Board and Chief Executive Officer	Devon Energy Corporation
Robert L. Parker, Sr.	Chairman of the Board	Parker Drilling Company
Douglas B. Petno	Managing Director and Energy Group Head	J.P. Morgan Securities Inc.
James E. Rogers	Chairman, President and Chief Executive Officer	Duke Energy Corporation
Peter R. Rose	Past President	American Association of Petroleum Geologists
Robert E. Rose	Chairman of the Board	GlobalSantaFe Corporation
Richard M. Schaeffer	Chairman of the Board	New York Mercantile Exchange, Inc.
Adam E. Sieminski	Chief Energy Economist, Global Markets/Commodities	Deutsche Bank AG
Matthew R. Simmons	Chairman of the Board	Simmons and Company Int'l.
Branko Terzic	Global and U.S. Regulatory Policy Leader, Energy and Resources	Deloitte Services LP

Carl F. Thorne	Non-Executive Chairman	ENSCO International Incorporated
Rex W. Tillerson	Chairman, President and Chief Executive Officer	Exxon Mobil Corporation
Philip K. Verleger, Jr.	President	PKVerleger, L.L.C.
J. Robinson West	Chairman	PFC Energy, Inc.
Patricia A. Woertz	Chairman, Chief Executive Officer and President	Archer Daniels Midland Company

COORDINATING SUBCOMMITTEE

Chair
Alan J. Kelly   Former General Manager,   Exxon Mobil Corporation
                            Corporate Planning

Government Cochair
James A. Slutz   Deputy Assistant Secretary for Oil and   U.S. Department of Energy
                            Natural Gas, Office of Fossil Energy

Assistant to the Chair
Thomas R. Eizember   Senior Planning Advisor,   Exxon Mobil Corporation
                            Corporate Planning – Strategy Division

Secretary
John H. Guy, IV   Deputy Executive Director   National Petroleum Council

Members
David K. Bellman   Director of Fundamental Analysis,   American Electric Power Co., Inc.
                            Corporate Planning & Budgeting

Fatih Birol   Chief Economist   International Energy Agency

James R. Burkhard   Managing Director, Global Oil Group   Cambridge Energy
                                                               Research Associates

Kateri A. Callahan   President   Alliance to Save Energy

Guy F. Caruso   Administrator,   U.S. Department of Energy
                            Energy Information Administration

Clifford C. Cook   Senior Vice President,   Marathon Oil Corporation
                            Supply, Distribution and Planning

Scott M. Hoyte   Energy Technology Strategic Initiatives   GE Energy

Rodney F. Nelson   Vice President,   Schlumberger Limited
                            Innovation and Collaboration

Marvin E. Odum   Executive Vice President – Americas   Shell Energy Resources Company

Donald L. Paul   Vice President and   Chevron Corporation
                            Chief Technology Officer

Douglas B. Petno   Managing Director and Energy Group Head   J.P. Morgan Securities Inc.

William C. Ramsay   Deputy Executive Director   International Energy Agency

David T. Seaton   Group President, Energy and Chemicals   Fluor Corporation

Philip R. Sharp   President   Resources for the Future

Adam E. Sieminski   Chief Energy Economist,   Deutsche Bank AG
                            Global Markets/Commodities

Frank A. Verrastro   Director and Senior Fellow, Energy Program   Center for Strategic &
                                                               International Studies

Alternative Assistant to the Chair
Charles E. Sheppard   Area Manager – U.S. and Mexico, Americas   ExxonMobil Exploration Company

Communications Assistants

| T. Evan Smith | Global Best Practices Advisor | Exxon Mobil Corporation |
| J. Donald Turk | Staff Consultant | National Petroleum Council |

Integration Team

Team Leader

| Mervyn T. Sambles | Vice President, Strategic Development | Fluor Corporation |

Members

Joseph A. Caggiano	Senior Consultant, Technology Projects	Chevron Energy Technology Co.
John J. Conti	Director, Office of Integrated Analysis and Forecasting, Energy Information Administration	U.S. Department of Energy
Thomas R. Eizember	Senior Planning Advisor, Corporate Planning – Strategy Division	Exxon Mobil Corporation
William R. Finger	Senior Associate	Cambridge Energy Research Associates
Mariano E. Gurfinkel	Project Manager, Center for Energy Economics, Bureau of Economic Geology	The University of Texas
Bryan J. Hannegan	Vice President, Environment	Electric Power Research Institute
Nancy L. Johnson	Director, Environmental Science and Policy Analysis, Office of Fossil Energy	U.S. Department of Energy
Keith C. King	New Business Development	ExxonMobil Exploration Company
Wilbur D. Kirchner	Chief Engineer, International Exploration New Ventures	Marathon Oil Corporation
Sarah O. Ladislaw	Fellow, Energy Program	Center for Strategic & International Studies
Joseph W. Loper	Vice President, Research and Analysis	Alliance to Save Energy
W. Howard Neal	Adjunct Associate Professor	The University of Texas
John H. Schaus	Executive Officer to the President	Center for Strategic & International Studies
Charles E. Sheppard	Area Manager – U.S. and Mexico, Americas	ExxonMobil Exploration Company
Surina Shukri	Energy Investment Banking	J.P. Morgan Securities Inc.
Adam E. Sieminski	Chief Energy Economist, Global Markets/Commodities	Deutsche Bank AG
Andrew J. Slaughter	Senior Energy and Economics Advisor – EP Americas	Shell Exploration & Production Company
Thomas H. Zimmerman	Schlumberger Fellow	Schlumberger Limited

COORDINATING SUBCOMMITTEE

Report Writing Team

Team Leader

Thomas R. Eizember	Senior Planning Advisor, Corporate Planning – Strategy Division	Exxon Mobil Corporation

Members

Mark A. Andersen	Manager, Oilfield Executive Communications, Executive Editor, *Oilfield Review*	Schlumberger Oilfield Services
Joseph A. Caggiano	Senior Consultant, Technology Projects	Chevron Energy Technology Co.
Edward C. Chow	Senior Fellow, Energy Program	Center for Strategic & International Studies
William R. Finger	Senior Associate	Cambridge Energy Research Associates
Mariano E. Gurfinkel	Project Manager, Center for Energy Economics, Bureau of Economic Geology	The University of Texas
William Lanouette	Editorial Consultant	National Petroleum Council
Joseph W. Loper	Vice President, Research and Analysis	Alliance to Save Energy
John H. Schaus	Executive Officer to the President	Center for Strategic & International Studies
Andrew J. Slaughter	Senior Energy and Economics Advisor – EP Americas	Shell Exploration & Production Company

Carbon Management Subgroup

Team Co-Leaders

Rodney F. Nelson	Vice President, Innovation and Collaboration	Schlumberger Limited
Michael C. Sheppard	Schlumberger Fellow, Schlumberger Oilfield Services	Schlumberger Cambridge Research

Members

David K. Bellman	Director of Fundamental Analysis, Corporate Planning & Budgeting	American Electric Power Co., Inc.
DeAnn Craig	Consultant, Business Planning	Chevron North America Exploration and Production Company
Thomas R. Eizember	Senior Planning Advisor, Corporate Planning – Strategy Division	Exxon Mobil Corporation
William R. Finger	Senior Associate	Cambridge Energy Research Associates
John H. Guy, IV	Deputy Executive Director	National Petroleum Council
Bryan J. Hannegan	Vice President, Environment	Electric Power Research Institute

Gardiner Hill	Director, Carbon Capture and Storage Technology	BP Alternative Energy Company
Allan R. Hoffman	General Engineer, Office of Planning, Budget and Analysis	U.S. Department of Energy
Scott M. Hoyte	Energy Technology Strategic Initiatives	GE Energy
Haroon S. Kheshgi	Advanced Research Associate, Corporate Strategic Research	ExxonMobil Research & Engineering Company
Scott M. Klara	Director, Office of Coal & Power R&D, National Energy Technology Laboratory	U.S. Department of Energy
Vello A. Kuuskraa	President	Advanced Resources International
Sarah O. Ladislaw	Fellow, Energy Program	Center for Strategic & International Studies
Arthur Lee	Principal Advisor, Global Policy and Strategy	Chevron Corporation
Marc Levinson	Economist	JPMorgan Chase & Co.
Richard G. Newell	Gendell Associate Professor of Energy and Environmental Economics, Nicholas School of the Environment and Earth Sciences	Duke University
Arnold R. Smith	Executive Director, Office of Technology	Fluor Corporation
Robert H. Socolow	Co-Director, The Carbon Mitigation Initiative	Princeton University
John M. Tombari	Vice President, North & South America	Schlumberger Carbon Services
Thomas H. Zimmerman	Schlumberger Fellow	Schlumberger Limited

Macroeconomic Subgroup

Team Leader

Douglas B. Petno	Managing Director and Energy Group Head	J.P. Morgan Securities Inc.

Assistant Leader

Surina Shukri	Energy Investment Banking	J.P. Morgan Securities Inc.

Members

Charles E. Bishop*	Director, Economics	Marathon Oil Corporation
Larry G. Chorn	Chief Economist	Platts
R. Dean Foreman	Senior Economist, Corporate Planning – Economics and Energy Division	Exxon Mobil Corporation
Marianne S. Kah	Chief Economist	ConocoPhillips
Marc Levinson	Economist	JPMorgan Chase & Co.

* Individual has since changed organizations but was employed by the specified company while participating in the study.

Richard G. Newell	Gendell Associate Professor of Energy and Environmental Economics, Nicholas School of the Environment and Earth Sciences	Duke University
Adam E. Sieminski	Chief Energy Economist, Global Markets/Commodities	Deutsche Bank AG
Katherine B. Spector	Executive Director, Global Head of Energy Strategy, Global Currency & Commodities Group	JPMorgan Chase Bank, N.A.

Antitrust Advisory Subgroup

Team Leader

Carter B. Simpson	Senior Counsel, Antitrust & Trade Regulation	Exxon Mobil Corporation

Members

Charles W. Corddry, III	Senior Antitrust Counsel	Shell Oil Company
Taik Haw Lim	Director of Corporate Legal	Schlumberger Limited
Margaret A. Ward	Attorney	Jones Day
R. Kenly Webster	Attorney at Law	NPC Counsel

Antitrust Counsel to the National Petroleum Council

Timothy J. Muris	Of Counsel	O'Melveny & Myers LLP
Christine C. Wilson	Partner, Antitrust and Competition Practice	O'Melveny & Myers LLP
Adam J. Coates	Associate	O'Melveny & Myers LLP

DEMAND TASK GROUP

Chair
James R. Burkhard — Managing Director, Global Oil Group — Cambridge Energy Research Associates

Government Cochair
Paul D. Holtberg — Director, Demand and Integration Division, Office of Integrated Analysis and Forecasting, Energy Information Administration — U.S. Department of Energy

Assistant to the Chair
William R. Finger — Senior Associate — Cambridge Energy Research Associates

Secretary
Benjamin A. Oliver, Jr. — Senior Committee Coordinator — National Petroleum Council

Members

David K. Bellman	Director of Fundamental Analysis, Corporate Planning & Budgeting	American Electric Power Co., Inc.
Fatih Birol	Chief Economist	International Energy Agency
Robbie Diamond	President	Securing America's Future Energy
Kathey A. Ferland	Project Manager, Texas Industries of the Future	The University of Texas
Mark P. Gilbert	Director, Economic Forecasting, Corporate Planning & Budgeting	American Electric Power Co., Inc.
Marianne S. Kah	Chief Economist	ConocoPhillips
Joseph W. Loper	Vice President, Research and Analysis	Alliance to Save Energy
Deron W. Lovaas	Vehicles Campaign Director	Natural Resources Defense Council
Dean A. Mathew	Project Manager II, Efficiency Projects & System Efficiency	Duke Energy Corporation
Alan Naisby	Director of Marketing, Global Petroleum Group	Caterpillar Inc.
William Prindle	Deputy Director	American Council for an Energy-Efficient Economy
Kevin P. Regan	Manager, Long-Term Energy Forecasting	Chevron Corporation
Adam E. Sieminski	Chief Energy Economist, Global Markets/Commodities	Deutsche Bank AG
Jaime Spellings	General Manager, Corporate Planning	Exxon Mobil Corporation
Edward J. Stones	Director, Energy Risk	The Dow Chemical Company
David P. Teolis	Manager, European Economics and Industry Forecasting, Adam Opel GmbH	General Motors Europe
Connie S. Trecazzi	Staff Analyst	American Electric Power Co., Inc.
Lowell W. Ungar	Senior Policy Analyst	Alliance to Save Energy
Michael A. Warren	National Manager, Americas Strategic Research & Planning Group	Toyota Motor North America, Inc.

DEMAND TASK GROUP

Coal Impact Subgroup

Team Leader

Connie S. Trecazzi	Staff Analyst	American Electric Power Co., Inc.

Members

Frank A. Clemente	Senior Professor of Social Science	Pennsylvania State University
Frederick L. Freme	Survey Statistician, Coal, Nuclear and Renewable Fuels Division, Energy Information Administration	U.S. Department of Energy
Daniel L. Keen	Assistant Vice President – Policy Analysis	Association of American Railroads
James A. Luppens	Project Chief, U.S. Coal Assessment	U.S. Geological Survey
Brenda S. Pierce	Program Coordinator, Energy Resources Program	U.S. Geological Survey
Craig F. Rockey	Vice President, Policy & Economics	Association of American Railroads
Keith Welham	Principal Energy Economist	Rio Tinto plc

Cultural, Social, & Economic Subgroup

Team Leader

Joseph W. Loper	Vice President, Research and Analysis	Alliance to Save Energy

Members

Stephen A. Capanna	Research Associate	Alliance to Save Energy
Helen M. Currie*	Director, Chief Economist's Office, Planning Strategy & Corporate Affairs	ConocoPhillips
D. Olandan Davenport	Attorney	Davenport & Associates
Zachary Henry	Manager, Americas Strategic Research & Planning Group	Toyota Motor North America, Inc.
F. Jerome Hinkle	Vice President, Policy and Government Affairs	National Hydrogen Association
Paul D. Holtberg	Director, Demand and Integration Division, Office of Integrated Analysis and Forecasting, Energy Information Administration	U.S. Department of Energy
Marianne S. Kah	Chief Economist	ConocoPhillips
John A. Laitner	Visiting Fellow and Senior Economist	American Council for an Energy-Efficient Economy
Deron W. Lovaas	Vehicles Campaign Director	Natural Resources Defense Council
Kevin P. Regan	Manager, Long-Term Energy Forecasting	Chevron Corporation
Jaime Spellings	General Manager, Corporate Planning	Exxon Mobil Corporation
David P. Teolis	Manager, European Economics and Industry Forecasting, Adam Opel GmbH	General Motors Europe

* Individual has since changed organizations but was employed by the specified company while participating in the study.

| Michael A. Warren | National Manager, Americas Strategic Research & Planning Group | Toyota Motor North America, Inc. |

Data Evaluation Subgroup

Team Leader
| William R. Finger | Senior Associate | Cambridge Energy Research Associates |

Members
James R. Burkhard	Managing Director, Global Oil Group	Cambridge Energy Research Associates
Robbie Diamond	President	Securing America's Future Energy
Paul D. Holtberg	Director, Demand and Integration Division, Office of Integrated Analysis and Forecasting, Energy Information Administration	U.S. Department of Energy
David S. Reed	Senior Energy Planner, Corporate Planning Department	Exxon Mobil Corporation

Industrial Energy Efficiency Subgroup

Team Leader
| Edward J. Stones | Director, Energy Risk | The Dow Chemical Company |

Members
| Kathey A. Ferland | Project Manager, Texas Industries of the Future | The University of Texas |
| Michelle R. R. Noack | Global Business Analyst, Energy | The Dow Chemical Company |

Power Generation Efficiency Subgroup

Team Leader
| David K. Bellman | Director of Fundamental Analysis, Corporate Planning & Budgeting | American Electric Power Co., Inc. |

Members
Brett D. Blankenship	Analyst – Power and Emissions	American Electric Power Co., Inc.
Joseph Philip DiPietro	Lead General Engineer, Office of Systems, Analysis and Planning, National Energy Technology Laboratory	U.S. Department of Energy
Carl H. Imhoff	Manager, Energy Products and Operations Product Line, Pacific Northwest National Laboratory	U.S. Department of Energy
Barry Rederstorff	Staff Engineer, Engineering Services	American Electric Power Co., Inc.
Xuejin Zheng	Senior Analyst – Coal	American Electric Power Co., Inc.

Residential/Commercial Efficiency Subgroup

Team Leader

Mark P. Gilbert	Director, Economic Forecasting, Corporate Planning & Budgeting	American Electric Power Co., Inc.

Members

Stephen A. Capanna	Research Associate	Alliance to Save Energy
Leslie Black Cordes	Branch Chief, Energy Supply and Industry	U.S. Environmental Protection Agency
Selin Devranoglu	Research Associate	Alliance to Save Energy
Joseph W. Loper	Vice President, Research and Analysis	Alliance to Save Energy
Matthew C. Rogers	Director	McKinsey & Company

SUPPLY TASK GROUP

Chair
Donald L. Paul   Vice President and Chief Technology Officer   Chevron Corporation

Government Cochair
Nancy L. Johnson   Director, Environmental Science and Policy   U.S. Department of Energy
                                Analysis, Office of Fossil Energy

Assistant to the Chair
Joseph A. Caggiano   Senior Consultant, Technology Projects   Chevron Energy Technology Co.

Alternate Government Cochair
Glen E. Sweetnam   Director, International, Economic and   U.S. Department of Energy
                                Greenhouse Gases Division,
                                Energy Information Administration

Secretary
John H. Guy, IV   Deputy Executive Director   National Petroleum Council

Members
David J. Bardin   Of Counsel (Retired Member)   Arent Fox LLP

Thomas P. Binder   President, ADM Research Division   Archer Daniels Midland Company

Fatih Birol   Chief Economist   International Energy Agency

Ronald R. Charpentier   Geologist   U.S. Geological Survey

Alicia M. Boutan   Vice President, Business Development   Chevron Technology Ventures LLC

William M. Cobb   2008 President-Elect   Society of Petroleum Engineers

DeAnn Craig   Consultant, Business Planning   Chevron North America Exploration
                                                                                 and Production Company

Linda E. Doman   International Energy Analyst,   U.S. Department of Energy
                                Energy Information Administration

Scott B. Gill   Managing Director, Co-Head Research   Simmons & Company International

Timothy C. Grant   Geologist, National Energy   U.S. Department of Energy
                                Technology Laboratory

Mariano E. Gurfinkel   Project Manager,   The University of Texas
                                Center for Energy Economics,
                                Bureau of Economic Geology

D. Ronald Harrell   Chairman Emeritus   Ryder Scott Company, L.P.

F. Jerome Hinkle   Vice President,   National Hydrogen Association
                                Policy and Govenment Affairs

Donald A. Juckett   Director, Geoscience and Energy Office   American Association of
                                                                                 Petroleum Geologists

Wilbur D. Kirchner   Chief Engineer,   Marathon Oil Corporation
                                International Exploration New Ventures

Charles D. Linville   Manager – Knowledge and Data Engineering,   Archer Daniels Midland Company
                                Research Division

SUPPLY TASK GROUP

Stephen K. London	Senior Global Account Manager	Halliburton Company
Brenda S. Pierce	Program Coordinator, Energy Resources Program	U.S. Geological Survey
Kevin P. Regan	Manager, Long-Term Energy Forecasting	Chevron Corporation
Peter R. Rose	Past President	American Association of Petroleum Geologists
Mervyn T. Sambles	Vice President, Strategic Development	Fluor Corporation
Charles E. Sheppard	Area Manager – U.S. and Mexico, Americas	ExxonMobil Exploration Company
Andrew J. Slaughter	Senior Energy and Economics Advisor – EP Americas	Shell Exploration & Production Company
Roger W. Smith	Director, Strategic Development	Fluor Corporation
Scott W. Tinker	Director, Bureau of Economic Geology and State Geologist of Texas	The University of Texas
Connie S. Trecazzi	Staff Analyst	American Electric Power Co., Inc.
David L. Whikehart	Optimization LP Manager	Marathon Oil Corporation
John H. Wood	Director, Reserves & Production Division, Energy Information Administration	U.S. Department of Energy

Biomass Subgroup

Team Leader

Thomas P. Binder	President, ADM Research Division	Archer Daniels Midland Company

Members

John R. Benemann	Director	Institute for Environmental Management, Inc.
Ralph P. Cavalieri	Associate Dean and Director, Agricultural Research Center	Washington State University
Andre P. C. Faaij	Associate Professor, Copernicus Institute for Sustainable Development and Innovation	Utrecht University
Richard Flavell	Chief Scientific Officer	Ceres, Inc.
Frank D. Gunstone	Professor Emeritus	University of St. Andrews
John S. Hickman	Principal Scientist	Deere & Company
Kenneth A. Kindler	Global Grain Channel Leader, Plant Genetics and Biotechnology	Dow AgroSciences
Charles D. Linville	Manager – Knowledge and Data Engineering, Research Division	Archer Daniels Midland Company
Sharon P. Shoemaker	Founder and Executive Director, California Institute of Food and Agricultural Research	University of California

| Michael A. Warren | National Manager, Americas Strategic Research & Planning Group | Toyota Motor North America, Inc. |
| Edwin H. White | Director, SUNY Center for Sustainable and Renewable Energy, College of Environmental Science and Forestry | State University of New York |

Data Interpretation & Warehouse Subgroup

Team Leader
| Charles E. Sheppard | Area Manager – U.S. and Mexico, Americas | ExxonMobil Exploration Company |

Data Warehouse Development
| Charles D. Linville | Manager – Knowledge and Data Engineering, Research Division | Archer Daniels Midland Company |

Data Warehouse Manager
| Scott J. Hills | GIS & Remote Sensing | Chevron Energy Technology Co. |

Data Warehouse Librarian
| Andrew P. Richardson | Project Manager, Rapid Response Team, Schlumberger Information Solutions | Schlumberger Oilfield Services |

Members
Anthony L. Barker	Senior Business Research Analyst, Strategic Planning and Portfolio	Marathon Oil Corporation
Frank A. Clemente	Senior Professor of Social Science	Pennsylvania State University
Linda E. Doman	International Energy Analyst, Energy Information Administration	U.S. Department of Energy
Patrick Gibson	Principal Oil Supply Analyst	Wood Mackenzie Ltd.
Timothy C. Grant	Geologist, National Energy Technology Laboratory	U.S. Department of Energy
Jason A. Gretencord	Scientific User Support Analyst, Research Division	Archer Daniels Midland Company
Mariano E. Gurfinkel	Project Manager, Center for Energy Economics, Bureau of Economic Geology	The University of Texas
Keith C. King	New Business Development	ExxonMobil Exploration Company
Wilbur D. Kirchner	Chief Engineer, International Exploration New Ventures	Marathon Oil Corporation
Stephen K. London	Senior Global Account Manager	Halliburton Company
Deron W. Lovaas	Vehicles Campaign Director	Natural Resources Defense Council
Pawel Olejarnik	Research Analyst, Economic Analysis Division	International Energy Agency

Raja V. Ramani	Professor of Mining Engineering and Geo-Environmental Engineering (Emeritus), Department of Energy and Geo-Environmental Engineering	Pennsylvania State University
Olivier Rech	Energy Analyst, Economic Analysis Division	International Energy Agency
Kevin P. Regan	Manager, Long-Term Energy Forecasting	Chevron Corporation
Glen E. Sweetnam	Director, International, Economic, and Greenhouse Gases Division, Energy Information Administration	U.S. Department of Energy
Connie S. Trecazzi	Staff Analyst	American Electric Power Co., Inc.

Hydrogen Subgroup

Team Leader
| F. Jerome Hinkle | Vice President, Policy and Government Affairs | National Hydrogen Association |

Members
Ethan W. Brown	Director, Government Business Development	Ballard Power Systems, Inc.
Daniel C. Cicero	General Engineer, Office of Coal and Power Research and Development, National Energy Technology Laboratory	U.S. Department of Energy
Raymond S. Hobbs	Future Fuels Program	Arizona Public Service
Michael J. Holmes	Deputy Associate Director for Research, Energy & Environment Research Center	University of North Dakota
Jay O. Keller	Manager, Hydrogen & Combustion Technologies, Sandia National Laboratories	U.S. Department of Energy
David H. Mann	Project Coordinator	National Hydrogen Association
Margaret K. Mann	Chemical Process Engineer, National Renewable Energy Laboratory	U.S. Department of Energy
Jonathan P. Mathews	Assistant Professor, Energy & Geo-Environmental Engineering	Pennsylvania State University
Robert N. Miller	Senior Contract Manager, Corporate Technology Partnerships	Air Products and Chemicals, Inc.
A. K. S. Murthy	Technology Fellow	The Linde Group
Frank J. Novachek	Director, Corporate Planning	Xcel Energy
W. Gerry Runte	General Manager, Clean Energy	ARES Corporation
Harold H. Schobert	Professor, Fuel Science, Energy & Geo-Environmental Engineering	Pennsylvania State University
Kenneth R. Schultz	Operations Director, Energy Group	General Atomics
Mary-Rose de Valladares	Hydrogen Implementing Agreement Secretariat	International Energy Agency

Infrastructure Subgroup

Team Leader

Roger W. Smith	Director, Strategic Development	Fluor Corporation

Members

Harry R. Homan	Senior Director, Strategic Development	Fluor Corporation
Francis C. Pilley	Manager, U.S. Pipelines	TransCanada Pipelines Limited
Craig F. Rockey	Vice President, Policy & Economics	Association of American Railroads
Douglas Sheffler	Manager, Research and Data Analysis	The American Waterways Operators
Tianjia Tang	Transportation Specialist, Federal Highway Administration	U.S. Department of Transportation
Cheryl J. Trench	President	Allegro Energy Consulting
Eric A. von Moltke	Analyst	Fluor Corporation
Kristin N. Walsh	Manager, Strategic Planning	Anadarko Petroleum Corporation

LNG & GTL Subgroup

Team Leader

Andrew J. Slaughter	Senior Energy and Economics Advisor – EP Americas	Shell Exploration & Production Company

Members

Robert F. Corbin	Natural Gas Analyst, Global Security and Supply, Office of Oil and Gas	U.S. Department of Energy
David M. A. Hendicott	Director, Global Gas LNG Strategy	ConocoPhillips
James T. Jensen	President	Jensen Associates
Kenneth B. Medlock, III	Visiting Professor, Department of Economics and Energy Consultant to the James A. Baker III Institute for Public Policy	Rice University
Kyle M. Sawyer	Consultant	El Paso Pipeline Group
Michael S. Speltz	Manager – Gas Market Analysis	Chevron Global Gas

Refining & Manufacturing Subgroup

Team Leader

David L. Whikehart	Optimization LP Manager	Marathon Oil Corporation

Members

Alison A. Keane	Environmental Protection Specialist, Office of Policy, Economics and Innovation	U.S. Environmental Protection Agency
Michael E. Leister	Fuels Technology Manager	Marathon Oil Corporation
David A. Sexton	Vice President, Strategy and Portfolio	Shell Oil Products U.S.
Philip Stephenson	Vice Chairman	The Rompetrol Group NV

SUPPLY TASK GROUP

Thomas H. White	Policy Analyst, Office of Oil and Gas Analysis	U.S. Department of Energy
James R. Wilkins	Refining HES Manager	Marathon Oil Corporation

Renewables Subgroup

Team Leader
Alicia M. Boutan	Vice President, Business Development	Chevron Technology Ventures LLC

Members
Thomas J. Bunting	Business Analyst	Chevron Technology Ventures LLC
Conor M. Duffy	Business Analyst	Chevron Technology Ventures LLC
Stephen M. Robinson	Planning Manager	Chevron Technology Ventures LLC
Geoffrey S. W. Styles	Managing Director	GSW Strategy Group, LLC

Resource Endowment Subgroup

Team Leader
Brenda S. Pierce	Program Coordinator, Energy Resources Program	U.S. Geological Survey

Members
Roberto F. Aguilera	Postdoctoral Fellow, Centro de Mineria, Escuela de Ingenieria	Pontificia Universidad Catolica de Chile
David J. Bardin	Of Counsel (Retired Member)	Arent Fox LLP
P. Jeffrey Brown	Senior Consultant, Exploration and Production Practice	Decision Strategies, Inc.
Joseph A. Caggiano	Senior Consultant, Technology Projects	Chevron Energy Technology Co.
Ronald R. Charpentier	Geologist	U.S. Geological Survey
Arthur R. Green	Geoscientist	Gig Harbor, Washington
D. Ronald Harrell	Chairman Emeritus	Ryder Scott Company, L.P.
Donald A. Juckett	Director, Geoscience and Energy Office	American Association of Petroleum Geologists
Keith C. King	New Business Development	ExxonMobil Exploration Company
W. C. Riese	Geoscience Advisor, North American Gas & Long Term Renewal	BP America Production Company
Peter R. Rose	Past President	American Association of Petroleum Geologists
Wolfgang E. Schollnberger	Energy Advisor	Potomac, Maryland
Floyd C. Wiesepape	Petroleum Engineer, Reserves and Production Division, Energy Information Administration	U.S. Department of Energy

| John H. Wood | Director, Reserves and Production Division, Energy Information Administration | U.S. Department of Energy |
| Margarita V. Zyrianova | Geophysicist, Central Energy Resources Team | U.S. Geological Survey |

Wide-Net Subgroup

Team Leader

| Scott B. Gill | Managing Director, Co-Head Research | Simmons & Company International |

Members

Timothy C. Grant	Geologist, National Energy Technology Laboratory	U.S. Department of Energy
Mariano E. Gurfinkel	Project Manager, Center for Energy Economics, Bureau of Economic Geology	The University of Texas
Wilbur D. Kirchner	Chief Engineer, International Exploration New Ventures	Marathon Oil Corporation
Stephen K. London	Senior Global Account Manager	Halliburton Company

Data Warehouse Quality Assurance

| Louis D. DeMouy | Consultant | National Petroleum Council |
| Richard D. Farmer | Consultant | National Petroleum Council |

TECHNOLOGY TASK GROUP

Chair
Rodney F. Nelson   Vice President, Innovation and Collaboration   Schlumberger Limited

Government Cochair
Guido DeHoratiis, Jr.   Director,   U.S. Department of Energy
                            Oil and Gas Research & Development,
                            Office of Fossil Energy

Assistant to the Chair
Thomas H. Zimmerman   Schlumberger Fellow   Schlumberger Limited

Secretary
Benjamin A. Oliver, Jr.   Senior Committee Coordinator   National Petroleum Council

Members
Mark A. Andersen   Manager,   Schlumberger Oilfield Services
                            Oilfield Executive Communications,
                            Executive Editor, *Oilfield Review*

David K. Bellman   Director of Fundamental Analysis,   American Electric Power Co., Inc.
                            Corporate Planning & Budgeting

Stephen M. Cassiani   President   ExxonMobil Upstream
                                                                            Research Company

Brian Clark   Schlumberger Fellow   Schlumberger Limited

Russell J. Conser   Manager, GameChanger   Shell International Exploration &
                                                                            Production Inc.

Mariano E. Gurfinkel   Project Manager,   The University of Texas
                            Center for Energy Economics,
                            Bureau of Economic Geology

Tobin K. Harvey   Senior Advisor, Immediate Office of the   U.S. Department of Energy
                            Assistant Secretary for Energy Efficiency
                            and Renewable Energy

Allan R. Hoffman   General Engineer, Office of Planning,   U.S. Department of Energy
                            Budget and Analysis

Stephen A. Holditch   Noble Endowed Chair and   Texas A&M University
                            Head of the Harold Vance
                            Department of Petroleum Engineering

Scott M. Hoyte   Energy Technology Strategic Initiatives   GE Energy

F. Emil Jacobs   Vice President, Research and Development   ExxonMobil Research and
                                                                            Engineering Company

Robert L. Kleinberg   Schlumberger Fellow   Schlumberger-Doll Research

Taik Haw Lim   Director of Corporate Legal   Schlumberger Limited

Ernest J. Moniz   Professor of Physics and Cecil and Ida   Massachusetts Institute of Technology
                            Green Distinguished Professor,
                            Department of Physics

W. Howard Neal	Adjunct Associate Professor	The University of Texas
T. S. Ramakrishnan	Scientific Advisor	Schlumberger Oilfield Services
Michael C. Sheppard	Schlumberger Fellow, Schlumberger Oilfield Services	Schlumberger Cambridge Research
Arnold R. Smith	Executive Director, Office of Technology	Fluor Corporation
M. Nafi Toksöz	Robert R. Shrock Professor of Geophysics, Department of Earth, Atmospheric & Planetary Sciences	Massachusetts Institute of Technology
Lowell W. Ungar	Senior Policy Analyst	Alliance to Save Energy

Carbon Capture & Sequestration Subgroup

Team Leader

| Michael C. Sheppard | Schlumberger Fellow, Schlumberger Oilfield Services | Schlumberger Cambridge Research |

Members

Michael J. Bowman	Manager, Energy Systems Laboratory	GE Global Energy
Steven L. Bryant	Assistant Professor, Petroleum and Geosystems Engineering	The University of Texas
S. Julio Friedmann	Carbon Management Program APL	Lawrence Livermore National Laboratory
Bjørn-Erik Haugan	Executive Director	Gassnova
David Hawkins	Director, Climate Center	Natural Resources Defense Council
Howard J. Herzog	Principal Research Engineer, Laboratory for Energy and the Environment	Massachusetts Institute of Technology
Gardiner Hill	Director, Carbon Capture and Storage Technology	BP Alternative Energy Company
Scott M. Klara	Director, Office of Coal & Power R&D, National Energy Technology Laboratory	U.S. Department of Energy
Vello A. Kuuskraa	President	Advanced Resources International
Arthur Lee	Principal Advisor, Global Policy and Strategy	Chevron Corporation
Geoffrey Maitland	Professor of Energy Engineering, Department of Chemical Engineering	Imperial College London
Thomas Mikus	CO2 Capture Team Leader	Shell Oil Company
Franklin M. Orr, Jr.	Keleen and Carlton Beal Professor of Petroleum Engineering, Department of Petroleum Engineering	Stanford University
T. S. Ramakrishnan	Scientific Advisor	Schlumberger Oilfield Services
Robert H. Socolow	Co-Director, The Carbon Mitigation Initiative	Princeton University
John M. Tombari	Vice President, North & South America	Schlumberger Carbon Services

TECHNOLOGY TASK GROUP

Coal to Liquids and Gas Subgroup

Team Leader

David K. Bellman	Director of Fundamental Analysis, Corporate Planning & Budgeting	American Electric Power Co., Inc.

Members

James Edward Burns	Business Development Manager	Shell U.S. Gas & Power LLC
Frank A. Clemente	Senior Professor of Social Science	Pennsylvania State University
Michael L. Eastman	General Engineer, Strategic Center for Coal, National Energy Technology Laboratory	U.S. Department of Energy
James R. Katzer	Visiting Scholar, Laboratory for Energy and the Environment	Massachusetts Institute of Technology
Gregory J. Kawalkin	Business Management Specialist, Strategic Center for Coal, National Energy Technology Laboratory	U.S. Department of Energy
George G. Muntean	Chief Engineer, Energy Science and Technology Division, Pacific Northwest National Laboratory	U.S. Department of Energy
Hubert W. Schenck	Business Development Manager, Clean Coal Energy	Shell U.S. Gas & Power LLC
Joseph P. Strakey	Director, Strategic Center for Coal, National Energy Technology Laboratory	U.S. Department of Energy
Connie S. Trecazzi	Staff Analyst	American Electric Power Co., Inc.

Deepwater Subgroup

Team Leader

Russell J. Conser	Manager, GameChanger	Shell International Exploration & Production Inc.

Members

Ronald M. Bass	Senior Staff Engineer, Deepwater Research & Development	Shell International Exploration & Production Inc.
Chryssostomos Chryssostomidis	Professor of Mechanical and Ocean Engineering	Massachusetts Institute of Technology
Elmer Peter Danenberger, III	Chief, Offshore Regulatory Programs, Minerals Management Service	U.S. Department of the Interior
C. Christopher Garcia	Deepwater Theme Manager, Gulf of Mexico USA	Schlumberger Oilfield Services
Michael G. Grecco*	DeepStar Director, Energy Technology Company	Chevron Corporation
James Longbottom	TEES Associate, Research Scientist	Texas A&M University

* Individual has since changed organizations but was employed by the specified company while participating in the study.

| Robert E. Sandström | Research Supervisor, Offshore Division – Marine Engineering Section | ExxonMobil Upstream Research Co. |
| Paul Tranter | Vice President, Performance and Operations | Transocean Inc. |

Exploration Technology Subgroup

Team Leader
| Stephen M. Cassiani | President | ExxonMobil Upstream Research Co. |

Members
Michael S. Bahorich	Executive Vice President, Exploration and Production Technology (Representing Society of Exploration Geophysicists)	Apache Corporation
David R. Converse	Senior Research Associate, Breakthrough Division	ExxonMobil Upstream Research Co.
William L. Fisher	Professor and Barrow Chair, Jackson School of Geosciences	The University of Texas
David Edward Nichols	Research Director	WesternGeco
W. C. Riese	Geoscience Advisor, North American Gas & Long Term Renewal (Representing American Association of Petroleum Geologists)	BP America Production Company
Saad J. Saleh	Program Manager, Frontier Exploration Opportunities R&D	Shell International Exploration & Production Inc.
Wolfgang E. Schollnberger	Energy Advisor	Potomac, Maryland
M. Nafi Toksöz	Robert R. Shrock Professor of Geophysics, Department of Earth, Atmospheric & Planetary Sciences	Massachusetts Institute of Technology

Heavy Oil Subgroup

Team Leader
| Brian Clark | Schlumberger Fellow | Schlumberger Limited |

Members
W. Gordon Graves	Petroleum Consultant	Pagosa Springs, Colorado
Mariano E. Gurfinkel	Project Manager, Center for Energy Economics, Bureau of Economic Geology	The University of Texas
Jorge E. Lopez-de-Cardenas	Perforating Domain and Technical Advisor	Schlumberger Reservoir Evaluation Wireline
Allan W. Peats	Business Development Manager, Heavy Oil	Schlumberger Oilfield Services

Nuclear Power Subgroup

Team Leader

| Scott M. Hoyte | Energy Technology Strategic Initiatives | GE Energy |

Members

Christopher E. Maslak	Marketing Program Manager, Nuclear	GE Energy
Ernest J. Moniz	Professor of Physics and Cecil and Ida Green Distinguished Professor, Department of Physics	Massachusetts Institute of Technology
John M. Stamos	Nuclear Engineer, Light Water Reactor Deployment, Office of Nuclear Energy	U.S. Department of Energy
Will van der Zalm	Senior Project Director	Fluor Corporation

Oil and Gas Technology Development Subgroup

Team Leader

| W. Howard Neal | Adjunct Associate Professor | The University of Texas |

Members

Matthew R. G. Bell*	Senior Investment Manager	Shell Technology Ventures
Christine A. Hansen	Executive Director	Interstate Oil and Gas Compact Commission
Robert W. Siegfried, II	Manager, Research & Development	Gas Technology Institute

Oil Shales and Hydrates Subgroup

Team Leader

| Robert L. Kleinberg | Schlumberger Fellow | Schlumberger-Doll Research |

Members

Edith C. Allison	Physical Scientist, Office of Future Oil and Gas Resources	U.S. Department of Energy
Timothy S. Collett	Research Geologist	U.S. Geological Survey
Robert A. Hardage	Senior Research Scientist, Bureau of Economic Geology	The University of Texas
Stephen A. Holditch	Noble Endowed Chair and Head of the Harold Vance Department of Petroleum Engineering	Texas A&M University
James J. Howard	Principal Scientist	ConocoPhillips
E. Dendy Sloan, Jr.	Weaver Endowed Chair in Chemical Engineering	Colorado School of Mines

* Individual has since changed organizations but was employed by the specified company while participating in the study.

Technology Impact on Arctic Subgroup

Team Leader
Thomas H. Zimmerman   Schlumberger Fellow   Schlumberger Limited

Members
Geir Utskot   Oilfield Services Arctic Manager   Schlumberger Oilfield Services

Technology Impact on Conventional Wells Subgroup

Team Leader
Thomas H. Zimmerman   Schlumberger Fellow   Schlumberger Limited

Members

Daniel R. Burns	Researcher, Department of Earth, Atmospheric, and Planetary Sciences	Massachusetts Institute of Technology
Akhil Datta-Gupta	Professor and LeSuer Chair in Reservoir Management, Petroleum Engineering	Texas A&M University
William L. Fisher	Professor and Barrow Chair, Jackson School of Geosciences	The University of Texas
J. Heine Gerretsen	Technology Strategy Advisor (EPT-RCT)	Shell International Exploration & Production Inc.
D. Ronald Harrell	Chairman Emeritus	Ryder Scott Company, L.P.
A. Daniel Hill	Associate Department Head, Graduate Program and R. L. Whiting Endowed Chair, Harold Vance Department of Petroleum Engineering	Texas A&M University
George J. Hirasaki	A. J. Hartsook Professor in Chemical Engineering, Chemical & Biomolecular Engineering Department	Rice University
John D. Kuzan	Upper Zakum Transition Manager	ExxonMobil Upstream Research Co.
John J. Pyrdol	Economist	U.S. Department of Energy

Technology Impact on Enhanced Oil Recovery Subgroup

Team Leader
Thomas H. Zimmerman   Schlumberger Fellow   Schlumberger Limited

Members

Swapan Kumar Das	Advisor, Thermal & HO EOR	ConocoPhillips
Birol Dindoruk	Principal Reservoir Engineer, Technology Applications & Research	Shell International Exploration & Production Inc.
Daniel T. Georgi	Director, Strategic Technology and Advanced Research, INTEQ	Baker Hughes Incorporated

George J. Hirasaki	A. J. Hartsook Professor in Chemical Engineering, Chemical & Biomolecular Engineering Department	Rice University
Jairam Kamath	Team Leader	Chevron Energy Technology Co.
Anthony R. Kovscek	Associate Professor, Department of Energy Resources Engineering	Stanford University
Fikri J. Kuchuk	Schlumberger Fellow and Chief Reservoir Engineer	Schlumberger Riboud Product Center
Vello A. Kuuskraa	President	Advanced Resources International
Kishore K. Mohanty	Professor and Director, Institute for Improved Oil Recovery, Chemical & Biomolecular Engineering	University of Houston
Hamdi A. Tchelepi	Associate Professor, Petroleum Engineering	Stanford University
Djebbar Tiab	Senior Professor of Petroleum Engineering, Mewbourne School of Petroleum and Geological Engineering	University of Oklahoma
John Roland Wilkinson	Regional Reservoir Manager – NA/SA/AP/ME	ExxonMobil Production Company

Technology Impact on Human Resources Subgroup

Team Co-Leaders

| Mark A. Andersen | Manager, Oilfield Executive Communications, Executive Editor, *Oilfield Review* | Schlumberger Oilfield Services |
| Hillary F. Dayton | Lead Analyst | Fluor Corporation |

Members

Ronald L. Albright	Senior Vice President, Construction & Procurement	Fluor Corporation
Richard M. Byrnes	Director, North and South America	Schlumberger Business Consulting
William L. Fisher	Professor and Barrow Chair, Jackson School of Geosciences	The University of Texas
H. Steven Gilbert	Senior Vice President, Human Resources	Fluor Corporation
Christine A. Hansen	Executive Director	Interstate Oil and Gas Compact Commission
Stephen A. Holditch	Noble Endowed Chair and Head of the Harold Vance Department of Petroleum Engineering	Texas A&M University
Larry G. Jackson	Vice President, Strategy & Sourcing Management	Fluor Corporation
Wm. Daryl Johnson	Marketing Director	Fluor Corporation
Mark A. Landry	Senior Director, Human Resources	Fluor Corporation
W. Howard Neal	Adjunct Associate Professor	The University of Texas

Rodney F. Nelson	Vice President, Innovation and Collaboration	Schlumberger Limited
Michael Oswalt	Spend Analyst	Fluor Corporation
Heidi C. Pozzo	Controller, Construction and Procurement	Fluor Corporation
M. Antoine Rostand	Global Managing Director	Schlumberger Business Consulting
Mervyn T. Sambles	Vice President, Strategic Development	Fluor Corporation
James A. Scotti	Vice President and Chief Procurement Officer	Fluor Corporation
Mukul M. Sharma	Professor, Petroleum & Geosystems Engineering	The University of Texas

Transportation Efficiency Subgroup

Team Leader

F. Emil Jacobs	Vice President, Research and Development	ExxonMobil Research and Engineering Company

Members

John K. Amdall	Director, Engine Research and Development	Caterpillar Inc.
Alicia M. Boutan	Vice President, Business Development	Chevron Technology Ventures LLC
Kevin L. Bruch	Assistant Director, Engine Research, Technical Services Division	Caterpillar Inc.
K. G. Duleep	Managing Director, Transportation	Energy and Environmental Analysis
William R. Finger	Senior Associate	Cambridge Energy Research Associates
David J. Friedman	Research Director, Clean Vehicles Program	Union of Concerned Scientists
Srini R. Gowda	Business Development Manager	General Electric – Aircraft Engines
Albert M. Hochhauser	Consultant	Essex Consulting, Inc.
Gilbert R. Jersey	Distinguished Research Associate	ExxonMobil Research and Engineering Company
Peter Lawson	Product Line Manager	General Electric – Transportation
James A. Spearot	Director, Chemical and Environmental Sciences Lab	General Motors Research & Development Center
Daniel Sperling	Director, Institute of Transportation Studies	University of California
Kevin C. Stork	Lead General Engineer, Office of FreedomCAR and Vehicle Technology Program	U.S. Department of Energy
Thomas Stricker	Director, Technical and Regulatory Affairs	Toyota Motor North America, Inc.
Rogelio A. Sullivan	Supervisory General Engineer, Office of the FreedomCAR and Vehicle Technology Program	U.S. Department of Energy

Unconventional Gas Subgroup

Team Leader

Stephen A. Holditch	Noble Endowed Chair and Head of the Harold Vance Department of Petroleum Engineering	Texas A&M University

Members

Walter B. Ayers	Visiting Professor of Petroleum Engineering, Harold Vance Department of Petroleum Engineering	Texas A&M University
John A. Bickley	Team Leader, Tight Gas Task Force, EP Americas	Shell Exploration & Production Co.
Thomas A. Blasingame	Professor and Holder of the Robert L. Whiting Professorship in Petroleum Engineering, Harold Vance Department of Petroleum Engineering	Texas A&M University
Mark L. Hoefner	Senior Engineering Associate	ExxonMobil Upstream Research Co.
Valerie A. Jochen	Technical Director, Unconventional Gas	Schlumberger Oilfield Services
W. John Lee	Professor and L. F. Peterson Endowed Chair, Harold Vance Department of Petroleum Engineering	Texas A&M University
Duane A. McVay	Associate Professor, Harold Vance Department of Petroleum Engineering	Texas A&M University
Kent F. Perry	Managing Director, Supply (Unconventional Gas) Sector	Gas Technology Institute
Mukul M. Sharma	Professor, Petroleum & Geosystems Engineering	The University of Texas
Catalin Teodoriu	Assistant Professor, Harold Vance Department of Petroleum Engineering	Texas A&M University
Carlos Torres-Verdín	Associate Professor, Petroleum & Geosystems Engineering	The University of Texas

GEOPOLITICS & POLICY TASK GROUP

Geopolitics Subgroup

Team Leader
Edward C. Chow[†]   Senior Fellow, Energy Program   Center for Strategic & International Studies

Government Coleader
David L. Pumphrey*   Deputy Assistant Secretary, International Energy Cooperation, Office of Policy and International Affairs   U.S. Department of Energy

Assistant to the Leader
Jennifer L. Bovair   Program Coordinator, Energy Program   Center for Strategic & International Studies

Secretary
Marshall W. Nichols   Executive Director   National Petroleum Council

Members

David P. Bailey   International Government Relations and Planning Manager   Exxon Mobil Corporation

Samuel C. Beatty   International Trade Specialist, Office of Energy and Environment, International Trade Agency   U.S. Department of Commerce

Ann A. Bordetsky   Policy Analyst   Natural Resources Defense Council

DeAnn Craig   Consultant, Business Planning   Chevron North America Exploration and Production Company

M. Reginald Dale   Senior Fellow, Europe Program   Center for Strategic & International Studies

J. Robert Garverick   Economic/Energy Officer, Bureau of Economic and Business Affairs   U.S. Department of State

Robert L. Grenier   Managing Director   Kroll Inc.

Rachel E. Halpern   International Trade Specialist, Office of Energy and Environment, International Trade Agency   U.S. Department of Commerce

Bryan J. Hannegan   Vice President, Environment   Electric Power Research Institute

Alexander L. Iannaccone   Intern 2006   Center for Strategic & International Studies

Sarah O. Ladislaw   Fellow, Energy Program   Center for Strategic & International Studies

Regis W. Matlak   CIA Chair   National War College

Richard G. Newell   Gendell Associate Professor of Energy and Environmental Economics, Nicholas School of the Environment and Earth Sciences   Duke University

† Replaced Alan S. Hegburg, who left CSIS to join DOE.
* Individual has since changed organizations but was employed by the specified organization while participating in the study.

Kevin M. O'Donovan	Director, Policy and State Government Relations, Government Affairs	Shell Oil Company
William C. Ramsay	Deputy Executive Director	International Energy Agency
D. Tate Rich	Policy Advisor, Office of the Deputy Assistant Secretary for Fossil Energy	U.S. Department of Energy
Mark E. Rodekohr	Director, Energy Markets and Contingency Information Division, Energy Information Administration	U.S. Department of Energy

Policy Subgroup

Team Leader

| Frank A. Verrastro | Director and Senior Fellow, Energy Program | Center for Strategic & International Studies |

Government Coleader

| David L. Pumphrey* | Deputy Assistant Secretary, International Energy Cooperation, Office of Policy and International Affairs | U.S. Department of Energy |

Assistants to the Leader

| John H. Schaus | Executive Officer to the President | Center for Strategic & International Studies |
| Jennifer L. Bovair | Program Coordinator, Energy Program | Center for Strategic & International Studies |

Secretary

| Marshall W. Nichols | Executive Director | National Petroleum Council |

Members

Douglas J. Arent	Principal Analyst	National Renewable Energy Laboratory
David K. Bellman	Director of Fundamental Analysis, Corporate Planning & Budgeting	American Electric Power Co., Inc.
James R. Burkhard	Managing Director, Global Oil Group	Cambridge Energy Research Associates
Kateri A. Callahan	President	Alliance to Save Energy
Charles B. Curtis	President and Chief Operating Officer	Nuclear Threat Initiative
Bruce M. Everett	Adjunct Assistant Professor, Edmund A. Walsh School of Foreign Service	Georgetown University
Jason S. Grumet	Executive Director	National Commission on Energy Policy
Alan J. Kelly	Former General Manager, Corporate Planning	Exxon Mobil Corporation

* Individual has since changed organizations but was employed by the specified organization while participating in the study.

William L. Kovacs	Vice President, Environment, Technology & Regulatory Affairs	U.S. Chamber of Commerce
Deron W. Lovaas	Vehicles Campaign Director	Natural Resources Defense Council
Shirley J. Neff	President	Association of Oil Pipe Lines
Rodney F. Nelson	Vice President, Innovation and Collaboration	Schlumberger Limited
Donald L. Paul	Vice President and Chief Technology Officer	Chevron Corporation
Erik R. Peterson	Senior Vice President	Center for Strategic & International Studies
Mervyn T. Sambles	Vice President, Strategic Development	Fluor Corporation
Philip R. Sharp	President	Resources for the Future
Adam E. Sieminski	Chief Energy Economist, Global Markets/Commodities	Deutsche Bank AG
Linda G. Stuntz	Partner	Stuntz, Davis & Staffier, P.C.

APPENDIX C
STUDY OUTREACH PROCESS AND SESSIONS

This appendix provides descriptions of the outreach process and sessions conducted for this study.

In addition to conducting a systematic review and evaluation of available information on the future oil and gas supply and demand picture, the study desired to ensure an open process that would be fully transparent to individuals, organizations, and non-U.S. governments with interests in global energy issues. Most importantly, the National Petroleum Council (NPC) wished to ensure that the study's approach would address the broad range of global issues associated with energy.

To solicit input from such a broad perspective of individuals and organizations, the NPC conducted an extensive communications outreach effort during the early phases of the study. Members from the various study groups and NPC staff participated in over 30 study outreach sessions with organizations and individuals with interests in the global energy issues. These sessions involved more than 1,000 individuals. Slide presentations were used to outline the reason for the study—Secretary Bodman's request, the planned scope of work, the study's organization and staffing, and how the study would proceed to conclusion. Participants were encouraged to offer comments during the sessions and to submit further comments if they so wished.

Sessions were held with representatives of members of the U.S. Congress and Congressional committees, non-governmental organizations (NGOs) of diverse interests, other third-parties, business associations, a wide-range of energy-related professional and trade associations, and, very importantly, non-U.S. government energy ministries. The comments received as a result of these sessions were captured and forwarded to the appropriate study group(s) for review and use during the fact-finding and analysis process.

Background information about the study—its scope, format, and progress, including updated versions of status presentations—was posted on the NPC's publicly accessible website, www.npc.org.

Outreach sessions were conducted with the following individuals and organizations:

- U.S. Congressional Staffs:
  - Staff Members, U.S. Senate Energy Committee
  - Staff Representative, U.S. Senate Foreign Relations Committee
  - Staff Representative, U.S. House of Representatives Committee on International Relations, Subcommittee on Middle East and Central Asia
  - Staff Member, U.S. Senator Feinstein
  - Staff Members, U.S. Senate Finance Committee
  - Staff Members, Joint Committee on Taxation

- Environmental NGOs:
  - Friends of the Earth
  - Alliance to Save Energy
  - National Environmental Trust
  - World Resources Institute
  - Resources for the Future
  - American Council for an Energy-Efficient Economy
  - Natural Resources Defense Council

- Non-environmental NGOs:
  - National Democratic Institute
  - International Crisis Group
  - Human Rights Watch
  - International Republican Institute

- Mercy Corps

- International Rescue Committee

- Catholic Relief Services

- USAID

- Other Pertinent Organizations:

  - International Energy Agency

  - National Commission for Energy Policy

  - Saudi National Security Assessment Project

  - Organization of Petroleum Exporting Countries (OPEC)

  - American Enterprise Institute

- General Business Associations:

  - U.S. Chamber of Commerce

  - Business Roundtable

  - National Association of Manufacturers

- Energy-Related Professional and Trade Associations:

  - American Petroleum Institute

  - National Petrochemical and Refiners Association

  - Center for Liquefied Natural Gas

  - Methane Hydrate Advisory Committee

  - American Association of Petroleum Geologists

  - Hedburg Conference on World Oil Resources

  - Independent Petroleum Association of America

  - American Gas Association

  - American Chemistry Council

  - Natural Gas Supply Association

  - Society of Petroleum Engineers

  - National Coal Council

Also, letters and/or phone calls were placed by representatives of the Department of Energy to the following U.S. government executive departments, inviting their participation, comments, and input:

- U.S. Department of the Interior

- U.S. Department of Agriculture

- U.S. Department of State

- U.S. Department of Transportations

- U.S. Department of Defense

- U.S. Environmental Protection Agency

- U.S. Department of the Treasury

- U.S. Department of Commerce

- U.S. Trade Representative

- Federal Energy Regulatory Commission

- Interstate Oil & Gas Compact Commission

In addition to the data-gathering methodology described elsewhere, Secretary Bodman sent letters in October 2006 to the following non-U.S. governments advising them of the study and seeking their participation, comments, and input:

- Australia

- Azerbaijan

- Brazil

- Canada

- Peoples Republic of China

- Germany

- India

- Indonesia

- Japan

- Kazakhstan

- Kuwait

- Mexico

- Nigeria

- Norway

- Qatar

- Russia

- Saudi Arabia

- United Arab Emirates

- United Kingdom

NPC study representatives were assigned responsibility for conducting follow-up contacts to provide more background information on the study and to elicit input from non-U.S. governments. Input received was forwarded to the appropriate study group(s) for review and use in the study. Visits were made to a number of energy ministries and representatives of non-U.S. governments and companies participated in some meetings of the study's Coordinating Subcommittee. Also, study status reports were sent in April and July 2007 to update all those initially contacted by Secretary Bodman.

APPENDIX D
PARALLEL STUDIES

PROCESS AND SUMMARIES

The summaries in this appendix were prepared by the NPC based on studies authored or published by other organizations, and are used with permission. To obtain a complete version of any study, readers should contact the study's sponsoring organization. Contact information is included in each summary. Nothing in this appendix should be understood as indicating endorsement or sponsorship by any other organization or the NPC.

Parallel Studies

A Parallel Studies process, which examined numerous recent reports regarding aspects of energy policy, was employed to inform the work of the NPC study's Coordinating Subcommittee. This process found that:

- Most current energy studies tend to be dominated by one or at most two of the three key concerns that we believe are critical to a complete understanding of global oil and natural gas.

- The best energy strategies for the U.S. to pursue to ensure greater economic stability and prosperity are likely to be found at the intersection of these three circles.

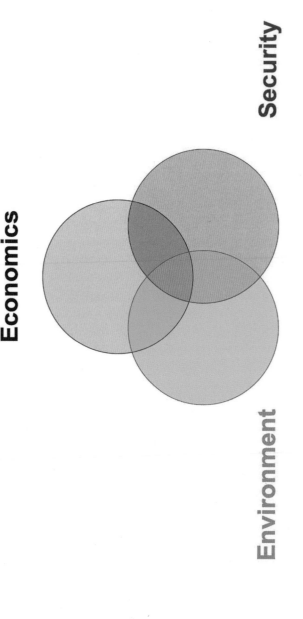

Economics

Security

Environment

Reports Examined

Overall Findings of Policy Studies

General Agreement on Policy Objectives

- Encourage Market Solutions
- Increase Energy Efficiency
- Ensure Access to Supplies
- Encourage Fuel Diversity
- Reduce Price and Supply Volatility
- Strengthen Energy Infrastructure
- Develop New Energy Technologies
- Protect the Environment

Overall Findings of Policy Studies

Diversity of Policies and Concerns

- CAFE standards
- Carbon taxes, caps, regulations
- Subsidies for alternate fuels
- Limits to imports / or to demand growth
- Efficiency standards
- Peak oil
- Data transparency
- Market imperfections / Over-regulation

National Commission on Energy Policy

- A consensus set of recommendations that aims to enhance American national security, strengthen the US economy, and protect the global environment and public health.

Leadership: John Holdren (Harvard University & Woods Hole Research Center)
William Reilly (Aqua Int'l Partners, formerly US EPA)
John Rowe (Exelon Corporation)

Structure: A bipartisan group of 20 energy experts – representing the senior ranks of industry, government, academia, labor, consumer and environmental protection organizations, with more than a dozen experienced analytical staff.

Timelines: Main study published in December 2004: Ending the Energy Stalemate:
Key recommendations at http://www.energycommission.org/files/finalReport/O82F4692.pdf

Updated recommendations published April 2007

Other reports/workshops include:
§ US Energy Infrastructure Vulnerability (June 2006)
§ Design Issues in Market-based Greenhouse Gas Reduction Strategies (Feb 2006)
§ Oil Shockwave – An Oil Crisis Executive Simulation (June 2005)

- Recommendations considered a thoughtful set of policies. Has made modest progress in a highly partisan Congressional atmosphere. Latest proposals include (1) increased auto efficiency standards, (2) interim nuclear waste storage, (3) deployment of carbon capture and storage technologies, and (5) a national renewable energy standard.

Website: **http://www.energycommission.org/**

NATIONAL COMMISSION
ON ENERGY POLICY

National Commission on Energy Policy

KEY RECOMMENDATIONS

1. ENHANCING OIL SECURITY

• Establish a national average new-vehicle fuel-economy improvement target of 4%/yr, while retaining the full discretionary authority of the National Highway Traffic Safety Administration (NHTSA) to modify the presumptive target up or down if safety, technology, or economic considerations warrant.

• Encourage and empower NHTSA to implement reforms aimed at making the existing CAFE program more cost-effective, market-oriented, and responsive to the jobs and competitiveness concerns of the automobile industry.

• Provide targeted consumer and manufacturer incentives to promote the domestic development, production, and deployment of advanced automotive technologies such as hybrid, plug-in hybrid, and advanced diesel vehicles.

• Pursue cost-effective opportunities to further reduce transportation energy use by improving heavy-truck fuel economy and by adopting efficiency standards for light-duty vehicle replacement tires.

2. REDUCING RISKS FROM CLIMATE CHANGE

• Adopt legislation this Congress to implement a mandatory, market-based program to limit economy-wide U.S. greenhouse gas emissions.

• Strengthen key parameters of the original NCEP climate proposal, including:
  -defining targets to aim for stabilizing emissions at current (2006) levels by 2020 and reducing emissions 15% below current levels by 2030;
  -raising the starting price of the safety valve to $10 per ton of carbon-dioxide equivalent emissions; and
  -increasing the rate of escalation in the safety-valve price to 5 percent per year in real (rather than nominal) terms.

• Address other program design issues by (1) allocating emission allowances in a manner that effectively directs substantial resources to aid in the transition to a low-carbon economy and that fairly compensates major affected industries for short-term economic dislocations incurred as a result of the policy, while also avoiding the potential for significant windfall gains; (2) placing the compliance obligation (point of regulation) at or near primary energy suppliers; and (3) including a well-designed offsets provision.

• Create stronger incentives for comparable action on the part of key trading partners by providing technical and financial resources for the transfer of low-carbon technology, by signaling that the United States will work with other countries to forcefully address trade and competitiveness concerns in the event other major emitting nations fail to take action within a reasonable timeframe, and by linking future U.S. emission-reduction commitments to progress in the international arena.

3. INCREASING ENERGY EFFICIENCY

• Enhance and extend tax incentives for efficiency investments introduced under the Energy Policy Act of 2005 (EPAct05).

• Ensure that the Department of Energy (DOE) follows through on its recent commitment to issue efficiency standards for 22 categories of appliances and equipment that capture all cost-effective and technically feasible energy savings.

Appendix D – Parallel Studies

D-7

KEY RECOMMENDATIONS (continued)

4. NATURAL GAS/ COAL / NUCLEAR

• Continue to focus on assuring future supply adequacy by following through on EPAct05 commitments with respect to the Alaska pipeline, LNG infrastructure, market transparency, and permitting and leasing. The Commission reiterates its call for a comprehensive inventory of on- and off-shore resources to inform future policy decisions and urges Congress to address concerns about the adequacy of related provisions in EPAct05 (both in terms of the relatively short timeframe specified for completing the inventory and in terms of constraints on the use of federal resources to conduct inventory-related activities in certain areas).

• Direct greater resources toward accelerating the commercialization of carbon capture and storage (CCS) by providing substantial deployment incentives. Specifically, the Commission believes CCS projects should be eligible for bonus allowances under a greenhouse gas trading program that are at least equal in value to incentives provided under the renewable energy production tax credit.

• Condition eligibility for public funding or subsidies on the actual inclusion of CCS with any new IGCC and other advanced coal projects going forward. CCS must be included from the outset in any taxpayer supported efforts to develop coal-to-liquids technology.

• Explore carbon capture options for non-IGCC plants.

• Ensure that the U.S. Environmental Protection Agency (EPA) completes a rigorous, formal public process to formulate effective regulatory protocols governing long-term carbon storage as soon as possible (recognizing that midcourse corrections will likely be needed as experience is gained).

• Ensure that new coal plants built without CCS are not "grandfathered" (i.e., awarded free allowances) in any future regulatory program to limit greenhouse gas emissions.

• Take action to address the current impasse on nuclear waste disposal, while reaffirming the ultimate objective of siting and developing one or more secure geologic disposal facilities, by amending the Nuclear Waste Policy Act (NWPA) to:

- Align its requirements with human engineering and scientific capabilities, while adequately protecting public health and safety and the environment.

- Require DOE to site and operate consolidated national or regional interim storage options.

- Undertake R&D to explore technological alternatives to the direct geologic disposal of waste from a once-through cycle that meet commercial requirements and non-proliferation objectives, reduce the challenge of waste disposal, ensure adequate protection of public health and safety, and extend fuel supply.

- Codify that interim storage and federal responsibility for disposal of nuclear waste is sufficient to satisfy the Nuclear Regulatory Commission's waste confidence requirement.

- Require the Secretary of Energy to take possession of and/or remove fuel from reactor sites that have been, or are in the process of being fully decommissioned.

National Commission on Energy Policy

KEY RECOMMENDATIONS (continued)

5. RENEWABLE ENERGY & BIOFUELS

• Continue to provide investment certainty by extending the eligibility period for federal production tax credits in five-year increments.

• Adopt a federal renewable portfolio standard to increase the share of electricity generated by renewable resources nationwide to at least 15% by 2020.

• Re-evaluate ethanol subsidies and tariffs in light of current fuel mandates and rationalize existing policies to direct a greater share of public resources to more promising options, such as cellulosic ethanol; biobutanol; and clean, high-quality diesel fuel from organic wastes.

• Address other hurdles to biofuels deployment, including hurdles related to the deployment of critical supporting infrastructures (including gathering systems, distribution systems, and refueling facilities) and compatible vehicle technologies.

• Take steps to ensure that policies aimed at reducing U.S. oil dependence do not promote environmentally unsustainable fuel alternatives. The Commission believes that California's recently introduced low-carbon fuel standard suggests a useful direction for future policy and deserves consideration at the national level.

6. ENERGY TECHNOLOGY INNOVATION

• Double annual direct federal expenditures on energy-technology research, development, and demonstration, corrected for inflation, with increases emphasizing public-private partnerships, international cooperation, and energy-technologies that offer high potential leverage against multiple challenges. Substantially increasing public investment in energy technology innovation is critical to the achievement of oil security and climate change objectives and can be funded using revenues generated by the proposed greenhouse-gas trading program.

• Triple federal funding specifically for cooperative international efforts in energy research, development, and deployment (where this proposed increase is within the overall expansion of federal expenditures recommended above).

Greenhouse Gas Emission Targets

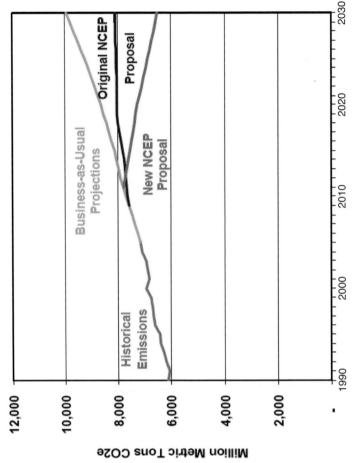

GHG PROPOSAL REVISED

While strengthening the overall stringency of its Greenhouse Gas (GHG) mitigation proposal, the new Commission proposal continues to rely on the core program elements first articulated in its 2004 report, especially: emission targets within a cap and trade system; providing market-based incentives for deployment of low-carbon technologies; linkage to greenhouse gas mitigation action by major U.S. trading partners, including China and India; and a cost-containment mechanism to prevent undue harm to the U.S. economy.

The reductions in greenhouse gas (GHG) emissions would result from a series of new policies proposed by the Commission, beginning with a revision of key elements of its initial cap and trade proposal for mitigating U.S. emissions. The proposal announced today increases the proposed "safety valve" or "cost cap" of the NCEP program from $7 to $10 per ton of carbon-dioxide equivalent emissions, and would increase the safety valve price by 5 percent above inflation per year. In addition, the Commission's new carbon cap does not rely on an "emissions intensity" metric, but instead calls for specific numerical reductions in greenhouse gas emissions for a given year.

The Commission's original proposal envisioned an initial ten-year implementation period during which program targets would first aim to slow the rate of growth in US emissions before proceeding to "stop" and "reverse" phases in which emissions would stabilize and then begin to decline. The Commission's new proposal strengthens the program targets to begin emissions reductions immediately upon implementation and achieve a 15% reduction below current emissions levels by 2030.

Business-as-usual projections for greenhouse gas emissions are taken from the Energy Information Administration's Annual Energy Outlook 2006.

ENERGY SECURITY LEADERSHIP COUNCIL

Energy Security Leadership Council

Securing America's Future Energy

The Council, a project of Securing America's Future Energy (SAFE), is led by Co-Chairmen Frederick W. Smith, Chairman and CEO of FedEx Corporation, and General P.X. Kelley (Ret.), former Marine Corps Commandant and member of the Joint Chiefs of Staff. The Energy Security Leadership Council includes prominent business and military leaders who support a comprehensive, long-term policy to reduce US oil dependence and improve energy security. The Council will work aggressively to build bipartisan support. SAFE is committed to reducing America's dependence on oil in order to improve our national security and strengthen the economy, while increasing US exports, protecting the environment, and creating US jobs.

Other members include Admiral Dennis Blair, USN (Ret.), CIC, US PACOM; Admiral Vern Clark, USN (Ret), former Chief of Naval Operations; Michael L. Eskew, Chairman and CEO, UPS, Inc; Adam Goldstein, President, Royal Caribbean International; General John A. Gordon, USAF (Ret.), former Homeland Security Advisor to the President; Maurice Greenberg, Chairman and CEO, C.V. Starr & Co., Inc.; Admiral Gregory Johnson, USN (Ret.), Commander, US Naval Forces, Europe; Robert Hormats, Vice Chairman, Goldman Sachs International; Herbert Kelleher, Exec.Chairman, Southwest Airlines; John F. Lehman, former Secretary of the US Navy; Andrew Liveris, CEO, The Dow Chemical Company; General Michael E. Ryan, USAF (Ret.), 16th Chief of Staff, USAF; David P. Steiner, CEO, Waste Management, Inc.; and General Charles F. Wald, USAF (Ret.), Former Deputy Commander, US European Command, Edgar M. Bronfman, Retired Chairman, The Seagram Company Ltd.; Jeffrey C. Sprecher, Chairman, IntercontinentalExchange (ICE); Josh S. Weston, Honorary Chairman, Automatic Data Processing, Inc.

SAFE has produced:

☐ **The Wescott Report:** This report gives an overview of the broad economic effects of a scenario in which oil prices surge to $120 a barrel due to coordinated terrorist attacks on global oil transportation infrastructure. The scenario was the basis for a simulation exercise conducted at the World Economic Forum Annual Meeting 2006 in Davos, Switzerland.

☐ **Oil ShockWave:** A scenario exercise developed by SAFE and the National Commission on Energy Policy (NCEP). This half-day simulation provided participants and observers with an opportunity to think through simulated emergency situations--in this case involving oil supply disruptions. (June 2005)

☐ Recommendations to the Nation on Reducing US Oil Dependence: December 2006

Website: http://www.secureenergy.org/

ENERGY SECURITY
LEADERSHIP
COUNCIL

Energy Security Leadership Council

Securing America's
Future Energy

Recommendations to the Nation on Reducing US Oil Dependence: December 2006

I. REDUCE OIL CONSUMPTION

A. Significantly reform and then annually strengthen fuel efficiency standards for passenger cars and light-duty trucks.

— Reform the Corporate Average Fuel Economy (CAFE) system in order to make it more market-, size-, and attribute-based and to allow for the application of different but increasingly stringent standards.

— Set a target of 4% for annual increases in fuel efficiency of all passenger cars and light-duty trucks weighing up to 10,000 lbs.

— Allow "off-ramps" if 4% is technically infeasible, unsafe, or not cost-effective for a given year.

B. Fund significant financial incentives for the domestic production and purchase of highly fuel efficient vehicles.

— Lift the current 60,000 vehicle-per-manufacturer cap on tax incentives for the purchase of advanced technology effi cient vehicles.

— Link the tax credit to the miles-per-gallon performance of the vehicles.

— Provide tax incentives for retooling to all manufacturers with existing U.S. facilities.

Projected savings: 4.3 million barrels of oil per day (mbd)

II. PROVIDE ALTERNATIVES

A. Grow the supply and demand sides of the biofuels market by creating incentives and obligations for infrastructure deployment, requiring increasing production of Flexible Fuel Vehicles (FFVs), and increasing federal assistance available for "first-mover" production of cellulosic ethanol and other promising large-volume biofuels.

— Create obligations and provide tax credits for installing ethanol fuel pumps and related infrastructure. Limit the credit for corporate-owned and branded stations when oil prices are high.

— Require 10% annual increases in the production of FFVs so that all major production models are compatible with rich ethanol blends by 2015.

— Establish a competitive program employing a variety of financial tools—grants, tax credits, direct loans, and loan guarantees—for federal assistance to six or more biorefineries employing a variety of feedstocks and located in various regions of the country.

Projected ethanol output: 30 billion gallons per year ≈ 2.0 mbd

Recommendations to the Nation on Reducing US Oil Dependence: December 2006 (continued)

III. EXPAND SUPPLY

A. Increase access to U.S. oil and natural gas reserves on the Outer Continental Shelf (OCS) with sharply increased and expanded environmental protections.

— Increase access to OCS oil and natural gas reserves with appropriate third-party monitoring, increased surety bond requirements, clear penalties for environmental damages to avoid protracted litigation, stronger administration of the current leasing program, and protection of coastal vistas.

Projected production: 1.0–2.0 mbd

B. Employ federal funds to accelerate the development and deployment of Enhanced Oil Recovery (EOR) techniques.

Projected production: 1.0 mbd

C. Make investment access a high profile aspect of U.S. trade negotiations and diplomatic efforts with oil-producing nations.

IV. MANAGE RISKS

A. In light of military threats to the global oil infrastructure, the U.S. should, where appropriate:

— Encourage burden sharing with U.S. allies and partners, including producing and consuming nations, in defense of global oil flows;

— Foster formal and informal security arrangements on multilateral, regional, and bilateral bases, capitalizing on the U.S.'s unique ability to arrange international security efforts;

— Provide diplomatic support as well as counter-terrorism training and military aid so that oil-producing nations can better assist in protecting petroleum supplies;

— Offer assistance to producing countries in their efforts to develop attractive investment climates backed by stable civil societies; and

B. Reassess the multiple dimensions of strategic reserves policy within the U.S. and at the International Energy Agency (IEA). In addition, revise the 1974 Organization for Economic Cooperation and Development (OECD) agreement to allow China and India to join the IEA and participate in updated global strategic petroleum reserve arrangements.

Energy Security Leadership Council

Securing America's Future Energy

Corollary Recommendations (December 2006)

I. REDUCE OIL CONSUMPTION

A. Extend federal subsidies for hybrid medium-duty vehicles (Classes 3–6) to 2012 and remove the cap on the number of eligible vehicles. Set and then annually increase fuel efficiency standards for medium-duty vehicles. Set the standards consistent with the energy efficiency benefits of hybridization. Projected savings: 0.2 mbd

B. Set and then annually strengthen fuel efficiency standards for heavy-duty vehicles (Class 7 and 8), employing federal subsidies as suitable. Projected savings: 0.9 mbd

C. Increase allowable weight to 97,000 lbs. gross vehicle weight for tractor-trailer trucks that have a supplementary sixth axle installed but which replicate current stopping distances and do not fundamentally alter current truck architecture. Further study the safety impacts of significantly longer and heavier tractor-trailers used in conjunction with slower speed limits. If safety can be proven, implementation could generate major efficiencies while simultaneously reducing road congestion and other non-fuel costs. Projected savings: will vary with extent of implementation

D. Require the Federal Aviation Administration (FAA) to implement improvements to commercial air traffic routing in order to increase safety and decrease fuel consumption. Projected savings: 0.4 mbd

II. PROVIDE ALTERNATIVES

A. Reform current ethanol per gallon subsidies to encourage private-sector investment in domestic ethanol and alternative biofuels production and infrastructure. "Smart subsidies" will secure the industry against short-term oil price drops, minimize the cost to the U.S. Treasury, and distinguish between feedstock technologies. Balance the benefits of domestic production capability with the advantages of environmentally responsible development of an international biofuels trade.

B. Grow the biodiesel market, while ensuring a biodiesel standard that mandates quality and reliability to satisfy the operational standards of users and also includes clear and consistent labeling of biodiesel blend ratios. Projected output: 3.3 billion gallons per year ≈ 0.2 mbd

C. Support federal investment in research, development, and commercialization of carbon sequestration technologies that can limit the adverse emissions impacts of oil shale, oil sands, and coal-to-liquids (CTL) production.

III. EXPAND SUPPLY and MANAGE RISKS

A. Increase access to U.S. reserves in Alaska. Increase access to Alaskan reserves with appropriate third-party monitoring, increased surety bond requirements, clear penalties for environmental damages to avoid protracted litigation, and stronger administration of the current leasing program. Projected production: 0.9 mbd

B. Evaluate policy approaches to expand the ability of U.S. refineries to process a wider variety of crude stocks and to make U.S. refining less vulnerable to extreme weather. Work to expand total U.S. capacity or to ensure that the U.S. will have secure access to product produced overseas.

Business Roundtable

- The Business Roundtable is an association of 160 chief executive officers of leading US companies that comprise nearly a third of the total value of the US stock market. The Energy Task Force was created in early 2006 to address the impact of higher energy costs on economic growth. CEOs report that rising energy costs are one of the top two cost pressures on their businesses and, as such, are committed to identifying solutions. Roundtable launched a comprehensive energy report publicly on June 6, 2007.

- Leadership: Michael G. Morris, CEO, American Electric Power Company,
coordinated by Tony Kavanagh, AEP, and Marian Hopkins, Director – Public Policy, Business Roundtable

More Diverse, More Domestic, More Efficient: A Vision for America's Energy Future

Improving Energy Efficiency in the Commercial, Residential and Electric Power Sectors
The United States should reduce energy intensity by at least 25 percent above the anticipated business-as-usual rate by:
- Substantially boosting the efficiency of new and existing commercial and residential buildings
- Deploying a broad portfolio of energy efficient technologies for building operations and appliances
- Increasing the efficiency of the transmission and distribution system
- Optimizing the power grid with new or advanced technologies to save energy and improve reliability
- Encouraging smart metering and other strategies that reduce peak period demand on the grid
- Improving the efficiency of the nation's power plant fleet through upgrades at existing units and by constructing new advanced technology units
- Accelerating the deployment of wind and solar-thermal power generation
- Increasing reliance on efficient combined heat and power (CHP) units at industrial facilities
- Challenging individual companies to set and meet ambitious energy efficiency goals

Increasing Energy Security in the Transportation Sector
The United States should aggressively reduce transportation fuel demand and diversify supply by:
- Developing and deploying energy efficient vehicle technologies to the maximum extent feasible
- Enhancing conventional domestic oil production by raising refinery output and expanding access to currently off-limit petroleum reserves, including reserves in Alaska
- Scaling up to 10% ethanol in gasoline as quickly as possible, undertaking intensive R&D on advanced biofuels such as biobutanol and cellulosic ethanol, and expanding their presence in fuel supply as warranted by technology advances in the vehicles and fuels sectors
- Increasing production of transportation fuels from unconventional sources like shale oil and coal-to-liquids processes
- Moderating fuel demand by adopting policies that reduce vehicle congestion and idling, and growth in vehicle miles traveled per capita
- Maintaining access to the world's energy resources by preserving the integrity of free markets and opportunities for robust foreign investment by our energy industry

Achieving a Better Supply/Demand Balance in Natural Gas Markets
The United States should provide stable and affordable supplies of natural gas over the long-term by:
- Increasing domestic production through expanded access to natural gas supplies in the Rocky Mountains, the Atlantic and Pacific Coasts, Alaska and the Eastern Gulf of Mexico
- Augmenting conventional natural gas supplies through gasification of coal and bio-mass
- Expanding our liquefied natural gas import and pipeline infrastructure
- Moderating demand through energy efficiency in the power distribution and home heating sectors

Maintaining a Viable and Growing Nuclear Power Sector
The United States should maintain a viable and growing nuclear power sector by:
- Establishing an efficient, predictable licensing system for new nuclear power plants
- Providing effective financial incentives for new plants
- Implementing a workable and effective program for the management and disposal of spent nuclear fuel

Website: http://www.businessroundtable.org/pdf/Energy/Business_Roundtable_Energy_Report_06062007.pdf

Congressional Checklist:

Website: http://www.nam.org

Affordable and reliable energy is essential to the long-term health of the U.S. economy and its citizens. Lower energy prices mean greater take-home pay for American workers, and access to competitively priced energy enables domestic producers of chemicals, plastics, fertilizers, paper goods, glass, metals and food products to effectively compete in the global economy.

Impressively, energy efficiency in the United States has doubled since 1970. But, our country's need for energy has risen 47 percent due to a growing economy. While investing in new energy sources and continuing to boost efficiency gains will play critical roles in meeting our country's energy demands in the future, increasing access to domestic sources of reliable energy will be essential to the long-term health of U.S. industry as well as the American worker.

A robust, comprehensive and forward-looking energy policy must consist of five crucial elements:

- **Making a national commitment to further reducing the energy intensity of the U.S. economy and educating consumers;**
- **Strengthening and focusing on public-private research and development efforts;**
- **Making existing statutes and regulations rational;**
- **Increasing domestic power generation; and**
- **Increasing domestic energy supply.**

- Reduce Energy Intensity: Establish a national goal for decreasing the energy intensity of the U.S. economy by 30 percent by 2021.

- Strengthen and Make Permanent the R&D Tax Credit: The credit is now set to expire for the thirteenth time. To stay competitive, Congress must encourage U.S.-based R&D activities.

- Fund a New Office Within the Department of Education: The office would promote increased visibility of energy concepts within primary and secondary education curricula.

- Establish a New Office of Federal Lands Energy Project Streamlining: This office should be within the Executive Office of the President.

- Codify and Enhance Two Major Clean Air Act Regulations: The Clean Air Interstate Rule (CAIR) and the Clean Air Mercury Rule.

- Fully Fund All Federal Energy Research Authorized by EPAct 2005.

- Fund Nuclear Research: Congress should authorize $100 million for new university-based nuclear physics programs.

- Permanently Reauthorize the Price-Anderson Act: To assure compensation to the public in the event of a nuclear accident and appropriately limit private- sector liability.

- Authorize Interim Storage of Spent Fuel: Congress should allow temporary storage at existing DOE facilities and other sites approved by a state legislature and governor.

- Fund Fuel Research: Authorize $500 million annually for research and development in advanced fuel cycles and reprocessing/recycling of spent nuclear fuel.

- Authorize Reverse Auctions: Allow a system of reverse auctions for awarding federal assistance to solar, ethanol, organic municipal solid waste and silvicultural cellulose material plants.

- Address ANWR: Authorize the U.S. Department of Interior to begin leasing activities in ANWR.

- Address OCS: Lift moratoria and reverse withdrawals for oil and gas production in the Outer Continental Shelf.

- Update EPAct 2005: Extend EPAct 2005 refinery expensing for oil shales to 2020 and make coal liquefaction facilities eligible for the same treatment.

- Fund R&D Initiatives: Authorize $1 billion annually for R&D in oil shales, coal liquefaction and production of natural gas from methane hydrate formations, while providing incentives for the production of petroleum from oil shales and transportation fuels from coal liquefaction.

- Set Standards: Establish uniform standards for the production of biodiesel and ethanol.

COUNCIL ON FOREIGN RELATIONS

CFR

A Nonpartisan Resource for Information and Analysis

The Council on Foreign Relations is an independent, national membership organization and a nonpartisan center for scholars dedicated to producing and disseminating ideas so that members, as well as policymakers, journalists, students, and interested citizens in the US and other countries, can better understand world and foreign policy choices.

Task Force Leadership: John Deutch and Jim Schlesinger, co-chairs;   David Victor, Project Director

Other Participants: Graham Allison, Belfer Center; Norman Augustine, Lockheed Martin; Robert Belfer, Belfer Management; Steven Bosworth, The Fletcher School; Helima Croft, Lehman Brothers; Charles DiBona, Sentient Council; Jessica Einhorn, SAIS; Martin Feldstein, NBER; David Goldwin, Goldwyn Int'l; Michael Granoff, Pomona Capital; Bennett Johnston; Johnston & Assoc; Arnold Kanter, The Scowcroft Group; Karin Lissakers, Soros Fund; Walter Massey, Morehouse College; Ernest Moniz, MIT; William Reilly, Aqua Int'l; Peter Schwartz, Global Business Network; Philip Sharp, RFF; James Steinberg, LBJ School; Linda Stuntz, Stuntz, Davis & Staffier; James Sweeney, Stanford Univ; Frank Verrastro, CSIS; J. Robinson West, PFC Energy

Recommends, "the adoption of incentives to slow and eventually reverse the growth in consumption of petroleum products, especially transportation fuels such as motor gasoline," and offers three options: a tax on gasoline; stricter and broader mandated Corporate Average Fuel Economy (CAFE) standards; and the use of tradable gasoline permits that would cap the total level of gasoline consumed in the economy.

Other recommendations include:

- Encourage supply of oil from all sources while recognizing that the world cannot "drill its way out of this problem."
- US should take a more active role in international arrangements to manage the revenues from oil in a more transparent way in oil-producing nations.
- Remove the protectionist tariff on imported ethanol. Increase efficiency of oil and gas use in the United States and elsewhere.
- Switch from oil-derived products to alternatives. Biofuels have significant potential.
- The Task Force favors greater use of nuclear power today and notes that over time electricity can replace liquid fuels for transportation.
- Make the oil and gas infrastructure more efficient and secure. Reexamine the management of the US SPR.
- Increase investment in new energy technologies. Promote the proper functioning and efficiency of energy markets.
- US should help improve efficiency in NOCs. Revitalize international institutions such as the International Energy Agency (IEA).
- Establish an energy security directorate within the National Security staff.
- Engage the Secretary of Energy in any foreign policy deliberations that involve energy issues.
- Include energy security considerations in all planning studies at the National Security Council, Defense and State departments, and the intelligence community.

Website: http://www.cfr.org/energy

Alliance for ENERGY & ECONOMIC GROWTH

Energy to secure America's future.

Alliance for Energy & Economic Growth

The Alliance for Energy and Economic Growth was formed in 2001 to build support for the adoption and implementation of a comprehensive, market-based energy policy that uses all forms of energy to meet consumer demand for reliable energy at reasonable prices, while at the same time ensuring the quality of the environment. The Alliance is a broad-based coalition of more than 1,200 members who develop, deliver, or consume energy from all sources.

The US Chamber of Commerce and the Nuclear Energy Institute (as founding sponsors) hosted an Energy Summit in July, 2006, "An Open National Discussion on US Energy Policy." Featuring: Samuel Bodman, Secretary of Energy, Dirk Kempthorne, Secretary of the Interior, Joseph T. Kelliher, FERC Chairman.

http://www.uschamber.com/issues/index/energy/060719_energyagenda.htm

Key policy recommendations include:

☐ Increase energy efficiency and conservation
☐ Ensure adequate energy supplies and generation
☐ Renew and expand the energy infrastructure
☐ Encourage investment in new energy technologies
☐ Provide energy assistance to low-income households
☐ Ensure appropriate consideration of the impact of regulatory policies on energy

The Alliance adopted a supplemental set of principles to help guide the debate on climate change:

☐ Promote the accelerated development, demonstration, and cost-effective commercial deployment of climate friendly technologies to reduce, avoid, or sequester greenhouse gas emissions
☐ Address barriers to the development, financing, regulation, storage, and use of domestic climate-friendly fuel sources
☐ Promote energy conservation and efficiency
☐ Preserve American jobs and the competitiveness of U.S. industry
☐ Minimize economic disruptions and disproportionate impacts on specific sectors or regions of the economy
☐ Permit maximum flexibility in achieving energy and environmental goals
☐ Recognize the economy-wide and international dimensions of the challenge
☐ Facilitate technology transfer to emerging economies to reduce the fastest growing emission sources globally and to include the participation of developing nations such as China and India

Website: http://www.yourenergyfuture.org/

World Energy Council

US Energy Association

The World Energy Council (WEC) covers all types of energy, including coal, oil, natural gas, nuclear, hydro, and renewables, and is UN-accredited, non-governmental, non-commercial and non-aligned. WEC is headquartered in London with member committees in 90 countries. Its goals include promoting research into the means of supplying and using energy having, short and long term, the greatest social benefit and the least harmful impact on the natural environment, and publishing or otherwise disseminating the results; holding of Congresses, workshops and seminars, to facilitate such supply and use of energy; and collaborating with other organizations in the energy sector.

Website: http://www.worldenergy.org/wec-geis/default.asp

The United States Energy Association (USEA) is the US member committee of the WEC. USEA is an association of public and private energy-related organizations. USEA sponsors policy reports and conferences dealing with global and domestic energy issues, as well as trade and educational exchange visits with other countries. The USEA published "Toward a National Energy Strategy" in February 2001 (and 10 other assessments of US Energy Policy. The policy recommendations were based on the results of workshops on key energy issues and a working group representing all sectors of the industry under the leadership of Richard Lawson, Chairman of its National Energy Policy Committee. Project was directed by Guy Caruso (now the head of the EIA at the US DOE).

Website: http://www.usea.org

Recommendations include:

- Encourage energy supply expansion
- Implement tax policies to spur capital investment
- Encourage competitive markets regarding pricing and selection of fuels and energy suppliers
- Increase funding for the low-income home energy assistance program and weatherization
- Promote US leadership in energy development
- Advocate market-based energy policies for foreign nations
- Avoid unilateral trade and economic sanctions
- Education programs to explain the importance of energy to economic security and development
- Government programs should avoid favoring selective fuels or technologies
- Improve the US energy transportation infrastructure
- Comprehensive electric industry restructuring should promote efficient competition
- Allow environmentally sound access to domestic resources
- Government policies should promote energy efficiency
- Eliminate tax rules the discourage foreign investment
- Foster more open legal and institutional structures overseas
- Focus R&D on a 20-30 year horizon
- Regulatory predictability to stabilize investment decisions

International Energy Agency

World Energy Outlook 2006 published November 2006

Reference Scenario: No new government policies are adopted

Alternative Policy Scenario: Energy-security & climate-change policies now under consideration are adopted

Focus on Special Issues:
- Impact of higher energy prices
- Current oil and gas investment trends
- Outlook for nuclear power & biofuels
- Energy for cooking in developing countries (http://www.iea.org/textbase/weo/cooking.pdf)
- Brazil's energy outlook (http://www.worldenergyoutlook.org/Brazil.pdf)

The world is facing twin energy threats:
Inadequate and insecure supplies at affordable prices
Environmental damage, including climate change

☐ Global energy system is on an unsustainable path
☐ Need to diversify energy sources & mitigate emissions is critical
☐ Urgent need to curb the growth in fossil-fuel demand & related emissions
☐ Strong new policies could sharply reduce the rate of increase in demand & emissions
☐ Economic cost of these policies would be more than outweighed by the economic benefits alone
☐ Governments need to tackle market barriers to ensure investment is forthcoming
☐ Considerable political will is needed to push policies through
☐ Rich countries need to help developing countries address energy poverty
☐ In the longer term, technology *development* will be critical to a sustainable energy system

Website: http://www.worldenergyoutlook.org

Facing the Hard Truths about Energy

International Energy Agency

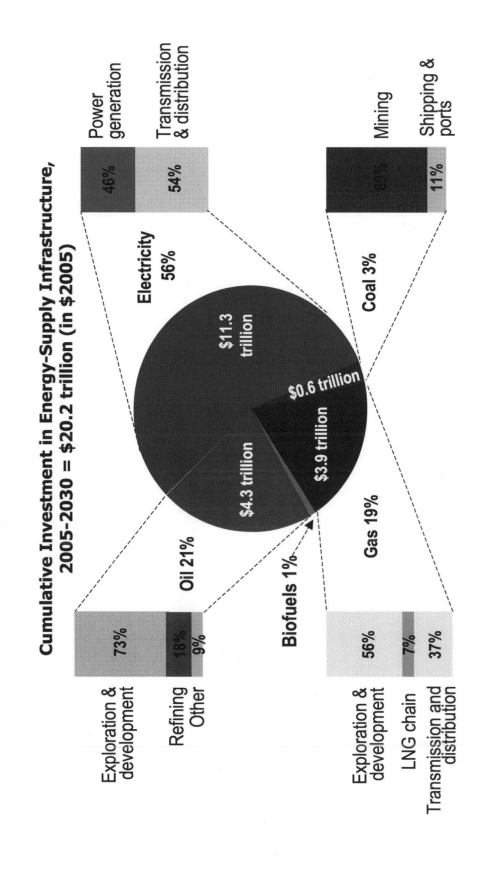

Cumulative Investment in Energy-Supply Infrastructure, 2005-2030 = $20.2 trillion (in $2005)

Power generation 46%
Transmission & distribution 54%

Electricity 56%

$11.3 trillion

Mining 89%
Shipping & ports 11%

Coal 3%

$0.6 trillion

$3.9 trillion

Gas 19%

$4.3 trillion

Exploration & development 73%
Refining 18%
Other 9%

Oil 21%

Biofuels 1%

Exploration & development 56%
LNG chain 7%
Transmission and distribution 37%

Source: IEA, World Energy Outlook 2006.

Energy Information Administration

Official Energy Statistics from the U.S. Government

International
Energy Outlook 2007

The Energy Information Administration (EIA) publishes its annual assessment of long-term world energy markets in its International Energy Outlook (IEO). The IEO2007 is the latest edition of this report and was released in May 2007; the NPC study, which was conducted prior to the IEO2007 release, is based upon the previous edition of this report, supplemented by projections from the Annual Energy Outlook 2007—the long-term energy outlook for U.S. energy markets. The report includes regional projections of world marketed energy use by fuel type (petroleum and other liquid fuels, natural gas, coal, nuclear power, and hydroelectricity and other renewable energy sources) and energy-related carbon dioxide emissions to the year 2030.

The projections in the IEO2007 provide an objective, policy-neutral reference case that can be used to analyze international energy markets. Models are abstractions of energy production and consumption activities, regulatory activities, and producer and consumer behavior. As a policy-neutral statistics and analysis organization, EIA does not propose, advocate, or speculate on future legislative and regulatory changes. Trends depicted in the analysis are indicative of tendencies in the real world rather than representations of specific real-world outcomes.

Highlights from the 2007 IEO include:

- In the IEO2007 reference case, world energy consumption is projected to increase by 57 percent between 2004 and 2030, rising to 702 quadrillion British thermal units (Btu).

- Much of the growth in worldwide energy use is projected for the non-OECD economies; energy use in the non-OECD exceeds that of the OECD by 2010.

- Non-OECD Asia (including China and India) accounts for half of the world's increase in marketed energy use in the IEO2007 reference case.

- World marketed energy consumption is projected to grow by 57 percent between 2004 and 2030, according to the reference case projection from the International Energy Outlook 2007 (IEO2007) released today by the Energy Information Administration (EIA). The IEO2007 shows the most rapid growth in energy demand for nations outside the Organization for Economic Cooperation and Development (OECD), especially in non-OECD Asia, where strong projected economic growth drives the increase in energy use.

Website: http://www.eia.doe.gov/oiaf/ieo

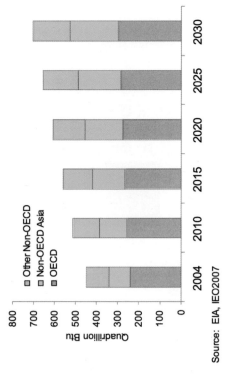

World Marketed Energy Consumption by Region

Source: EIA, IEO2007

World Marketed Energy Use by Fuel Type

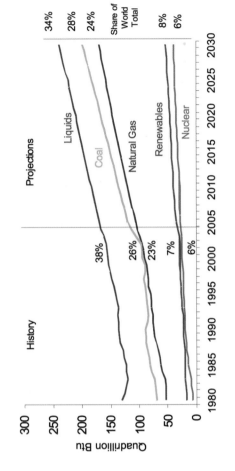

History | Projections

Quadrillion Btu

| | 1980 | 1985 | 1990 | 1995 | 2000 | 2005 | 2010 | 2015 | 2020 | 2025 | 2030 |

Liquids — 38% → 34%
Coal — 26% → 28%
Natural Gas — 23% → 24%
Renewables — 7% → 8%
Nuclear — 6% → 6%

Share of World Total

Source: EIA, IEO2007

World Energy Consumption by Fuel, 2004-2030

	2004	2015	2030	Average Annual Percent Change 2004-2030
	(Quadrillion Btu)			
Liquids	168.2	197.6	238.9	1.4
Natural Gas	103.4	134.3	170.4	1.9
Coal	114.4	151.6	199.1	2.2
Nuclear	27.5	32.5	39.7	1.4
Renewables	33.2	43.4	53.5	1.9
Total	**446.7**	**559.4**	**701.6**	**1.8**

- Petroleum and other liquid fuels remain the dominant energy source worldwide through 2030, though relatively high world oil prices in the mid-term erode their share of total energy use from 38 percent in 2004 to 34 percent in 2030.

- Coal is the fastest-growing energy source, increasing by 2.2 percent per year over the projection period.

- Higher fossil fuel prices, energy security concerns, improved reactor designs, and environmental considerations are expected to improve prospects for nuclear power capacity in many parts of the world, and a number of countries are expected to build new nuclear power plants. World nuclear capacity is projected to rise from 368 gigawatts in 2004 to 481 gigawatts in 2030. Declines in nuclear capacity are projected only in OECD Europe, where several countries (including Germany and Belgium) have either plans or mandates to phase out nuclear power, and where some old reactors are expected to be retired and not replaced.

- Higher fuel prices—especially for natural gas in the power sector, along with government policies and programs to support renewable energy, allow renewable fuels to compete economically. The renewable share of total world energy use increases from 7 percent in 2004 to 8 percent in 2030.

World Oil Prices in Three Cases

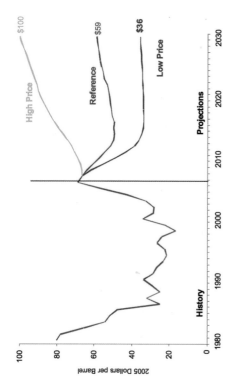

- In the IEO2007 reference case, world oil prices decline from $68 per barrel in 2006 (in real 2005 U.S. dollars) to $49 per barrel in 2014, then rise to $59 per barrel in 2030 ($95 per barrel on a nominal basis).

- High and low world oil price cases reflect the substantial degree of uncertainty about future oil prices. In 2030, prices range from $36 per barrel to $100 per barrel (real 2005 dollars) and the respective liquids demand ranges from 134 million barrels per day to 103 million barrels per day.

Source: EIA, IEO2007

- To meet the increment in world liquids demand in the reference case, total supply in 2030 is projected to be 35 million barrels per day higher than the 2004 level of 83 million barrels per day.

- OPEC conventional production contributes about 21 million barrels per day to the total increase in supply; non-OPEC conventional another 6 million barrels per day to the increase.

- Unconventional resources (including biofuels, coal-to-liquids, and gas-to-liquids) are expected to become increasingly competitive and account for 9 percent of total world liquids supply in 2030, on an oil equivalent basis.

Worldwide Liquids Production

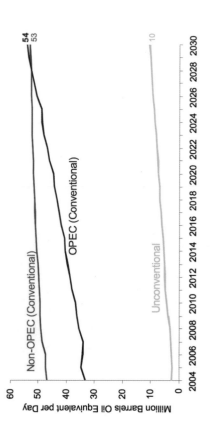

Source: EIA, IEO2007

Industrial Sector Energy Consumption

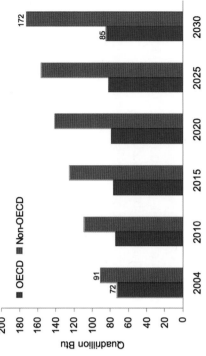

Source: EIA, IEO2007

- The IEO2007 includes regional projections of delivered energy at the end use sector. In 2004 the OECD accounted for 44 percent of the world's industrial sector energy use; that share declines to 33 percent in 2030.

- Industrial sector energy use—driven by energy intensive industries—expands more rapidly in the non-OECD countries where investors are attracted by lower costs and fewer environmental constraints, than in the OECD countries.

- In the IEO2007 reference case, which does not include specific policies to limit greenhouse gas emissions, energy-related carbon dioxide emissions are projected to rise from 26.9 billion metric tons in 2004 to 33.9 billion metric tons in 2015 and 42.9 billion metric tons in 2030.

- From 2003 to 2004, carbon dioxide emissions from the non-OECD countries grew by almost 10 percent, while emissions in the OECD countries grew by less than 2 percent. The result of the large increase in non-OECD emissions was that 2004 marked the first time in history that emissions from the non-OECD exceeded those from the OECD countries.

- Because of the expectation that non-OECD countries will rely on fossil fuels to supply much of their future energy demand growth, carbon dioxide emissions from the non-OECD countries in 2030 are projected to exceed those from the OECD by 57 percent.

Energy-Related World Carbon Dioxide Emissions

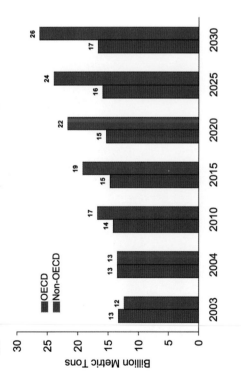

Source: EIA, IEO2007

ExxonMobil

Taking on the world's toughest energy challenges.

The 2006 Outlook for Energy
A View to 2030

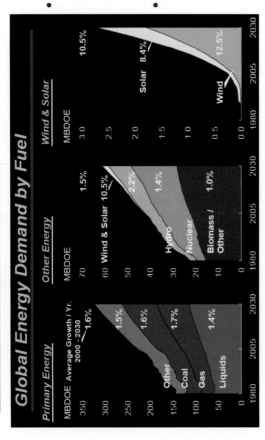

Global Energy Demand by Fuel

- Reflecting global population and GDP gains, we expect energy demand to rise by an average of 1.6% each year through 2030, reaching close to 325 million barrels per day of oil-equivalent (MBDOE). That's 60% higher than in 2000. Energy demand will rise fastest in non-OECD nations, which will account for approximately 80% of the global increase.

- A wide range of energy sources will contribute to meeting this growing global energy demand. Wind and solar energy, for example, are expected to grow at a rate of about 10 percent per year. But even at that rate, by 2030 they will likely still provide less than 1 percent of the world's total energy needs.

- Most of the world's growing energy needs through 2030 will continue to be met by oil, gas and coal. Today, fossil fuels account for 80% of energy usage, and that percentage is expected to remain stable through 2030.

- Driven by increasing needs in non-OECD countries, global liquids demand for transportation is expected to outpace gains in industrial and residential/commercial demand. Total liquids demand for transportation in 2030 will be about 65 million barrels a day, or about 50% higher than today.

- Ongoing access to affordable, reliable energy supplies is the foundation for future growth and prosperity around the globe.

- Meeting the world's growing energy needs will depend, as it has in the past, on advances in technology. Technology not only expands the range of where we produce, but it also extends the types of supplies available to meet demand. Many of the world's largest exploration and production projects are made possible by recent advances in technology.

Website: http://www.exxonmobil.com/Corporate/Citizenship/Imports/EnergyOutlook06/index.html

The 2006 Outlook for Energy
A View to 2030

Taking on the world's toughest energy challenges.

Global Oil Resource Base

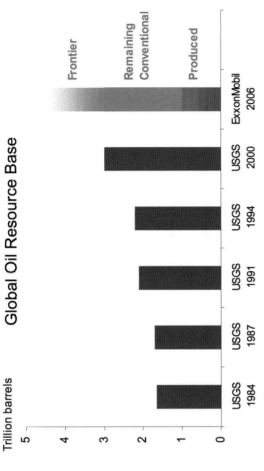

Trillion barrels

Legend: Frontier / Remaining Conventional / Produced

Chart categories: USGS 1984, USGS 1987, USGS 1991, USGS 1994, USGS 2000, ExxonMobil 2006

- Technology (and prices) can impact estimates of oil resources. Global projections of the level of ultimately recoverable reserves for oil have grown over time.

- In 1984, the US Geological Survey (USGS) estimated that there were less than 2 trillion barrels of conventional oil that could be recovered globally. But that estimate has grown steadily, to more than 3 trillion barrels, as new technologies have expanded the possibilities for exploration and production.

- The ExxonMobil "2006 Outlook for Energy" adds estimated "frontier" resources (such as heavy oil and shale oil) to "conventional" oil and estimates the world's recoverable oil base is over 4 trillion barrels. Since only about 1 trillion barrels of the world's conventional oil has been produced so far, we see ample resources available to meet growing demand for oil through 2030.

- Looking to 2030, we expect global liquids trade will increase more than 50%. Globally, more volume will originate from the Middle East and Russia/Caspian regions. Also significant will be increased flows to Europe and Asia Pacific.

The 2006 Outlook for Energy
A View to 2030

CO₂ Mitigation Options

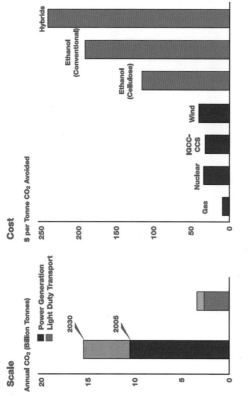

Scale
Annual CO₂ (Billion Tonnes)

- Power Generation
- Light Duty Transport

2030
2005

Cost
$ per Tonne CO₂ Avoided

Gas
Nuclear
IGCC-CCS
Wind
Ethanol (Cellulose)
Ethanol (Conventional)
Hybrids

Sources SFA Pacific, JEC WTW Study (Dec. 2005)

- We expect global CO2 emissions to increase by 1.6%/yr through 2030, in line with overall energy growth and the expected uses of oil, gas and coal that result in CO2 emissions. Most of that growth will occur in the non-OECD countries, where strong energy demand growth along with heavy reliance on coal will drive CO2 emissions up by 2.6%/yr.

- Many options exist that will help mitigate CO2 emissions. Nuclear power is clearly an option, though it carries issues regarding new plant siting and waste management. Clean coal technology – where carbon is captured and sequestered – is another option, albeit a costly one. Other sectors are important too, including transportation, where we expect better vehicle technologies, including HCCI and hybrids, as well as cleaner fuels.

- In terms of scale, power generation is the single largest source of CO2 emissions. CO2 emissions from this sector now total 10 billion tonnes per year, and by 2030 are likely to exceed 15 billion tonnes, or 40% of energy-related CO2 emissions. CO2 emissions from light-duty vehicle transportation are also significant, but far smaller.

- In the case of power generation, the lowest-cost mitigation option involves the use of natural gas to generate power compared to a conventional coal-fired power plant, while the highest-cost option shown above is wind power. In the middle-cost range are nuclear and clean-coal technologies with carbon capture and sequestration.

ExxonMobil

Taking on the world's toughest energy challenges.

The 2006 Outlook for Energy
A View to 2030

- By 2030, energy demand will increase by about 60% compared to 2000, driven by population growth and economic progress. While the vast majority of this increase will occur in non-OECD nations, efficiency gains throughout the world will remain important.

- The global energy mix will look very similar 25 years from now. Oil, gas and coal will be predominant.

- Resources are adequate to support global demand growth. However, access to these resources and large, timely investments will be needed to ensure people have access to reliable energy supplies. Global trade, particularly for oil and natural gas, will continue to grow.

- Providing this energy is not easy or automatic. Fortunately, many approaches exist which, working together, can help address these challenges. These include:

  – Supporting free and open markets to enable consumers to access the energy they need, and to spur continued innovation

  – Wise and efficient use of energy to help conserve global energy supplies and reduce greenhouse gas emissions

  – Technology advances to extend supplies and make the use of energy more efficient

  – Securing the benefits of energy trade in international markets to help ensure reliable and affordable supplies to meet growing demand

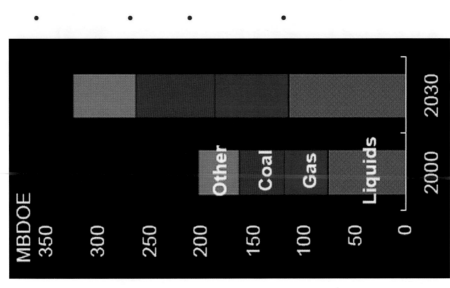

PEAKING OF WORLD OIL PRODUCTION
IMPACTS, MITIGATION, & RISK MANAGEMENT

**THE ONLY U.S. NATIONAL LABORATORY
DEVOTED TO FOSSIL ENERGY TECHNOLOGY**

☐ The peaking of world oil production presents the US and the world with an unprecedented risk management problem. As peaking is approached, liquid fuel prices and price volatility will increase dramatically, and, without timely mitigation, the economic, social, and political costs will be unprecedented. Viable mitigation options exist on both the supply and demand sides, but to have substantial impact, they must be initiated more than a decade in advance of peaking.

☐ A unique aspect of the world oil peaking problem is that its timing is uncertain, because of inadequate and potentially biased reserves data from elsewhere around the world. In addition, the onset of peaking may be obscured by the volatile nature of oil prices.

☐ Oil peaking will create a severe liquid fuels problem for the transportation sector, not an energy crisis in the usual sense that term has been used.

☐ Waiting until world oil production peaks before initiating crash program mitigation leaves the world with a significant liquid fuel deficit for more than two decades.

☐ Initiating a mitigation crash program 20 years before peaking offers the possibility of avoiding a world liquid fuels shortfall for the forecast period.

☐ If mitigation were to be too little, too late, world supply/demand balance will be achieved through massive demand destruction (shortages), which would translate to significant economic hardship. With adequate, timely mitigation, the costs of peaking can be minimized.

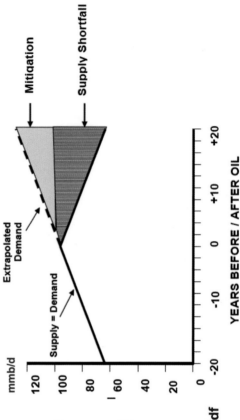

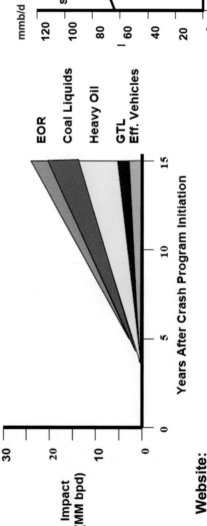

Website:
http://www.netl.doe.gov/publications/others/pdf/Oil_Peaking_NETL.pdf

US Government Accountability Office

GAO

Accountability * Integrity * Reliability

The Government Accountability Office, the audit, evaluation and investigative arm of Congress, exists to support Congress in meeting its constitutional responsibilities and to help improve the performance and accountability of the federal government. The GAO has published reports on a number of key energy issues and is currently working many on others. Among GAO's views, the agency recommends investigation of topics such as:

Ensure the Adequacy of National Energy Supplies and Related Infrastructure: Meeting rising demand could require significant investments into infrastructure such as power plants, transmission lines, refineries, and other key equipment and technologies.

Key Topics Needing Congressional Oversight
• Evaluate the risks, benefits, and implications for national security of investments that deepen US ties to international energy markets (e.g. overseas refineries, oil imports).
• Examine the Nuclear Regulatory Commission's licensing process for new power plants.
• Examine the implications of the Department of Energy's R&D portfolio.
• Assess development of evolving renewable energy markets.
• Evaluate programs that encourage energy efficiency and reduced energy demand.

Selected GAO Products
• Peak Oil GAO-07-283, February 2007
• Impact of petroleum inventories and refining capacity on refined product prices and price volatility (expected 2007)
• US Strategic Petroleum Reserve. GAO-06-872, August 2006
• Issues Related to Potential Reductions in Venezuelan Oil Production. GAO-06-668, June 2006
• Natural Gas: Factors Affecting Prices and Potential Impacts on Consumers. GAO-06-420T. February 2006.
• Electricity Restructuring: Key Challenges Remain. GAO-06-237. November 2005.
• Meeting Energy Demand in the 21st Century: Many Challenges and Key Questions. GAO-05-414T. March 2005.

Website: http://www.gao.gov

Peak Oil Study

Uncertainty about Future Oil Supply Makes It Important to Develop a Strategy for Addressing a Peak and Decline in Oil Production

What GAO Found

Most studies estimate that oil production will peak sometime between now and 2040. This range of estimates is wide because the timing of the peak depends on multiple, uncertain factors that will help determine how quickly the oil remaining in the ground is used, including the amount of oil still in the ground; how much of that oil can ultimately be produced given technological, cost, and environmental challenges as well as potentially unfavorable political and investment conditions in some countries where oil is located; and future global demand for oil. Demand for oil will, in turn, be influenced by global economic growth and may be affected by government policies on the environment and climate change and consumer choices about conservation.

In the US, alternative fuels and transportation technologies face challenges that could impede their ability to mitigate the consequences of a peak and decline in oil production, unless sufficient time and effort are brought to bear. For example, although corn ethanol production is technically feasible, it is more expensive to produce than gasoline and will require costly investments in infrastructure, such as pipelines and storage tanks, before it can become widely available as a primary fuel. Key alternative technologies currently supply the equivalent of only about 1% of US consumption of petroleum products, and the Department of Energy (DOE) projects that even by 2015, they could displace only the equivalent of 4% projected US annual consumption. In such circumstances, an imminent peak and sharp decline in oil production could cause a worldwide recession. If the peak is delayed, however, these technologies have a greater potential to mitigate the consequences. DOE projects that the technologies could displace up to 34% of US consumption in the 2025 through 2030 time frame. The level of effort dedicated to overcoming challenges will depend in part on sustained high oil prices to encourage sufficient investment in and demand for alternatives.

Federal agency efforts that could reduce uncertainty about the timing of peak oil production or mitigate its consequences are spread across multiple agencies and are generally not focused explicitly on peak oil. Federally sponsored studies have expressed concern over the potential for a peak, and agency officials have identified actions that could be taken to address this issue. For example, DOE and United States Geological Survey officials said uncertainty about the peak's timing could be reduced through better information about worldwide demand and supply, and agency officials said they could step up efforts to promote alternative fuels and transportation technologies. However, there is no coordinated federal strategy for reducing uncertainty about the peak's timing or mitigating its consequences.

Peak Oil Study

Why GAO Did This Study: The US economy depends heavily on oil, particularly in the transportation sector. World oil production has been running at near capacity to meet demand, pushing prices upward. Concerns about meeting increasing demand with finite resources have renewed interest in an old question: How long can the oil supply expand before reaching a maximum level of production—a peak—from which it can only decline?

How GAO Performed the Analysis: (1) examined when oil production could peak, (2) assessed the potential for transportation technologies to mitigate the consequences of a peak in oil production, and (3) examined federal agency efforts that could reduce uncertainty about the timing of a peak or mitigate the consequences. To address these objectives, GAO reviewed studies, convened an expert panel, and consulted agency officials.

What GAO Recommends: To better prepare for a peak in oil production, GAO recommends that the Secretary of Energy work with other agencies to establish a strategy to coordinate and prioritize federal agency efforts to reduce uncertainty about the likely timing of a peak and to advise Congress on how best to mitigate consequences.

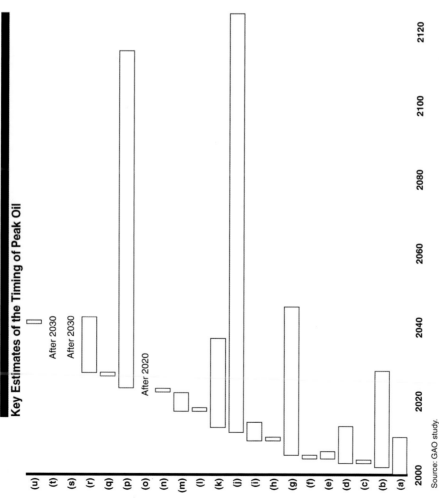

Key Estimates of the Timing of Peak Oil

Source: GAO study.

Note: These studies are listed in appendix II of the GAO report. Estimates of 90 percent confidence intervals using two different reserves data sources are provided for study g. One additional study that is not represented in this figure, referenced as study v, states that the timing of the peak is "unknowable."

AMERICAN ENTERPRISE INSTITUTE

American Enterprise Institute for Public Policy Research

The American Enterprise Institute for Public Policy Research is a private, nonpartisan, not-for-profit institution dedicated to research and education on issues of government, politics, economics, and social welfare. AEI sponsors research and conferences and publishes books, monographs, and periodicals. Its website, www.aei.org, posts its publications, videos and transcripts of its conferences, biographies of its scholars and fellows, and schedules of upcoming events. A number of these postings relate to energy policy:

Strategic Options for Bush Administration Climate Policy (November 2006) book

Lee Lane, the executive director of the Climate Policy Center, explores options that policymakers might consider, as well as the costs and benefits of current policies. His conclusions will surprise many environmental advocates: President Bush was right to reject the Kyoto Protocol and should continue to reject calls for "cap-and-trade" programs modeled on Kyoto. Emissions trading would be expensive and ineffective; the costs would be significant but the environmental benefits would be negligible. With the threat of Kyoto-style cap-and-trade programs looming larger with each passing year, Lane argues that the Bush administration should consider adopting a modest carbon tax. This would be vastly more efficient than emissions trading and would cut off the growing political momentum towards reengaging with the Kyoto system. (At the very least, a cap should include a "safety valve," providing an unlimited supply of affordable credits, essentially transforming the trading program into a tax.) Lane also argues that greater attention should be paid to ambitious approaches to climate change such as geo-engineering and the development of breakthrough clean-energy technologies that could reduce emissions enough to curtail projected warming. Costly cap-and-trade programs that produce trivial reductions in greenhouse gas emissions are simply a waste of money; our resources should focus instead on actual solutions, not ineffective interim steps.

What Would a Rational Energy Tax Policy Look Like (November 2006) article

Kevin Hassett and Gilbert Metcalf explore tax policy options for energy, arguing that US energy tax policy is misguided in at least three ways. First, a policy to promote energy independence through reduced oil imports is based on a fundamental misunderstanding of how energy markets function. A policy that attempts to establish energy independence by promoting domestic fossil fuel production is especially misguided. Second, our policy relies heavily on energy subsidies, most of which are socially wasteful, inefficient, and driven by political rather than energy considerations. Third, current energy taxes are deficient on a number of levels. If one accepts the view that U.S. reliance on oil is a problem, then we can do much better than the policies mentioned above. A rational U.S. energy tax policy would include (1) an end to energy supply subsidies; (2) a green tax swap; (3) an end to the gas guzzler tax loophole and possible use of "feebates"; and (4) conservation incentive programs. Ending subsidies for fossil fuel production would level the playing field among energy sources and shift us from a policy of promoting fossil fuel supply to encouraging a reduction in fossil fuel consumption. It would also move us away from a woefully inefficient reliance on corn-based ethanol. A green tax swap uses revenue from environmentally motivated taxes to lower other taxes in a revenue-neutral reform. For example, Congress could reduce reliance on oil and other polluting sources of energy by implementing a carbon tax. The revenue could be used to finance corporate tax reform or reductions in the payroll tax.

Website: http://www.aei.org

AMERICAN ENTERPRISE INSTITUTE

American Enterprise Institute
for Public Policy Research

Climate Change: Caps vs. Taxes

Kenneth P. Green, Steven F. Hayward, Kevin A. Hassett.   As the Kyoto Protocol's 2012 expiration date draws near, a general theme dominates the global conversation: leadership and participation by the United States are critical to the success of whatever climate policy regime succeeds the Kyoto Protocol. Two general policy approaches stand out in the current discussion. The first is national and international greenhouse gas (GHG) emissions trading, often referred to as "cap-and-trade." Cap-and-trade is the most popular idea at present, with several bills circulating in Congress to begin a cap-and-trade program of some kind. The second idea is a program of carbon-centered tax reform—for example, the imposition of an excise tax based on the carbon emissions of energy sources (such as coal, oil, and gasoline), offset by reductions in other taxes. In this paper we address the strengths and weaknesses of both ideas and the framework by which legislators should evaluate them.
http://www.aei.org/publications/filter.all,pubID.26286/pub_detail.asp

Website: http://www.aei.org

WMO

UNEP

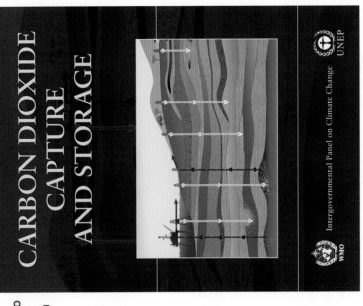

CARBON DIOXIDE
CAPTURE
AND STORAGE

WMO

Intergovernmental Panel on Climate Change

UNEP

The Intergovernmental Panel on Climate Change (IPCC) has been established by WMO and UNEP to assess scientific, technical and socio-economic information relevant for the understanding of climate change, its potential impacts, and options for adaptation and mitigation. It is currently finalizing its Fourth Assessment Report "Climate Change 2007".

The Panel meets in plenary sessions about once a year. It accepts/approves/adopts IPCC reports, decides on the mandates and work plans of the Working Groups and the Task Force, the structure and outlines of its reports. A main activity of the IPCC is to provide in regular intervals an assessment of the state of knowledge on climate change. The reports by the three Working Groups provide a comprehensive and up-to-date assessment of the current state of knowledge on climate change.

The IPCC has three Working Groups:
- Working Group I assesses the scientific aspects of the climate system and climate change.
  Report published February 2007
- Working Group II assesses the vulnerability of socio-economic and natural systems to climate change, negative and positive consequences of climate change, and options for adapting to it.
  Report published April 2007
- Working Group III assesses options for limiting greenhouse gas emissions and otherwise mitigating climate change. Report published May 2007

The Synthesis Report for the Fourth Assessment Report will be released in November 2007. This will provide the key findings of all three Working Groups of the IPCC Fourth Assessment Report.

Website: http://www.ipcc.ch

The graphic on this page depicts one of the many Special Reports undertaken by the IPCC.

INTERGOVERNMENTAL PANEL ON CLIMATE CHANGE

WMO

UNEP

Radiative Forcing Components

RF Terms	(graph)	RF values (W m⁻²)	Spatial scale	LOSU
Long-lived greenhouse gases	CO₂	1.66 [1.49 to 1.83]	Global	High
	N₂O / CH₄ / Halocarbons	0.48 [0.43 to 0.53] 0.16 [0.14 to 0.18] 0.34 [0.31 to 0.37]	Global	High
Ozone	Stratospheric / Tropospheric	-0.05 [...] 0.35 [0.25 to 0.65]	Continental to global	Med
Stratospheric water vapour from CH₄		0.07 [0.02 to 0.12]	Global	Low
Surface albedo	Land use / Black carbon on snow	-0.2 [...] 0.1 [0.0 to 0.2]	Local to continental	Med - Low
Total Aerosol — Direct effect		-0.5 [...]	Continental to global	Med - Low
— Cloud albedo effect		-0.7 [...]	Continental to global	Low
Linear contrails		0.01 [0.003 to 0.03]	Continental	Low
Solar irradiance		0.12 [0.06 to 0.30]	Global	Low
Total net anthropogenic		1.6 [0.6 to 2.4]		

Anthropogenic

Natural

Radiative Forcing (W m⁻²)

CLIMATE CHANGE 2007

The Physical Science Basis

Working Group I

Global atmospheric concentrations of carbon dioxide, methane and nitrous oxide have increased markedly as a result of human activities since 1750 and now far exceed pre-industrial values determined from ice cores spanning many thousands of years. The global increases in carbon dioxide concentration are due primarily to fossil fuel use and land-use change, while those of methane and nitrous oxide are primarily due to agriculture.

The understanding of anthropogenic warming and cooling influences on climate has improved since the Third Assessment Report (TAR), leading to very high confidence that the globally averaged net effect of human activities since 1750 has been one of warming, with a radiative forcing of +1.6 [+0.6 to +2.4] W m⁻².

Key impacts as a function of increasing global average temperature change

Working Group II

Illustrative examples of global impacts are projected for climate changes (and sea-level and atmospheric carbon dioxide where relevant) associated with different amounts of increase in global average surface temperature in the 21st century.

The black lines link impacts, dotted arrows indicate impacts continuing with increasing temperature. Entries are placed so that the left hand side of text indicates approximate onset of a given impact. Quantitative entries for water scarcity and flooding represent the additional impacts of climate change relative to the conditions projected across the range of Special Report on Scenarios (SRES) scenarios A1FI, A2, B1 and B2.

Adaptation to climate change is not included in these estimations. All entries are from published studies recorded in the chapters of the Assessment. Sources are given in the right hand column of the Table. Confidence levels for all statements are high.

Global mean annual temperature change relative to 1980-1999 (°C)

	0	1	2	3	4	5 °C	
WATER		Increased water availability in moist tropics and high latitudes					3.4.1, 3.4.3
		Decreasing water availability and increasing drought in mid-latitudes and semi-arid low latitudes					3.ES, 3.4.1, 3.4.3
		Hundreds of millions of people exposed to increased water stress					3.5.1, T3.3, 20.6.2, TS.B5
ECOSYSTEMS			Up to 30% of species at increasing risk of extinction	Significant† extinctions around the globe			4.ES, 4.4.11
		Increased coral bleaching — Most corals bleached — Widespread coral mortality					T4.1, F4.4, B4.4, 6.4.1, 6.6.5, B6.1
			Terrestrial biosphere tends toward a net carbon source as: ~15% ~40% of ecosystems affected				4.ES, T4.1, F4.2, F4.4
		Increasing species range shifts and wildfire risk					4.2.2, 4.4.1, 4.4.4, 4.4.5, 4.4.6, 4.4.10, B4.5
			Ecosystem changes due to weakening of the meridional overturning circulation				19.3.5
FOOD		Complex, localised negative impacts on small holders, subsistence farmers and fishers					5.ES, 5.4.7
			Tendencies for cereal productivity to decrease in low latitudes	Productivity of all cereals decreases in low latitudes			5.ES, 5.4.2, F5.2
			Tendencies for some cereal productivity to increase at mid- to high latitudes	Cereal productivity to decrease in some regions			5.ES, 5.4.2, F5.2
COASTS		Increased damage from floods and storms					6.ES, 6.3.2, 6.4.1, 6.4.2
				About 30% of global coastal wetlands lost‡			6.4.1
			Millions more people could experience coastal flooding each year				T6.6, F6.8, TS.B5
HEALTH		Increasing burden from malnutrition, diarrhoeal, cardio-respiratory, and infectious diseases					8.ES, 8.4.1, 8.7, T8.2, T8.4
		Increased morbidity and mortality from heat waves, floods, and droughts					8.ES, 8.2.2, 8.2.3, 8.4.1, 8.4.2, 8.7, T8.3, F8.3
		Changed distribution of some disease vectors					8.ES, 8.2.8, 8.7, B8.4
			Substantial burden on health services				8.6.1

Global mean annual temperature change relative to 1980-1999 (°C)

WMO

UNEP

INTERGOVERNMENTAL PANEL ON CLIMATE CHANGE

Mitigation of Climate Change   Working Group III

Sector	Key mitigation technologies and practices currently commercially available.	Key mitigation technologies and practices projected to be commercialized before 2030.
Energy Supply [4.3, 4.4]	Improved supply and distribution efficiency; fuel switching from coal to gas; nuclear power; renewable heat and power (hydropower, solar, wind, geothermal and bioenergy); combined heat and power; early applications of CCS (e.g. storage of removed CO_2 from natural gas)	Carbon Capture and Storage (CCS) for gas, biomass and coal-fired electricity generating facilities; advanced nuclear power; advanced renewable energy, including tidal and waves energy, concentrating solar, and solar PV
Transport [5.4]	More fuel efficient vehicles; hybrid vehicles; cleaner diesel vehicles; biofuels; model shifts from road transport to rail and public transport systems; non-motorised transports (cycling, walking); land-use and transport planning	Second generation biofuels; higher efficiency aircraft; advanced electric and hybrid vehicles with more powerful and reliable batteries
Buildings [6.5]	Efficient lighting and daylighting; more efficient electrical appliances and heating and cooling devices; improved cook stoves, improved insulations; passive and active solar design for heating and cooling; alternative refrigeration fluids, recovery and recycle of fluorinated gases	Integrated design of commercial buildings including technologies, such as intelligent meters that provide feedback and control; solar PV integrated in buildings
Industry [7.5]	More efficient end-use electrical equipment; heat and power recovery; material recycling and substitution; control of non-CO_2 gas emissions; and a wide array of process-specific technologies	Advanced energy efficiency; CCS for cement, ammonia, and iron manufacture; inert electrodes for aluminium manufacture
Agriculture [8.4]	Improved crop and grazing land management to increase soil carbon storage; restoration of cultivated peaty soils and degraded lands; improved rice cultivation techniques and livestock and manure management to reduce CH_4 emissions; improved nitrogen fertilizer application techniques to reduce N_2O emissions; dedicated energy crops to replace fossil fuel use; improve energy efficiency	Improvements of crops yields
Forestry/forests [9.4]	Afforestation; reforestation; forest management; reduced deforestation; harvested wood product management; use of forestry products for bioenergy to replace fossil fuel use	Tree species improvements to increase biomass productivity and carbon sequestration. Improved remote sensing technologies for analysis of vegetation/soil carbon sequestration potential and mapping land use change
Waste [10.4]	Landfill methane recovery; waste incineration with energy recovery; composting of organic waste; controlled waste water treatment; recycling and waste minimization	Biocovers and biofilters to optimize CH_4 oxidation

WMO

UNEP

INTERGOVERNMENTAL PANEL ON CLIMATE CHANGE

Mitigation of Climate Change   Working Group III

A wide variety of national policies and instruments are available to governments to create the incentives for mitigation action. Their applicability depends on national circumstances and an understanding of their interactions, but experience from implementation in various countries and sectors shows there are advantages and disadvantages for any given instrument (high agreement, much evidence). Four main criteria are used to evaluate policies and instruments: environmental effectiveness, cost effectiveness, distributional effects including equity, and institutional feasibility.

General findings about the performance of policies are:

☐ Integrating climate policies in broader development policies makes implementation and overcoming barriers easier.

☐ Regulations and standards generally provide some certainty about emission levels. They may be preferable to other instruments when information or other barriers prevent producers and consumers from responding to price signals. However, they may not induce innovations and more advanced technologies.

☐ Taxes and charges can set a price for carbon, but cannot guarantee a particular level of emissions. Literature identifies taxes as an efficient way of internalizing costs of GHG emissions.

☐ Tradable permits will establish a carbon price. The volume of allowed emissions determines their environmental effectiveness, while the allocation of permits has distributional consequences. Fluctuation in the price of carbon makes it difficult to estimate the total cost of complying with emission permits.

☐ Financial incentives (subsidies and tax credits) are frequently used by governments to stimulate the development and diffusion of new technologies. While economic costs are generally higher than for the instruments listed above, they are often critical to overcome barriers.

☐ Voluntary agreements between industry and governments are politically attractive, raise awareness among stakeholders, and have played a role in the evolution of many national policies. The majority of agreements has not achieved significant emissions reductions beyond business as usual. However, some recent agreements, in a few countries, have accelerated the application of best available technology and led to measurable emission reductions.

☐ Information instruments (e.g. awareness campaigns) may positively affect environmental quality by promoting informed choices and possibly contributing to behavioural change, however, their impact on emissions has not been measured yet.

☐ RD&D can stimulate technological advances, reduce costs, and enable progress toward stabilization.

Global Warming Debate: Skepticism persists but science has improved

Comments below courtesy Wikipedia, The Free Encyclopedia

Material excerpted from entry titled "Global cooling" available at http://en.wikipedia.org/wiki/Global_cooling#_note-16

Wikipedia's informative entry titled "Global warming" available at http://en.wikipedia.org/wiki/Global_warming

1975 Newsweek article

April 28, 1975 article in Newsweek magazine: Titled "The Cooling World," it pointed to "ominous signs that the Earth's weather patterns have begun to change" and pointed to "a drop of half a degree [Fahrenheit] in average ground temperatures in the Northern Hemisphere between 1945 and 1968." The article claimed "The evidence in support of these predictions [of global cooling] has now begun to accumulate so massively that meteorologists are hard-pressed to keep up with it." The Newsweek article did not state the cause of cooling; it stated that "what causes the onset of major and minor ice ages remains a mystery" and cited the NAS conclusion that "not only are the basic scientific questions largely unanswered, but in many cases we do not yet know enough to pose the key questions."

The article mentioned the alternative solutions of "melting the Arctic ice cap by covering it with black soot or diverting arctic rivers" but conceded these were not feasible. The Newsweek article concluded by criticizing government leaders: "But the scientists see few signs that government leaders anywhere are even prepared to take the simple measures of stockpiling food or of introducing the variables of climatic uncertainty into economic projections of future food supplies...The longer the planners (politicians) delay, the more difficult will they find it to cope with climatic change once the results become grim reality." The article emphasized sensational and largely unsourced consequences – "resulting famines could be catastrophic", "drought and desolation," "the most devastating outbreak of tornadoes ever recorded", "droughts, floods, extended dry spells, long freezes, delayed monsoons," "impossible for starving peoples to migrate," "the present decline has taken the planet about a sixth of the way toward the Ice Age."

On October 23, 2006, Newsweek issued a correction, over 31 years after the original article, stating that it had been "so spectacularly wrong about the near-term future" (though editor Jerry Adler claimed that the article was not "inaccurate" in a journalistic sense).

Present level of knowledge

Thirty years later, the concern that the cooler temperatures would continue, and perhaps at a faster rate, can now be observed to have been incorrect. More has to be learned about climate, but the growing records have shown the cooling concerns of 1975 to have been simplistic and not borne out.

Climate science has improved

Scientific knowledge regarding climate change was more uncertain [in the 1970s] than it is today. At the time that Rasool and Schneider wrote their paper (published in the journal Science in July 1971), climatologists had not yet recognized the significance of greenhouse gases other than water vapor and carbon dioxide, such as methane, nitrous oxide and chlorofluorocarbons. Early in that decade, carbon dioxide was the only widely studied human-influenced greenhouse gas. The attention drawn to atmospheric gases in the 1970s stimulated many discoveries in future decades. As the temperature pattern changed, global cooling was of waning interest by 1979.

The Solar Effect

NewScientist

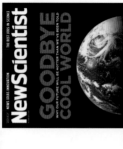
It is one of the few areas where the sceptics' argument has had some force. What role has the sun played in recent climate change? As if to underline the controversy, [the IPCC] debate on this issue lasted some 10 hours.

The scientists wanted to halve their previous estimate of the maximum possible solar influence on warming over the past 250 years, from 40 percent to 20 percent. Government delegations from China and Saudi Arabia refused to accept that, based on new ideas about cosmic rays from outer space.

Cosmic rays ionise the atmosphere, which could, the theory goes, create clouds. Thus, anything that reduces the amount of cosmic rays could diminish cloud cover and so warm the Earth's surface. An increase in solar activity would do just that - by deflecting cosmic rays away from Earth. China and Saudi Arabia were buoyed by claims that small changes in radiation from the sun could be amplified by their potential effect on clouds. Thus, they said, the sun could have a greater effect than the scientists claimed.

Most climate scientists are unconvinced. "Right now there is no evidence," says IPCC author Piers Forster of the University of Leeds, UK. In any case, IPCC scientists believe, most of today's warming can be explained by man-made influences (see Charts). But with a book due from solar-radiation proponent Henrik Svensmark of the Danish National Space Center, this may not be the end of the matter.

Source: *NewScientist* magazine, 10 February 2007

Website: http://www.newscientist.com

THE SUN VERSUS HUMANS

Amount of radiation (or heat) entering the Earth's climate system, known as radiative forcing

NATURAL SOLAR RADIATION

MAN-MADE EFFECTS

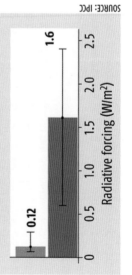

SOURCE: IPCC

0.12

1.6

Radiative forcing (W/m^2)

0   0.5   1.0   1.5   2.0   2.5

Note: The "circles" graphic is an amended version of the original appearing in *NewScientist* — to show the estimated contributions as equal areas and not equal diameters.

Stern Review on The Economics of Climate Change

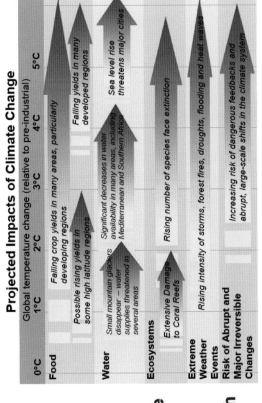

Projected Impacts of Climate Change

Global temperature change (relative to pre-industrial)

	0°C	1°C	2°C	3°C	4°C	5°C
Food			Falling crop yields in many areas, particularly developing regions			
			Possible rising yields in some high latitude regions		Falling yields in many developed regions	
Water		Small mountain glaciers disappear — water supplies threatened in several areas	Significant decreases in water availability in many areas, including Mediterranean and Southern Africa			Sea level rise threatens major cities
Ecosystems		Extensive Damage to Coral Reefs		Rising number of species face extinction		
Extreme Weather Events			Rising intensity of storms, forest fires, droughts, flooding and heat waves			
Risk of Abrupt and Major Irreversible Changes			Increasing risk of dangerous feedbacks and abrupt, large-scale shifts in the climate system			

- **There is still time to avoid the worst impacts of climate change, if we take strong action now.**

- **Climate change could have very serious impacts on growth and development.**

- **The costs of stabilising the climate are significant but manageable; delay would be dangerous and much more costly.**

- **Action on climate change is required across all countries, and it need not cap the aspirations for growth of rich or poor countries.**

- **A range of options exists to cut emissions; strong, deliberate policy action is required to motivate their take-up.**

- **Climate change demands an international response, based on a shared understanding of long-term goals and agreement on frameworks for action.**

Website:
http://www.hm-treasury.gov.uk/independent_reviews/stern_review_economics_climate_change/sternreview_index.cfm

Global Emissions by Sector

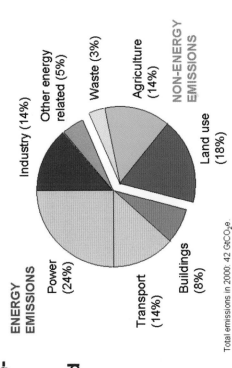

ENERGY EMISSIONS
- Power (24%)
- Industry (14%)
- Other energy related (5%)
- Transport (14%)
- Buildings (8%)

NON-ENERGY EMISSIONS
- Waste (3%)
- Agriculture (14%)
- Land use (18%)

Total emissions in 2000: 42 GtCO$_2$e.

Stern Review on The Economics of Climate Change

Key elements of future international frameworks should include:

- **Establishing a carbon price,** through tax, trading or regulation is an essential foundation for climate change policy

- **Emissions trading:** Expanding and linking the growing number of emissions trading schemes around the world is a powerful way to promote cost-effective reductions in emissions and to bring forward action in developing countries. Strong targets in rich countries could drive flows amounting to tens of billions of dollars each year to support the transition to low-carbon development paths.

- **Technology cooperation:** Informal co-ordination as well as formal agreements can boost the effectiveness of investments in innovation around the world. Globally, support for energy R&D should at least double, and support for the deployment of new low-carbon technologies should increase up to five-fold. International cooperation on product standards is a powerful way to boost energy efficiency.

- **Action to reduce deforestation:** The loss of natural forests around the world contributes more to global emissions each year than the transport sector.

- **Curbing deforestation** is a highly cost-effective way to reduce emissions; large scale international pilot programmes to explore the best ways to do this could get underway very quickly.

- **Adaptation:** The poorest countries are most vulnerable to climate change. It is essential that climate change be fully integrated into development policy, and that rich countries honour their pledges to increase support through overseas development assistance. International funding should also support improved regional information on climate change impacts, and research into new crop varieties that will be more resilient to drought and flood.

Global Roundtable on Climate Change

The Earth Institute
AT COLUMBIA UNIVERSITY

GLOBAL ROUNDTABLE
ON CLIMATE CHANGE

Statement Executive Summary

Climate change is an urgent problem requiring global action to reduce emissions of carbon dioxide (CO2) and other greenhouse gases (GHGs). Energy use is vital for a modern economy. Burning fossil fuels produces CO2. Thus, confronting climate change depends, in many ways, on adopting new and sustainable energy strategies that can meet growing global energy needs while allowing for the stabilization of atmospheric CO2 concentrations at safe levels.

- The world's governments should set scientifically informed targets, including an ambitious but achievable interim, mid-century target for global CO2 concentrations, for "stabilization of greenhouse gas concentrations in the atmosphere at a level that would prevent dangerous anthropogenic interference with the climate system," in accordance with the stated objective of the Framework Convention on Climate Change (UNFCCC).

- All countries should be party to this accord, which should include specific near- and long-term commitments for action in pursuit of the agreed targets. Commitments for actions by individual countries should reflect differences in levels of economic development and GHG emission patterns and the principles of equity and common but differentiated responsibilities.

- Clear, efficient mechanisms should be established to place a market price on carbon emissions that is reasonably consistent worldwide and across sectors in order to reward efficiency and emission avoidance, encourage innovation, and maintain a level playing field among possible technological options.

- Government policy initiatives should address energy efficiency and de-carbonization in all sectors, allow businesses to choose among a range of options as they strive to minimize GHG emissions and costs, encourage the development and rapid deployment of low-emitting and zero-emitting energy and transportation technologies, and provide incentives to reduce emissions from deforestation and harmful land management practices.

- Governments, the private sector, trade unions, and other sectors of civil society should undertake efforts to prepare for and adapt to the impacts of climate change, since climate change will occur even in the context of highly effective mitigation efforts.

- Signatories to this statement will support scientific processes including the Intergovernmental Panel on Climate Change (IPCC); work to increase public awareness of climate change risks and solutions; report information on their GHG emissions; engage in GHG emissions mitigation, which can include emissions trading schemes; champion demonstration projects; and support public policy efforts to mitigate climate change and its impacts.

Website: http://www.earthinstitute.columbia.edu/grocc/grocc4_statement.html

Global Roundtable on Climate Change

GLOBAL ROUNDTABLE
ON CLIMATE CHANGE

Management:

Jeffrey Sachs: Chair, Global Roundtable on Climate Change; Director, The Earth Institute at Columbia University; Quetelet Professor of Sustainable Development and Professor of Health Policy and Management, Columbia University.

David Downie: Director, Global Roundtable on Climate Change. Associate Director, Graduate Program in Climate and Society. Dr. Downie's research focuses on the creation, content, and implementation of international environmental policy.

Kate Brash: Assistant Director, Global Roundtable on Climate Change, The Earth Institute at Columbia University

Lyndon Valicenti: Program Coordinator, Global Roundtable on Climate Change, The Earth Institute at Columbia University

In addition, the Earth Institute's full time events staff in information technology, communications and events-planning facilitates the day-to-day operations of the Roundtable and all Roundtable and Working Group meetings. To contact the Roundtable, please send email to grocc@ei.columbia.edu.

Released February 20, 2007

The Path to Climate Sustainability:
A Joint Statement by the Global Roundtable on Climate Change

The signatories include Air France, Alcoa, Allianz, American Electric Power, Bayer, China Renewable Energy Industry Association, Citigroup, DuPont, Electricity Generating Authority of Thailand, ENDESA, Eni, Eskom, FPL Group, General Electric, Iberdrola, ING, Interface, Marsh & McLennan Companies, Munich Re, NRG Energy, Patagonia, Ricoh, Rolls Royce, Stora Enso North America, Suntech Power, Swiss Re, Vattenfall, Volvo, World Council of Churches, World Petroleum Council, and many others.

European Commission

World Energy
Technology Outlook - 2050

The WETO-H2 study has developed a Reference projection of the world energy system to test different scenarios for technology and climate policies in the next half-century. It has a particular focus on the diffusion of hydrogen as a fuel. This Reference projection adopts exogenous forecasts for population and economic growth in the different world regions and it makes consistent assumptions for the availability of fossil energy resources and for the costs and performances of future technologies. It uses a world energy sector simulation model – the POLES model – to describe the development to 2050 of the national and regional energy systems and of their interactions through international energy markets, under constraints on resources and from climate policy.

Conclusions

• In the Reference Case, by 2050 the "size" of the world energy system and corresponding CO_2 emissions will be twice that of today.

• Relative scarcity of oil and gas ("plateau"): Coal comes to be increasingly the swing primary source in the world energy balance, which aggravates the problem raised by the energy-related CO_2 emissions.

• Two alternative policy scenarios have been elaborated: A "Carbon Constraint Case" (CCC) and the "Hydrogen Scenario" (H2).

• The CCC scenario expects a very high carbon value (up to 200 €/tCO2 for Europe by 2050) to achieve a "factor two" reduction of emissions in the industrialised countries and progressive efforts from developing countries in order to get a stabilisation of emissions. In the CCC, there is important penetration of: (1) Carbon capture and storage (50% of thermal electricity in Europe), (2) Nuclear and renewables (75% of electricity), and (3) Low and very low energy buildings and vehicles (40%).

• The H2 scenario assumes technological breakthroughs in clusters of technologies concerning hydrogen production, distribution, storage, and end-use technologies. It has a substantial impact on transportation since by 2050 nearly 30% of total passenger cars run on hydrogen.

Annex

• Mean-variance portfolio (MVP) theory can help provide new insights to energy investment strategies. It demonstrates the range of possible mixes with technology shares that are +/- 20% from the POLES Reference. This enables policy makers to compare alternative 2050 outcomes, which may present more desirable CO_2, energy diversity and other characteristics.

• The challenge of this research has been to merge the technically rich descriptive power of POLES with the ability of portfolio analysis to trade-off risk and reward. Optimisation identifies portfolios with better balances of cost and risk and other improved characteristics.

• The optimised mixes show improvements that may be attainable and which lie within close to the Reference. The remaining challenge is to identify policy changes that produce such optimised outcomes, a task to which the POLES simulation is ideally suited.

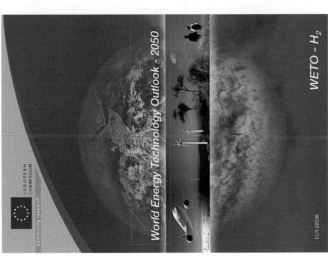

World Energy Technology Outlook - 2050

WETO - H_2

EUR 22038

European Commission
Directorate-General for Research
Information and Communication Unit
B-1049 Brussels
Internet:
http://ec.europa.eu/research/energy/pdf/
weto-h2_en.pdf

2000 - 2050 North American Transportation Energy Futures

Future US Highway Energy Use: A Fifty Year Perspective - May 2001

In the summer of 2000, the transportation program within the US Department of Energy launched its effort to analyze the long-term (to 2050) energy future of highway transportation in the US, with a focus on fuel supply and demand. The initial report examined the potential for efficient technologies to reduce demand. In working on this report, it became apparent that within a couple of decades the US will probably need to begin to transition away from conventional oil use in general and in the transportation sector in particular, because world conventional oil production will peak within that time frame.

Features
- Six strategies to reduce oil use and carbon emissions were compared
- Light vehicle oil use in 2050 dramatically less than the base case across all strategies
- No costs estimated for strategies; feedback between US and world oil markets not considered
- Estimates the energy, oil, carbon and cost implications of alternative transportation futures

Philip Patterson, US DOE   David Greene, Oak Ridge National Laboratory
Elyse Steiner, National Renewable Energy Laboratory
Steve Plotkin, Margaret Singh, Anant Vyas, Marianne Mintz,
Dan Santini, and Steve Folga, Argonne National Laboratory
Jim Moore, TA Engineering, Inc.
Peter Reilly-Roe, Kevin Cliffe, Ruth Talbot, Paul Khanna, and
Vernel Stanciulescu, Natural Resources Canada

2000 - 2050 North American Transportation Energy Futures, the second phase (completed in the spring of 2003), is a joint study by the US Department of Energy and Natural Resources Canada on the evolution of transportation fuels and vehicle technologies under three North American transportation scenarios over a fifty year time period. It expands on the work done by DOE for Future US Highway Energy Use: A Fifty Year Perspective by adding a Canadian perspective to the analysis, including vehicle and fuel costs, and by developing a world oil market model. The goals of the study were to: (a) develop and understand the evolution of the North American transportation sector to 2050 under various scenarios; (b) identify the technology and fuel options that may be important to these evolutions; and (c) analyze the costs and potential energy consumption, especially of petroleum, and the environmental impacts of the scenarios relative to a base case. The major focus of the study is on-road transport due to its dominant share of the North American transportation market and its nearly exclusive dependence on petroleum-based fuels.

The study sought to explore the following questions:
- How can North America manage the predicted decline of conventional oil supplies during this time period?
- What are the implications, economic and otherwise, of a transition from conventional oil to alternative feedstocks and/or energy carriers?
- What options are available to minimize North America's reliance on imported oil?
- In light of the above issues, how can North America achieve lower greenhouse gas emission levels that might be required in the future?

Among the study's conclusions were the following:
- World conventional oil production peaks before 2050 in all scenarios.
- Oil from Canadian oil sands will be an important contributor to future North American supply, but considerable uncertainty remains – especially about long-term costs and the potential for large increases in production.
- Even in the most optimistic scenario, oil continues to dominate highway transportation energy use.
- Still, hydrogen and ethanol can play major roles, though transitions to them as postulated in the scenarios examined will require large early capital investments.
- Oil reduction can be achieved with changes in behavior and/or with technological advances.
- For different environmentally-driven scenarios – different views of what the future will look like – there is similar potential for reducing North American oil use and greenhouse gas emissions at relatively similar total costs, but through different means and with different timing of benefits."

Tools of the Study
- Scenarios of possible futures using rate of innovation, environmental responsiveness and degree of North American energy market integration as drivers
- Models for analysis of energy demand, greenhouse gas emissions, oil markets and costs
- Resource Papers on key topics to provide context, technical detail and cost data

Website: http://www.eere.energy.gov

SIGMA XI
THE SCIENTIFIC RESEARCH SOCIETY

UNITED NATIONS FOUNDATION

Confronting Climate Change

CONFRONTING CLIMATE CHANGE
AVOIDING THE UNMANAGEABLE AND MANAGING THE UNAVOIDABLE

Website: http://www.unfoundation.org/SEG

Highlights of the resulting report include:

The United Nations Department of Economic and Social Affairs (DESA) seeks to facilitate contributions by the scientific community to the work of the UN Commission on Sustainable Development. Accordingly, DESA invited Sigma Xi, the Scientific Research Society, to convene an international panel of scientific experts to prepare a report outlining the best measures for mitigating and adapting to global warming for submission to the CSD. **The UN Foundation was funded by the Turner Gift.**

To carry out this task, the Scientific Expert Group on Climate Change and Sustainable Development (SEG) was formed and is comprised of 18 distinguished international scientists. The panel was asked to consider innovative approaches for mitigating and/or adapting to projected climate changes, and to anticipate the relationship of response measures to sustainable development.

To avoid a entering a regime of sharply rising danger of intolerable impacts on humans, policy makers should limit temperature increases from global warming to 2-2.5°C above the 1750 pre-industrial level. It is still possible to avoid unmanageable changes in the future, but the time for action is now. Avoiding temperature increases greater than 2-2.5°C would require very rapid success in reducing emissions of methane and black soot worldwide, and global carbon dioxide emissions must level off by 2015 or 2020 at not much above their current amount, before beginning a decline to no more than a third of that level by 2100.

• **The technology exists to seize significant opportunities around the globe to reduce emissions and provide other economic, environmental and social benefits,** including meeting the United Nations' Millennium Development Goals. To do so, policy makers must immediately act to reduce emissions by: (1) Improving efficiency in the transportation sector through measures such as vehicle efficiency standards, fuel taxes, and registration fees/rebates that favor purchase of efficient and alternative fuel vehicles. (2) Improving design and efficiency of commercial and residential buildings through building codes, standards for equipment and appliances, incentives for property developers and landlords to build and manage properties efficiently, and financing for energy-efficiency investments. (3) Expanding the use of biofuels through energy portfolio standards and incentives to growers and consumers. (4) Beginning immediately, designing and deploying only coal-fired power plants that will be capable of cost-effective and environmentally-sound retrofits for capture and sequestration of their carbon emissions.

• **Some level of climate change and impacts from it is already unavoidable.** Societies must do more to adapt to ongoing and unavoidable changes in the Earth's climate system by: (5) Improving preparedness/response strategies and management of natural resources to cope with future climatic conditions that will be. fundamentally different than those experienced for the last 100 years. (6) Addressing the adaptation needs of the poorest and most vulnerable nations, which will bear the brunt of climate change impacts. (7) Planning and building climate resilient cities. (8) Strengthening international, national, and regional institutions to cope with weather-related disasters and an increasing number of climate change refugees.

• **The international community, through the UN and related multilateral institutions, can play a crucial role in advancing action** to manage the unavoidable and avoid the unmanageable by: (9) Helping developing countries and countries with economies in transition to finance and deploy energy efficient and new energy technologies. 10) Accelerating negotiations to develop a successor international framework for addressing climate change and sustainable development. (11) Educating all about the opportunities to adopt mitigation and adaptation measures.

National Security and the Threat of Climate Change
The CNA Corporation

Global climate change presents a serious national security threat which could impact Americans at home, impact United States military operations and heighten global tensions, according to a new study released by a blue-ribbon panel of retired admirals and generals from all branches of the armed services.

The CNA Corporation (CNA) is a non-profit organization that provides research and analysis to inform public sector leaders. CNA brought together eleven retired senior admirals and generals to provide advice, expertise and perspective on the impact of climate change. CNA writers and researchers compiled the report under the board's direction and review. The study, "National Security and the Threat of Climate Change," explores ways projected climate change is a threat multiplier in already fragile regions, exacerbating conditions that lead to failed states — the breeding grounds for extremism and terrorism.

FINDINGS

- Projected climate change poses a serious threat to America's national security

- Climate change acts as a threat multiplier for instability in some of the most volatile regions of the world

- Projected climate change will add to tensions even in stable regions of the world

- Climate change, national security and energy dependence are a related set of global challenges

RECOMMENDATIONS

- The national security consequences of climate change should be fully integrated into national security and national defense strategies.

- The US should commit to a stronger national and international role to help stabilize climate changes at levels that will avoid significant disruption to global security and stability.

- The US should commit to global partnerships that help less developed nations build the capacity and resiliency to better manage climate impacts.

- The Department of Defense should enhance its operational capability by accelerating the adoption of improved business processes and innovative technologies that result in improved US combat power through energy efficiency.

- The Department of Defense should conduct an assessment of the impact on US military installations worldwide of rising sea levels, extreme weather events, and other possible climate change impacts over the next thirty to forty years.

Website: http://securityandclimate.cna.org

The Future of Coal   Massachusetts Institute of Technology

Leading academics from an interdisciplinary Massachusetts Institute of Technology (MIT) team issued a report that seeks to examine how the world can continue to use coal, an abundant and inexpensive fuel, in a way that mitigates, instead of worsens, the global warming crisis.

The goal of this MIT energy study, one of a series, was to evaluate the performance of different technologies, which in combination with policy and technology innovations, will reduce global emissions of CO2 and other greenhouse gases by mid-century.

Given that coal is likely to remain an important source of energy in any conceivable future energy scenario.

In particular, the focus is on carbon capture and sequestration (CCS) — the separation of the CO2 combustion product that is produced in conjunction with the generation of electricity from coal and the transportation of the separated CO2 to a site where the CO2 is sequestered from the atmosphere.

Website: http://web.mit.edu/coal/The_Future_of_Coal_Summary_Report.pdf

---

BOX 1 ILLUSTRATING THE CHALLENGE OF SCALE FOR CARBON CAPTURE

- Today fossil sources account for 80% of energy demand: Coal (25%), natural gas (21%), petroleum (34%), nuclear (6.5%), hydro (2.2%), and biomass and waste (11%). Only 0.4% of global energy demand is met by geothermal, solar and wind.[1]

- 50% of the electricity generated in the U.S. is from coal.[2]

- There are the equivalent of more than five hundred, 500 megawatt, coal-fired power plants in the United States with average age of 35 years.[2]

- China is currently constructing the equivalent of two, 500 megawatt, coal-fired power plants per week in a capacity comparable to the entire UK power grid each year.[3]

- One 500 megawatt coal-fired power plant produces approximately 3 million tons/year of carbon dioxide (CO_2).[3]

- The United States produces about 1.5 billion tons per year of CO_2 from coal-burning power plants.

- If all of this CO_2 is transported from sequestration, the quantity is equivalent to three times the weight and, under typical operating conditions, one-third of the annual volume of natural gas transported by the U.S. gas pipeline system.

- If 60% of the CO_2 produced from U.S. coal-based power generation were to be captured and compressed to a liquid for geologic sequestration, its volume would about equal the total U.S. oil consumption of 20 million barrels per day.

- At present the largest sequestration project is injecting one million tons/year of carbon dioxide (CO_2) from the Sleipner gas field into a saline aquifer under the North Sea.[3]

1 IEA Key World Statistics (2006)
2 EIA 2005 annual statistics (www.eia.doe.gov)
3 Derived from the MIT Coal Study

Key Findings

- Coal is a low-cost, per BTU, mainstay of both the developed and developing world, and its use is projected to increase. Because of coal's high carbon content, increasing use will exacerbate the problem of climate change unless coal plants are deployed with very high efficiency and large scale CCS is implemented.

- CCS is the critical enabling technology because it allows significant reduction in CO_2 emissions while allowing coal to meet future energy needs.

Table 1   Exajoules of Coal Use (EJ) and Global CO_2 Emissions (Gt/yr) in 2000 and 2050 with and without Carbon Capture and Storage*

	BUSINESS AS USUAL		LIMITED NUCLEAR 2050		EXPANDED NUCLEAR 2050	
	2000	2050	WITH CCS	WITHOUT CCS	WITH CCS	WITHOUT CCS
Coal Use: Global	100	448	161	116	121	78
U.S.	24	58	40	28	25	13
China	27	88	39	24	31	17
Global CO_2 Emissions	24	62	28	32	26	29
CO_2 Emissions from Coal	9	32	5	9	3	6

* Universal, simultaneous participation, High CO_2 prices and EPPA-Ref gas prices.

- A significant charge on carbon emissions is needed in the relatively near term to increase the economic attractiveness of new technologies that avoid carbon emissions and specifically to lead to large-scale CCS in the coming decades. We need large-scale demonstration projects of the technical, economic and environmental performance of integrated CCS systems.

- The U.S. government should provide assistance only to coal projects with CO2 capture in order to demonstrate technical, economic and environmental performance.

- Today, IGCC appears to be the economic choice for new coal plants with CCS. However, this could change with further RD&D, so it is not appropriate to pick a single technology winner at this time, especially in light of the variability in coal type, access to sequestration sites, and other factors. The government should provide assistance to several "first of a kind" coal utilization demonstration plants, but only with carbon capture.

- Congress should remove any expectation that construction of new coal plants without CO2 capture will be "grandfathered" and granted emission allowances in the event of future regulation. This is a perverse incentive to build coal plants without CO2 capture today.

- Emissions will be stabilized only through global adherence to CO2 emission constraints. China and India are unlikely to adopt carbon constraints unless the U.S. does so and leads the way in the development of CCS technology.

- Key changes must be made to the current Department of Energy RD&D program to successfully promote CCS technologies.

Is a Home-Grown Fuel Policy Undermining US Energy Security?

The Energy Policy Research Foundation, Inc. (EPRINC), formerly PIRINC is a not-for-profit organization that studies energy economics with special emphasis on oil.

In a recently published report, EPRINC examines the viability of a proposal that calls for the use of 35 billion-gallons/year of renewable fuels (primarily ethanol) by 2017.

Key Findings of the Ethanol Study

During the 1990's, the most commonly used gasoline oxygenate was MTBE. But due to concerns over MTBE contaminating the ground water, its phase-out in early 2006 created an opportunity for ethanol. Rapid growth in use during 2006 saw ethanol end the year at an annualized consumption rate of about 6 billion gallons, much higher than the 4 billion gallon estimate under the renewable fuel mandate - EPAct 05.

This success suggested that policy makers may have underestimated ethanol's inherent potential which led to the new proposal by President Bush, calling for the use of 35 billion-gallons/year of renewable fuels (primarily ethanol) by 2017.

But numerous challenges must be overcome before this much ethanol could be integrated into the US fuel supply.

Website: http://www.eprinc.org

Table 1:
Renewable Fuel Mandate — EPAct 05

YEAR	BILLION GAL.
2006	4.0
2007	4.7
2008	5.4
2009	6.1
2010	6.8
2011	7.4
2012	7.5

EPRINC
formerly PIRINC

Challenges Ahead: Ethanol

- Ethanol's limited availability, higher cost, and incompatibility with existing petroleum fuels.

- Ethanol transportation costs around 15 cents/gallon compared with just a few cents for gasoline.

- Lack of a robust transport system to provide universal distribution

- The availability of an estimated 13 billion bushels of corn to manufacture this amount of ethanol

- A needed technology breakthrough to manufacture ethanol from cellulosic plant material.

- A sustained rise in grain prices driven by ethanol feedstock demand could lead to higher US and world food prices.

Ethanol contains one-third less energy per unit of volume than gasoline. If the president's proposal is to be realized, the limited availability of E-85 ethanol (only 1158 retail outlets carry E-85), a limited supply of attractive FFV vehicles (despite Corporate Average Fuel Economy (CAFE) credits for manufacturers), and general disinterest among would-be fleet operators are factors that must be overcome.

Additionally, as new ethanol plants come on line, they appear to be driving ethanol prices down—and corn prices up—creating an adverse set of economics for this new industry.

OTHER EPRINC STUDIES OF INTEREST   http://www.eprinc.org/publications.html

Why Do Oil Prices Jump So High When Supply Glitches Occur? November 2006

Does the Hubbert Method Provide a Reliable Means of Predicting Future Oil Production? October 2006

Challenges Ahead: Ethanol

U.S. Fuel Ethanol Consumption: 2002-2006 (million gallons)

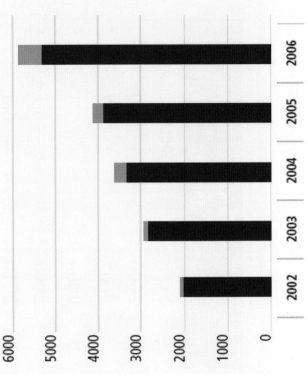

US Climate Action Partnership

USCAP
United States
Climate Action
Partnership

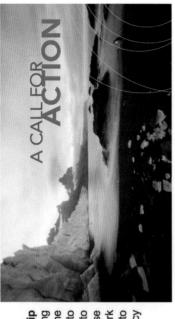

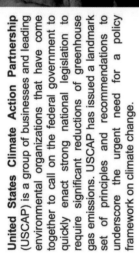

Six Design Principles

Account for the global dimensions of climate change

Create incentives for technology innovation

Be environmentally effective

Create economic opportunity and advantage

Be fair to sectors disproportionately impacted

Reward early action

Website: http://www.us-cap.org

United States Climate Action Partnership (USCAP) is a group of businesses and leading environmental organizations that have come together to call on the federal government to quickly enact strong national legislation to require significant reductions of greenhouse gas emissions. USCAP has issued a landmark set of principles and recommendations to underscore the urgent need for a policy framework on climate change.

USCAP Members Include: Alcan Inc., Alcoa, American International Group, Inc., Boston Scientific Corporation, BP America Inc., Caterpillar Inc., Chrysler Group, ConocoPhillips, Deere & Company, The Dow Chemical Company, Duke Energy, DuPont, Environmental Defense, Ford Motor Company, FPL Group, Inc., General Electric, General Motors Corp., Johnson & Johnson, Marsh, Inc., National Wildlife Federation, Natural Resources Defense Council, The Nature Conservancy, NRG Energy, Inc., PepsiCo, Pew Center on Global Climate Change, PG&E Corporation, PNM Resources, Shell, Siemens Corporation, World Resources Institute, Xerox Corporation.

USCAP offers the following interconnected set of recommendations for the general structure and key elements of climate protection legislation that we urge Congress to enact as quickly as possible. The legislation should require actions to be implemented on a fast track while a cap and trade program is put in place. We recommend these fast track actions begin within one year of enactment.

- Take a stepwise cost-effective approach
- Cap and Trade is essential
- Establish short and mid-term GHG emission targets
- GHG inventory and registry
- Credit for early action
- Aggressive technology research and development
- Policies to discourage new investments in high-emitting facilities
- Accelerated deployment of zero and low-emitting technologies and energy efficiency

Energy Action Group

The Energy Action Group works to identify financial, macroeconomic, industry and business specific issues of concern and solutions. It addresses the security of the energy supply; improvement of the investment climate for energy and development; North American energy integration; energy supply to the region; and alternative energy sources such as Liquefied Natural Gas. As a key part of this initiative, the Council of the Americas leads ongoing discussions with diplomats, visiting dignitaries and senior policy officials to create an open forum for energy issues.

Energy Action Group Themes:

Security of Energy Supply — Oil and gas supplies in the Western Hemisphere are very important to the United States and the region. Current political situations in several countries make this a crucial and on-going issue.

Energy Industry Investment Issues — Topics including investment climate safety, security of commitments, and investment dispute resolution will be discussed.

North American Energy Integration — We are working to advance the North American energy integration dialogue, in conjunction with the Mexico-US (MEXUS) Business Committee, a committee of the Council of the Americas. Through MEXUS, we bring together energy companies of NAFTA countries to promote one agenda to policy makers.

Supplying Energy to the Region — As industrialization continues in the Western Hemisphere, there will be a larger demand for reliable production and transmission of electricity. Historically, energy consumption increases at twice the rate of GDP growth. If this trend continues, the region's largest economies will not be able to meet demand.

Alternate Energy Sources — As the United States and the rest of the Western Hemisphere look to broaden their energy sources, they have begun to look at alternative sources of power. Among them are Liquefied Natural Gas (LNG), Hydroelectric Power, and Solar Energy.

Setting An Agenda — EAG members play an active role in setting the agenda for the group. By keeping the Council and the rest of the EAG informed of current issues, we are working together to promote discussion, advancement, and favorable resolutions.

Energy in the Americas
Building a Lasting Partnership
for Security and Prosperity

A Report of the Council of the Americas' Energy Action Group

Website:
http://www.counciloftheamericas.org/

http://www.americas-society.org/coa/events/2006events/2005/October/EnergyReport/FINAL%20-%20COA%20Energy%20Action%20Group%20Report.pdf

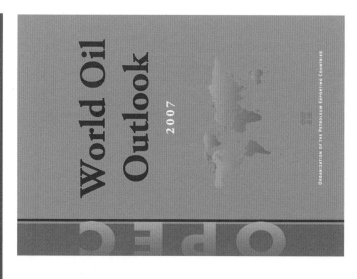

- **The OPEC Secretariat** has, for many years, produced a medium- to long-term outlook of the global oil scene. Results and analysis have offered insights into many important issues that producing countries and the oil industry have been, and may be confronted with in the future.

- In our reference case, with an average global economic growth rate of 3.5% per annum (purchasing power parity basis), and oil prices assumed to remain in the $50–60/b range in nominal terms for much of the projection period, oil demand is set to rise from the 2005 level of 83 mb/d to 118 mb/d by 2030. This also assumes that no particular departure in trends for energy policies and technologies takes place. This is a very important caveat for there are inherent downside risks to demand, something that is specifically addressed in this outlook.

- The transportation sector will be the main source of future oil demand increases. Of the non-transportation oil use, the main expected source of increase will be in the industrial and residential sectors of developing countries, which see a combined growth to 2030 of over 11 mboe/d in the reference case.

- Initial increases in both crude and non-crude supply pushes total non-OPEC supply up to 54 mb/d in 2010. This is 5 mb/d higher than in 2005. After 2010, non-OPEC crude supply, including NGLs, stabilises, then eventually falls. Yet with non-conventional oil supply increasing at strong rates, over the entire projection period, total non-OPEC supply actually continues to rise.

- The amount of crude oil supply expected from OPEC increases post-2010, rising, in this reference case, to 38 mb/d by 2020 and 49 mb/d by 2030.

- There is a great deal of uncertainty over future demand and non-OPEC supply, which translates into large uncertainties over the amount of oil that OPEC Member Countries will eventually need to supply. Investment requirements are very large, and subject to considerably long lead-times and pay-back periods. It is therefore essential to explore these uncertainties in the context of alternative scenarios.

- Taking into account the most likely changes in the future supply and demand structures and their quality specifications, the global downstream sector will require in the period 2006–2020, 13 mb/d of additional distillation capacity, around 7.5 mb/d of combined upgrading capacity, 18 mb/d of desulphurisation capacity and 2 mb/d of capacity for other supporting processes, such as alkylation, isomerisation and reforming.

Website: http://www.opec.org/library/World%20Oil%20Outlook/pdf/WorldOilOutlook.pdf

World Oil Outlook 2007

Annual growth in oil demand, 2005–2030

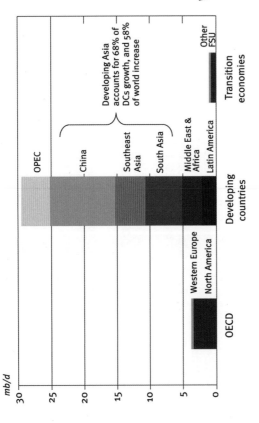

OECD countries, currently accounting for close to 60% of world oil demand, see a further growth of 4 mb/d by 2030, reaching 53 mb/d. Developing countries account for most of the rise in the reference case, with consumption doubling from 29 mb/d to 58 mb/d. Asian developing countries account for an increase of 20 mb/d, which represents more than two-thirds of the growth in all developing countries.

World oil supply, 2005–2030

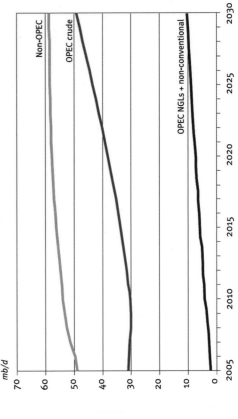

Inter-regional oil trade should increase by 13 mb/d to almost 63 mb/d of oil exports in 2020. Both crude and products exports will increase appreciably, with products exports growing faster than crude oil exports. Correspondingly, the reference case outlook calls for a total tanker fleet requirement in 2020 of 460 million dwt. This compares to 360 million dwt as of the end of 2006.

ENERGY
CHARTER
SECRETARIAT

PUTTING A PRICE ON
ENERGY

International
Pricing Mechanisms
for Oil and Gas

ENERGY CHARTER SECRETARIAT

The Energy Charter Treaty

The Energy Charter Treaty provides a multilateral framework for energy cooperation that is unique under international law. It is designed to promote energy security through the operation of more open and competitive energy markets, while respecting the principles of sustainable development and sovereignty over energy resources.

A core principle of the Energy Charter is 'market-oriented price formation' for the energy sector, within the framework of sovereign rights over energy resources. But this begs the question: how can these two elements be combined and how are they reflected in the formation of oil and gas prices in international trade?

Overall Conclusions   **Website: http://www.encharter.org**

This report looks at the pricing mechanisms for oil and gas by also using approaches of some more specialised parts of economic theory, mainly transaction cost theory dealing with different pricing and contract mechanism of open markets, long-term contracts and vertical integration, the theory of finite resources as reflected in Hotelling and Ricardian rent and the principal-agent theory. They suggest the following analysis:

The transaction cost theory suggests that the combination of marketplaces, long-term contracts and vertical integration depends on technology, market structure and regulation, and that it will change to reflect their development. Geology and geography provide the overall context, but the impact of endowments changes with the development of technology, as well as of markets and regulations. An important element in order to understand differences in pricing mechanisms is that there are two actors on the supply side: the resource owner, usually represented by a national government, which takes decisions determining the depletion of its resources, and the producing company, which takes the decision to invest.

Oil has already been traded internationally for more than a century, and trade in oil has developed all the features of a global commodity market. However, natural gas has not (yet) followed suit, and whether and how a global gas market might emerge is a hotly debated topic in international energy.

What we see instead, in the case of natural gas, are strong variations in the pricing mechanisms for international gas trade into different regional and national markets. This study examines possible reasons for these differences, starting with the physical properties of natural gas and the distribution of gas reserves, and continuing with a detailed consideration of the mechanisms that have emerged to determine gas prices in North America, in the UK and in Continental Europe. It also examines the role of liquefied natural gas in providing a link between different markets.

The aim of this study is to encourage an informed debate about international oil and gas pricing, which itself is a key to understanding many current developments on international energy markets. The study, available on the Energy Charter's website, does not recommend a particular model for national energy markets or for international commercial arrangements. However, and particularly where gas is traded through pipelines, it underlines that the international gas trade depends on long-term decisions that are taken along the entire energy chain. This in turn strengthens the significance of the Energy Charter as an instrument for international energy cooperation, since the Charter establishes binding disciplines protecting these long-term investment and trade decisions.

APPENDIX E
ADDITIONAL MATERIALS ON THE CD

This appendix provides detailed descriptions of additional study materials contained on the CD included with the final printed version of the National Petroleum Council (NPC) report, *Facing the Hard Truths about Energy: A Comprehensive View to 2030 of Global Oil and Natural Gas.* The CD contains the following files:

- Final Report
- Report Glossary
- Report Slide Presentation
- Webcast of NPC Meeting and Press Conference
- Study Topic Papers
- Study Data Warehouse Files

The contents of the CD also can be viewed and downloaded from the NPC website (www.npc.org) and additional or replacement copies of the CD can be purchased from the same site.

FINAL REPORT

The final report, as approved by the members of the National Petroleum Council and submitted to Secretary Bodman, is included on the report's CD. This copy of the printed report is in PDF format, contains hyperlinks among sections, and is searchable using Adobe software. It provides the report sections as follows:

- Transmittal Letter to Secretary Bodman (2-page summary of report)
- Table of Contents
- Preface
- Executive Summary

- Report Chapters
  - Chapter One: Energy Demand
  - Chapter Two: Energy Supply
  - Chapter Three: Technology
  - Chapter Four: Geopolitics
  - Chapter Five: Carbon Management
  - Chapter Six: Recommendations
  - Chapter Seven: Methodology
- Appendices
  - Appendix A: Request Letter and Description of the NPC
  - Appendix B: Study Group Rosters
  - Appendix C: Study Outreach Process and Sessions
  - Appendix D: Parallel Studies Process and Summaries
  - Appendix E: Additional Materials on the CD
- Acronyms and Abbreviations

REPORT GLOSSARY

The report's CD contains a detailed glossary of terms used in the report, which was drawn almost in its entirety from a glossary provided by EIA. The glossary is provided in PDF format. The NPC is appreciative of EIA allowing the use of this document and assumes responsibility for any modifications that have been made to it.

REPORT SLIDE PRESENTATION

On July 18, 2007, a detailed slide presentation on the report, *Facing the Hard Truths about Energy,* was delivered to Secretary of Energy Samuel W. Bodman and the membership of the National Petroleum Council. This slide presentation is included on the report's CD to allow readers access to materials that were used to help explain the study process and results. Two versions are provided in PDF format:

- Slides only
- Slides with presenter's text as notes.

WEBCAST OF NPC MEETING AND PRESS CONFERENCE

The report's CD also contains a webcast of the July 18, 2007 NPC meeting as follows:

- Presentation on the report to the NPC membership
- Report approval and delivery to Secretary of Energy, Samuel W. Bodman
- Remarks by Secretary Bodman
- Press conference on July 18, 2007, following the NPC meeting.

STUDY TOPIC PAPERS

On July 18, 2007, the National Petroleum Council in approving its report, *Facing the Hard Truths about Energy,* also approved making available certain materials used in the study process, including detailed, specific subject matter papers prepared by the Task Groups and their Subgroups. These Topic Papers were part of the analyses that led to development of the summary results presented in the report's Executive Summary and Chapters. The final report's CD includes final versions of these papers.

These Topic Papers represent the views and conclusions of the authors. The National Petroleum Council has not endorsed or approved the statements and conclusions contained in these documents but approved the publication of these materials as part of the study process.

The NPC believes that these papers will be of interest to the readers of the report and will help them better understand the study results. These materials are being made available in the interest of transparency.

A list of these Topic Papers with brief abstracts for each follows.

Demand Task Group

Paper #1: Coal Impact

The United States has the largest coal reserves in the world, followed by Russia and China. Coal now provides about a quarter of the energy used in the United States. The share of U.S. energy to be supplied by coal is projected to increase modestly to 2030. Coal use worldwide exhibits the same characteristics as in the United States. The largest increase in coal use through 2030 is projected to be in China, followed by the United States and India. Coal is consumed in large quantities throughout the United States, while most production is focused in a few states, requiring significant quantities of coal to be transported long distances. To that end, U.S. coal consumers and producers have access to the world's most comprehensive and efficient coal transportation system. The extent to which coal is able to help meet future U.S. energy challenges will depend heavily on the performance of coal transporters.

Paper #2: Cultural/Social/Economic Trends

Population and the economy are normally directly associated with projecting energy use trends, but other factors play an important role in understanding these trends. This topic paper examined 8 of these trends, which were thought to be the most significant. These trends include the relationship between the structural change in the economy and energy use, the importance of oil and natural gas to future energy use patterns, carbon dioxide emissions and their relationship to fossil-fuel use, China and its anticipated energy use growth, the energy use conundrum related to the introduction of new energy consuming technologies into the market place, the potential for energy use savings in the light-duty vehicle fleet, energy use and its association with energy price, and the impact of fuel-switching capability in the transportation sector.

Paper #3: Demand Data Evaluation

This report contains the findings of the Demand Data Evaluation Subgroup of the Demand Task Group, which reviewed, analyzed, and compared projection data collected in the NPC data warehouse through surveys for both public and proprietary projections of world energy demand. Major "drivers" underpinning the demand projections are population and economy. In all cases, worldwide and U.S. energy demand is projected to increase. In a general sense, the worldwide increase in energy is expected to be about 60 percent by 2030, matching the worldwide increase over the last 25 years. Detailed analyses were conducted using input from the U.S. Energy Information Administration (EIA) and the International Energy Agency (IEA). Other public studies were less complete than those produced by the EIA and the IEA, but confirmed the observations made from those studies as did the aggregated proprietary data collection effort.

Paper #4: Electric Generation Efficiency

Expected improvements in electric generation efficiency are projected to mainly come from the replacement of old plants with new plants that are constructed using contemporary technology with better efficiencies. Existing unit efficiency is not projected to improve significantly as replacement of auxiliary equipment is the only area where contemporary technology can be introduced. There are regional differences in the rate of improvement in electric generation efficiencies as developing regions have less installed capacity and are projected to add new electric generating capability at a faster rate than in industrialized regions.

Paper #5: Industrial Efficiency

This topic paper examines industrial energy use trends, the potential impact of energy efficiency technologies, and barriers to their adoption. The industrial sector is a large and price-responsive energy consumer. Energy efficiency opportunities of 5 quadrillion Btu per year, or over 15 percent of industrial energy use, exist broadly across the industrial sector. While 40 percent of these opportunities could be captured using existing technology and systems, further research-and-development is required to implement the rest. Areas of opportunity include waste-heat recovery, separations, and combined heat and power. By providing fuel-switching capability, the industrial sector serves as a quickly responding buffer against supply or demand shocks. Unfortunately, industrial fuel-switching capability has decreased in recent years.

Paper #6: Residential Commercial Efficiency

About 40 percent of U.S. energy is consumed in the residential and commercial sectors. If "achievable" cost-effective energy-efficiency measures were deployed, energy use in these two sectors could be roughly 15-20 percent below that anticipated in a business-as-usual future. Most energy consumed in these sectors is for traditional uses such as heating, cooling and lighting. However, a growing portion is being used to power new devices, many of which were rare or even nonexistent just a few years ago. Significant efficiency improvements have been made in building shells, systems, and appliances. But these improvements have been offset to some extent by additional demand for energy services resulting from trends toward bigger structures, use of increasing numbers of traditional appliances, and introduction of new energy consuming devices. Buildings typically last decades if not centuries. Many of the features of buildings that affect their energy consumption largely will go unchanged throughout the life of the building. Technologies and practices affecting energy use in these long-lived systems will be slow to penetrate and affect overall efficiency.

Supply Task Group

Paper #7: Global Access to Oil and Gas

For environmental and other policy reasons, governments around the world, including the U.S., have reduced access to oil and natural gas resources. This paper is a detailed description of resource types, locations, and volumes subject to U.S. federal access restrictions or moratoria. The paper also includes data about restricted global and North American access as well as oil and gas production from marginal U.S. wells.

Paper #8: Biomass

Biomass is part of the global resource endowment for supplying energy. This paper is a detailed survey of biomass, particularly cultivated crops, as a source of both energy and food. The paper considers the range of estimates for energy supplied by biomass; agricultural capacity to meet projected fuel and food demands; and the conditions needed to optimize energy crop production, including bioengineered or genetically modified crops. It also discusses infrastructure considerations and second-generation conversion technologies needed to secure biomass as a significant source of energy supply.

Paper #9: Gas to Liquids (GTL)

The term gas to liquids refers to technologies that convert natural gas to liquid fuels, as an alternative to refining crude oil and other commercialization paths

Appendix E – Additional Materials on the CD

E-3

for natural gas. Interest in large-scale GTL has grown over the past 10 years, based on strong demand for diesel fuel, particularly in Europe and Asia; increasingly stringent environmental specifications for diesel fuel; the commercial potential in monetizing stranded gas; and requirements to reduce flaring of natural gas and develop economic uses for the gas. This paper describes recent GTL developments and assesses potential capacity additions and commercial prospects.

Paper #10: Geologic Endowment

The geologic endowment of oil, natural gas, coal, or other hydrocarbons is a fundamental consideration for energy policy. This paper defines the major types of hydrocarbons and essential concepts such as reserves and resources that are used in energy discussions. The paper discusses a wide range of global resource estimates, their underlying methodologies, and the challenges in making resource assessments. The discussion concludes with a call to update estimates of global hydrocarbon resources using best-practice assessment techniques.

Paper #11: Hydrogen

Hydrogen is of great interest in the longer-term as the potential basis for a non-hydrocarbon energy economy. This paper describes the potential role of hydrogen at large scale in reducing U.S. petroleum imports and carbon emissions. The paper summarizes a range of estimates for hydrogen's share of energy supply through 2030 and beyond and discusses the R&D, distribution, and infrastructure requirements needed to make hydrogen a viable supply option.

Paper #12: Infrastructure

Transportation infrastructure is a vast, complex network of pipelines, railways, waterways, and roads that deliver energy from sources of supply to points of demand. Much of the U.S. transportation system was in place by the 1970s. This paper concludes that the network is approaching a tipping point as aging infrastructure contends with growing and increasingly diversified demand. Fragmented or outdated data about infrastructure add to the uncertainty in assessing the current state or planning for future requirements. The paper concludes that energy transportation infrastructure should become a national priority in the interests of economic security and national security.

Paper #13: Liquefied Natural Gas (LNG)

Liquefied natural gas is gas that has been cooled as a liquid for transport when pipelines are not economically or otherwise feasible. This paper describes the principal elements of the global LNG trade, defines the LNG "value chain," and assesses the prospects of emerging LNG exporters and consumers.

Paper #14: Non-Bio Renewables

This paper surveys the economic, technical, and policy prospects for non-bio renewable energy sources, including wind, solar, tidal, and geothermal power. Although these energy sources do not produce liquid fuels that compete with petroleum products, they all generate electricity or heat that can displace hydrocarbon power sources such as natural gas or coal. While each renewable source has unique features, they all share such characteristics as high construction or installation costs but low operating costs. The paper discusses these characteristics and their implications for potential timing, scale, and rate of adoption of renewable energy sources.

Paper #15: Summary Discussions on Peak Oil

This paper defines "peak oil" as one class of oil production forecasts and summarizes the arguments made for this point of view. The paper is based on two teleconferences with peak-oil forecasters, and a third teleconference with forecasters who do not share their view. The paper describes key concepts and indicators for the peak-oil position, including new field discoveries, production maxima in some oil-producing countries, and the inability of some producing countries to meet both domestic and export demand. The report concludes that concerns about supply shortfalls due to post-peak production have merit and warrant further consideration. It also warns that inconsistent definitions and reporting of production and reserve data raise uncertainty in supply forecasts.

Paper #16: Refining and Manufacturing

This paper addresses questions about the refining capacity that will be needed over the next 25 years; the location of that capacity; the technology required to process unconventional feedstock; and policy or regulatory issues that inhibit new refining capacity. The paper concludes that all projections for 2015 show that primary oil demand will exceed projected refining capacity, even assuming that all announced refinery expansion projects are implemented. Growing oil demand in the United States is projected to outpace the increase in domestic refining capacity, leading to increased imports of finished products. Increasing technical complexity, regulatory requirements, and lengthy permitting procedures will have a combined effect on capacity expansion.

Technology Task Group

Paper #17: Carbon Capture and Sequestration (CCS)

It is likely that the world is moving into an era of carbon management involving several measures to reduce CO_2 emissions, including improvements in the efficiency of energy use and the use of alternatives to fossil fuels such as biofuels, solar, wind, and nuclear power. However, to meet the energy demands of the nation, the United States will continue using fossil fuels, including coal, extensively over the next 50 years or more. To do so it will be necessary to capture and sequester a large fraction of the CO_2 produced by burning these fossil fuels, as discussed in this report.

Paper #18: Coal to Liquids and Gas

This Topic Report focuses on the potential of coal to liquids and coal to gas technologies, and potential advances in these conversion processes. It examines the inputs and assumptions from various publications and the range of production estimates from these technologies.

Paper #19: Conventional Oil and Gas (including Arctic and Enhanced Oil Recovery)

Large volumes of technically recoverable, domestic oil resources—estimated at 400 billion barrels—remain undeveloped and are yet to be discovered, from undeveloped remaining oil in place of over a trillion barrels. This resource includes undiscovered oil, stranded light oil amenable to CO_2-EOR technologies, unconventional oil (deep heavy oil and oil sands), and new petroleum concepts, such as residual oil in reservoir transition zones. The status of these resources is the topic of this report.

Paper #20: Deepwater

Deepwater oil and natural gas resources are conventional reserves in an unconventional setting. The Topic Report describes the top priority deepwater-specific technological challenges. These are reservoir characterization, extended system architecture, high-pressure and high-temperature (HPHT) completion systems, and metocean (meteorological and subsurface) forecasting and systems analysis.

Paper #21: Exploration Technology

The exploration topic study group identified five core exploration technology areas in which future developments have the potential to significantly impact exploration results over the next 25 years. These areas are seismic technologies, controlled source electromagnetism, interpretation technology, earth-systems modeling, and subsurface measurements. The Topic Report describes these and other aspects of exploration technology.

Paper #22: Heavy Oil

Heavy oil, extra-heavy oil, and bitumen are unconventional oil resources that are characterized by high viscosity (resistance to flow) and high density compared to conventional oil. Production methods currently in use and those needed in the future are described in the Topic Report.

Paper #23: Human Resources

The majority of oil and natural gas industry professionals are less than ten years from retirement eligibility. There are fewer academic departments in petrotechnical areas now than 20 years ago, and significantly fewer petrotechnical students are being trained to replace upcoming retirees. The upcoming demographic shift in employees is described in the Topic Report.

Paper #24: Hydrates

Gas hydrates are found within and under permafrost in arctic regions, and also within a few hundred meters of the seafloor on continental slopes and in deep seas and lakes. The reservoir architecture, technology needs, and eventual economic importance of hydrates in arctic and marine environments may be very different. Arctic hydrates lack validated methods for economical production, but for marine hydrate resources the added challenge is even more fundamental: a validated means of reliably finding them in significant deposits.

Paper #25: Nuclear Power

Nuclear power is expected to have a greater impact on use of coal rather than oil or natural gas, because it provides base-load power. This Topic Report discusses the predictions of future nuclear power usage.

Paper #26: Oil and Gas Technology Development

Since the beginning of the modern age of oil and natural gas, technology has played a fundamental role in supporting the efficient production of hydro-carbons. Payoff from a new technology can be huge, both for the individual company and for national energy security. However, commercializing technology in the oil and gas market is costly and time intensive; with an average of 16 years from concept to widespread commercial adoption. The Topic Report describes the technology development process.

Paper #27: Oil Shales

Globally, it is estimated that there are roughly 3 trillion barrels of shale oil in place, which is comparable to the original world endowment of conventional oil. About half of this immense total is found near the common borders of Wyoming, Utah, and Colorado. The Topic Report describes very recent advances in recovering this resource and the additional challenges ahead.

Paper #28: Transportation Efficiency

Improved efficiency in transportation can have a significant influence on future energy usage. This report examines several studies on transportation technologies and discusses the efficiency gains to be obtained in segments of light-duty vehicles, heavy-duty vehicles, air transport, marine shipping, and rail transport.

Paper #29: Unconventional Gas

Unconventional natural gas resources constitute some of the largest components of remaining natural gas resources in the United States. The Topic Report describes in detail tight sand, coalbed methane, and gas shale resources, and discusses advances needed in these areas.

Geopolitics & Policy Task Group

Paper #30: Historical Perspective on Energy Crises and U.S. Policy Responses

Section I excerpted from 1987 NPC Report, *Factors Affecting U.S. Oil & Gas Outlook.*

Macroeconomic Subgroup Reference Reports

Paper #31: Energy Markets Grow Up: How the Changing Balance of Participation Influences Oil Price, Katherine Spector, 6/15/05

This report explores who trades financial energy today, and how they participate in the market. The increase in the number of would-be buyers of energy over the past few years—including energy consumers, fundamentally inspired speculators, and passive investors—coincided, as prices rose, with a marked decline in hedging by producers, the market's natural sellers. The result is a sharp increase in the competition for forward price that has changed the way the market responds to bullish energy fundamentals.

Paper #32: Energy Markets Grow Up Part II: Who Trades Energy Now and How Much Does It Matter? Katherine Spector, 1/8/07

This is the follow-up report to "Energy Markets Grow Up: How the Changing Balance of Energy Market Participation Influences Price," a report which looked at who trades energy and why, and explained how the development of the financial energy market has changed the path of not only energy prices, but the shape of the futures curve and volatility. This report updates that discussion, examines what has changed in the past year, and—in a market with so little hard data on money flows—attempts to quantify the role that some of these market participants play. Specifically, this report estimates the per-commodity inflows and outflows associated with index investment on a quarterly basis since 2002. This report attempts to isolate the flow of money from rebalancing pure index positions to maintain fixed allocations to commodities. The report also explores some of the strategies that investors are using to improve returns—and that banks are using to manage the risk associated with selling index style products to real money customers.

Paper #33: Oil Shocks and the Global Business Cycle, David Hensley, 5/12/06

This report examines the increase in oil prices in the 1970s and the increase in oil prices in the 2000s and identifies the factors that contributed to the different outcomes in the two periods, including the difference in energy intensity, the rapidity of the price rise, and geopolitical tensions.

Paper #34: The Good, the Bad and the Ugly about the Oil Shock Impact on Emerging Markets, Luis Oganes & Katherine Spector, 10/21/05

This report examines the impact of the increase in oil prices seen in 2003–2005 on net oil exporters in Emerging Market.

Paper #35: Three Propositions on the Economics of Greenhouse-Gas Regulation, Marc Levinson, 2/14/07

This presentation was presented by Marc Levinson at the NPC Carbon Management meeting on February 14, 2007 in Princeton. Three propositions about climate change include: (1) If greenhouse-gas emissions cause social harm, emitters should bear a cost intended to discourage emissions; (2) Although it is impossible to calculate an "optimal" cost of emissions, the cost must be high enough to discourage consumption of greenhouse-gas-intensive goods and services; (3) The real cost of emissions should rise on a predictable path over an extended period of time, as extremely sharp or erratic price changes have the potential to cause significant economic harm.

Paper #36: Capturing the Gains from Carbon Capture, Marc Levinson, 4/11/07

Carbon sequestration—the burying of carbon dioxide captured from power generation and manufacturing—is likely to develop into an extremely large industry in the face of mounting concern about climate change. Investor interest in climate change has so far centered on utilities and fossil-fuel producers. This report seeks to widen this focus and look at opportunities for the industrial companies that are staking out roles in the infant capture-and-sequestration industry.

Paper #37: Carbon Dioxide: A Commodity Market Perspective, Scott Speaker, 3/27/07

This report intends to assess the emerging risks and opportunities of impending regulation of carbon dioxide emissions from U.S. power generators and heavy industries from a commodity market perspective and quantify potential impacts where possible.

Paper #38: All You Ever Wanted to Know About Carbon Trading, January 2007

This report provides an introduction to carbon trading and examines the emerging risks and opportunities of impending regulation of carbon dioxide emissions.

STUDY DATA WAREHOUSE FILES

To make the study's broad-ranging and original sources easily available to all participants, a data warehouse was developed. This provided for centralized management of the multidimensional data collected. By the time it concluded, the study had compiled and used nearly 100 energy forecasts or outlooks. These forecasts and several hundreds of papers/documents on various aspects of the energy sector were used in the interpretations that formed the basis of the study findings and recommendations.

The data warehouse was designed to be the main analytical tool for the Task Groups, accepting all data collected from the survey questionnaire and other data sources. Once in the data warehouse, selected values or ranges of values for any or all dimensions could be applied as a filter to enable analysis.

As with the Topic Papers, the National Petroleum Council has not endorsed or approved the contents of the study's Data Warehouse but approved making available this information as part of the study process.

The NPC believes that the information in the Data Warehouse will be of interest to the readers of the report and will help them better understand the study results. The structured data used in the NPC study, along with software to display data and graphics, are being made available in the interest of transparency.

ACRONYMS AND ABBREVIATIONS

ACEE	American Council for an Energy-Efficient Economy
AEO	*Annual Energy Outlook* (annual publication from EIA)
AIChE	American Institute of Chemical Engineers
ANWR	Arctic National Wildlife Refuge
APEC	Asia-Pacific Economic Cooperation (a group of energy ministers from 21 countries)
ASPO	Association for the Study of Peak Oil
Btu	British thermal unit
CAFE	Corporate Average Fuel Economy
CBM	coalbed methane
CCS	carbon capture and sequestration
CCSP	U.S. Climate Change Science Program
CHP	combined heat and power
CO₂	carbon dioxide
CSEM	controlled source electromagnetism
CSS	cyclic steam stimulation
CTG	coal-to-gas
CTL	coal-to-liquids
EC	European Commission (see also WETO)
DOE	U.S. Department of Energy
E&P	exploration and production

EOR	enhanced oil recovery
EIA	DOE's Energy Information Administration
EPRI	Electric Power Research Institute
FAO	Food and Agriculture Organization of the United Nations
GDP	gross domestic product
GTL	gas-to-liquids
HOV	high-occupancy vehicle
HVAC	heating-ventilation-air conditioning systems
IEA	International Energy Agency
IEO	*International Energy Outlook* (annual publication from EIA)
IGCC	integrated gasification combined cycle
IOCs	international oil companies
IOGCC	Interstate Oil and Gas Compact Commission
IPCC	Intergovernmental Panel on Climate Change
LDV	light duty vehicle
LNG	liquefied natural gas
MB/D	million barrels per day
mpg	miles per gallon
MMS	U.S. Minerals Management Service

NAFTA	North American Free Trade Agreement	**R&D**	research and development
NGL	natural gas liquid	**R/P**	reserves-to-production
NIMBY	not in my back yard	**RPSEA**	Research Partnership for a Secure Energy America
NGOs	non-governmental organizations	**SAGD**	steam-assisted gravity drainage
NOCs	national oil companies	**SPR**	Strategic Petroleum Reserve
NOx	nitrogen oxides	**SSEB**	Southern States Energy Board
NPC	National Petroleum Council	**TCF**	trillion cubic feet
OECD	Organisation for Economic Co-operation and Development	**URR**	ultimately recoverable resources
OPEC	Organization of Petroleum Exporting Countries	**USGS**	United States Geological Survey
		WEC	World Energy Council
PDVSA	Petroleos de Venezuela (Venezuela's national oil company)	**WEO**	*World Energy Outlook* (annual publication from IEA)
ppmv	parts per million by volume	**WETO**	*World Energy Technology Outlook 2050* (published in 2006 by European Commission)
PPP	purchasing power parity		
Quad	quadrillion Btu	**WETO-H2**	WETO Hydrogen Case
RECS	EIA's Residential Energy Consumption Survey	**WTO**	World Trade Organization

■

Note: A detailed glossary of terms used in this report is available at www.npc.org and on the CD that accompanies the printed report.

CONVERSION FACTORS

1 barrel = 42 U.S. gallons = 159 liters = 0.16 cubic meters (m^3)

1 cubic foot = 0.028 cubic meters (m^3)

1 cubic meter (m^3) = 35.7 cubic feet

1 short ton = 0.91 metric tons

1 metric ton = 1.1 cubic feet

APPROXIMATE BTU CONTENT[1]

100 million metric tons of oil equivalent = 4 quadrillion Btu

1 quadrillion Btu = 25.2 million metric tons of oil equivalent

1 barrel of crude oil = 6.0 million Btu

1 million barrels of oil per day = 2.12 quadrillion Btu per year

1 cubic foot of natural gas = 1,030 Btu

1 billion cubic feet per day = 0.38 quadrillion Btu per year

1 short ton of coal = 20.3 million Btu

1 million short tons of coal per day = 7.4 quadrillion Btu per year

1 gigawatt-hour of electricity = 3,412 million Btu

2,400 gigawatt-hours of electricity per day = 3 quadrillion Btu per year

1 barrel of motor gasoline = 5.2 million Btu

1 barrel of distillate fuel = 5.8 million Btu

1 barrel of residual fuel oil = 6.3 million Btu

---

1 Actual heat values vary over time and by source. The values shown are an approximation.

DATE DUE

6 2011